To Tracy,

Happy Reading

With Love
Fiona, Viv & Ziggy

July 2002
xxx

SUN, MOON
&
STONEHENGE

First published 1998
© Bluestone Press 1998

Published by Bluestone Press, Cardigan, Wales

British Library Cataloguing in Publication Data
Heath, Robin
Sun, Moon & Stonehenge

A CIP catalogue record for this book is
available from the British Library

ISBN 0 9526151 7 7

Printed in Great Britain
by The Cromwell Press Ltd,
Trowbridge, Wiltshire.

SUN, MOON
&
STONEHENGE

HIGH CULTURE IN ANCIENT BRITAIN

ROBIN HEATH

BLUESTONE PRESS

To Tricia with love.

Contents

Chronology, dimensions & evolution of the site. Aubrey and Sarsen circles. The history of the Bluestones. The four Station Stones. The five Trilithons.

Sun and Moonwatching at megalithic sites. Solar and lunar alignments. Calendar design - the year and the month. The two lunar cycles.

Measuring Sun and Moon motion. Sun-Moon integration. The Aubrey calendar. Predicting full and new Moons and Forecasting eclipses.

The octagonal geometry of Stonehenge. The Station Stone Rectangle and the use of Pythagorean geometry. The 5:12:13 triangle at Stonehenge.

The evidence for the Lunation Triangle. Using it as an accurate aid to soli-lunar astronomy. Ancient astronomy connecting ancient units of length.

The design process for megalithic stone rings. Practical methods to construct megalithic designs.

Understanding the culture which built the megaliths. Their siting and design. Castle Rigg and Stonehenge as designs of a high culture.

Evidence for cultural interchange at Stonehenge. Larger questions concerning the megalithic culture and synchronising it to other cultures.

The geometry and astronomy of Stonehenge. Ancient units of length and area - their derivation and use at Stonehenge and other sites.

The cultural legacy of Stonehenge. Evidence for high culture in the ancient world. Stonehenge and the Arthurian legends. Celtic geomantics.

Foreword

There are very few constructions in the world as old and as enigmatic as Stonehenge; perhaps the Great Pyramid, or the Nasca pictograms. Five thousand years ago our ancestors were building cosmological temples which are still effortlessly here today - compare this with our modern vacuous virtual reality most of which is designed to vanish in the blink of an eye! We may feel that we know nothing important enough to consciously leave behind for future millenia, but others in our past were not the same. Could it be that we might have something to learn from the ancients?

For some years now it has been becoming ever more obvious that these early structures are masterpieces of design, construction, mathematics and astronomy, and that a very high level of science must have existed in the British Isles, Egypt, China and elsewhere around five thousand years ago. This science seems to have involved the marriage of numbers to the various elements of the heavens, via geometry and harmony. It is a science we have largely lost, and what is left of it now tends to be either dismissed or blindly worshipped in fragments. Where now is the Bard who can predict eclipses, who understands the harmonies of the harp, who can decipher the patterns of nature in space and time, and who can help unify it all?

Robin Heath's work is at the forefront of the ongoing research in this field. In this astonishing book he provides a remarkable answer to one of the oldest riddles of Stonehenge. It seems to prove that the ancients had achieved a simple, accurate and meaningful solution to the number of full moons in a year, and that they deliberately created a massive picture of this profound solution across the British landscape. It is a picture which was designed to survive, in stone and in legend. If Robin Heath is right, and I strongly suspect that he is, then what he has unearthed is perhaps the single most important piece of the megalithic puzzle to surface for decades, for it raises even larger questions about the origins of this ancient science, and its possible function.

Whatever you may think about Stonehenge, and whether or not you are interested in learning about matters heavenly, cultural and mathematical, I can only heartily recommend this book as a gripping read and as a milestone in the ongoing search for our origins.

John Martineau

" But it must not be forgotten that the recent work could not have been so fruitful, had we not the results of the earlier work, confused and inadequate though they may be, as a foundation on which to build. Moreover, however much we may be convinced of the superiority of modern methods and modern attitudes to those of the past, we can be sure that the archaeologists of the future will not hold us blameless. To hope otherwise would be to deny the possibility of progress, whether at Stonehenge or elsewhere. "

Richard Atkinson, *Stonehenge*, final paragraph.

"Whatever we do we must avoid approaching the study with the idea that megalithic man was our inferior in ability to think."

Alexander Thom, *Megalithic Sites in Britain*, final paragraph.

Introduction

The first edition of *A Key to Stonehenge* began with a budget of five hundred pounds and a determination to present a no-nonsense comprehensible book enabling a non-specialist reader to begin the process of understanding Stonehenge and the culture which produced it. I was discouraged by nearly everyone I discussed the project with. "There are far too many books on Stonehenge" was going to become my epitaph. Now, five years and two reprints further on, *A Key to Stonehenge* sells throughout the world and not one of its original ideas has been demolished.

During the past five years I have applied the evident astronomy of the site into a wide range of practical applications. As a result, there are now several hundred 'Aubrey' calendar/eclipse predictors in use around the globe, derived from the original design on Salisbury Plain, and each will readily yield the calendar date, the state of the tides, the phase of the Moon, the dates of full Moons and eclipses. Knowledge of such things was once "required of every understanding person".

Sun, Moon and Stonehenge is the much expanded and enlarged replacement to *A Key to Stonehenge* and it takes a much deeper look at the whole vexed question of neolithic culture in Britain. Rising public awareness of the importance of Stonehenge within the British cultural landscape is demanding that the vague fog surrounding this monument be lifted, yet an astonishing number of books on Stonehenge tell the reader *almost nothing* about the aspirations of the culture that erected it, nor the effect of that culture on our subsequent history. This text, based on research over the past fifteen years and taken largely from recent lectures, seminars and workshops, is my contribution to this much needed educative process.

Against the vast backdrop of time, cultural phenomena come, have their moment, culminate and then fade from the social landscape to be eventually superceded by a different endeavour. The earlier belief system or fashion then becomes consigned to the historical record, the accuracy of which will depend on how amicable the new cultural paradigm is towards its vanquished past. Further along the road of time, often after several cultural shifts have taken place, a more fair and unbiassed historical overview may be written, this at least, even if it serves no other task, offering a decent burial to the old beliefs.

This book concerns itself particularly with the cultural phenomenon which built large stone monuments throughout northwestern Europe over a period of at least 2,000 years, from about 3500 BC. For most of that period, Stonehenge was evolving. Then, remarkably suddenly, the phenomenon of moving and placing huge stones was over and something very unusual happened - the purpose and meaning of the stones, and the culture which deemed them so important, apparently became lost to us. The normal historical recording process apparently never took place.

So little recognisable material was available to later historians that a definitive history of the megalithic culture was never written, and later cultures appear to have found very little time for these fusty relics in their landscape, nor for the philosophy underpinning their construction. Furthermore, new philosophies arose which were inimicable to the megalithic culture and its pagan roots. Some early versions of Christianity attempted to eradicate or censure what little historical detail was left to historians, whilst more recently the scientific materialism of the past two centuries has presented a distorted model of the world where almost *all* byegone ages are seen as primitive and having nothing useful to tell us. This text will show this belief to be erroneous and will demonstrate that the megalithic culture left an indelible imprint on the cultures which followed it, despite its omission in the history books.

There are five main routes up this sacred mountain that leads to the understanding of the megalithic culture. These are (i) traditional Archaeology, (ii) Archaeo-astronomy, sometimes also written astro-archaeology, (iii) Sacred Geometry and the Canon of Measure, (iv) the so-called Earth Mysteries and (v) the 'shamanistic' approach. Although the boundaries are somewhat loose between these groupings, particularly between (i) and (ii), (ii) and (iii), and (iv) and (v), there has not been enough contact between each group to enable a recognisable corpus of material concerning the megalithic culture to be assembled.

Archaeology is the traditional well trodden route, and whilst it has delivered remarkable information concerning the dating, social patterns and extent of this culture it has not fared well in answering why so many enormous groups of stones were assembled at certain sites.

Within the last few decades, archaeo-astronomy has discovered a new and apparently faster route to the summit whereby the stellar, solar and lunar alignments of a particular location have been shown to resonate with human constructions on the ground there. The unsung hero of this subject was the late Professor Alexander Thom, who also established the unit of length, the Megalithic yard, used by the builders, and he established many of the ground rules for evaluation of the astronomy of ancient sites.

From the ancient traditions, the protagonists of Sacred Geometry and the Canon of Measure follow a long and well established line of mysterious chivalric orders which were essentially hermetic. By definition, we can never know to what extent ancient wisdom has been preserved by such orders, although this century has seen some most useful attempts to recover lost knowledge from past cultures. Professor Keith Critchlow, John Michell and others have opened up a much more coherent pathway along this route, and a reliable corpus of material is now available to all.

The fourth route up the megalithic mountain is that of the so-called 'earth mysteries' school. Since the discovery in recent times, by Alfred Watkins, of the phenomenon which has come to be known as *leylines*, the vexed questions it has posed have perplexed and baffled many traditional scientists, whilst dowsers, psychics and other sensitive souls have happily discovered a new route by which they can apparently reach the summit. The flowering of the alternative culture in the 'sixties led to a great upsurge of interest in the ritual practices of the pagan past as more and more people sought to break free from the imposed restrictions of an industrial society. They added colour to a previously grey landscape, and they restored *ritual* to our sacred places, providing a necessary balancing of the excesses of scientific arrogance shown in the past towards ritual's importance to human well-being.

Finally, megalithic monuments have always attracted theories concerning the unknown. In our times, this is tagged onto our current liking for extra-terrestrials, although in the past it was the faery kingdom, dragons and ghosts. This is the traditional territory of the witch and *shaman*, and it has become the concern of anthropologists and other interested groups to understand better the psychic processes undergone by these people, and their followers, when the veil between this world and *the Otherworld* is temporarily rent in twain.

The evidence in this book suggests that some understanding of all five of the listed categories is required in order to understand *and experience* what the megalithic culture was about.

The megalithic culture was until recently never considered to be other than an isolated phenomenon, a cultural oddity, and any possible links with other cultures were vehemently denied. Finding examples of connection between the megalithic culture and other cultures has been possible because of two main sources - textual and metrological. *The Book of Enoch* contains an account of astronomical observations of the Sun and Moon taken from a similar latitude to Stonehenge. The units of length used to build stone circles may also be found elsewhere, and these are interconnected through a most intelligent metrology which integrates astronomy and geometry.

Stonehenge has survived fifty centuries and it is still, more or less, there on the ground for all to ponder on. There is no doubt any longer about the *form* of the original monument, the spacings between the stones, the type of stones used nor the location of the original sites of these stones. Yet this has not been enough: despite enjoying nearly a million visitors a year, despite all the books, research, articles and documentaries, we are still almost totally uneducated in the knowledge of how or why a culture could evolve such a profoundly complex monument over more than a millenium and a half, and what drove this culture to build such an enduring monument.

In other words, the solution to Stonehenge is still up for grabs - over three centuries of archaeological and other specialist endeavour has still not enabled our culture to come to grips with this astonishing *thing*. Baldly, we still do not have an owner's workshop manual, nor consensus on the likely uses to which the monument was put. This book therefore formulates a first *Owner's Manual for Stonehenge*, where I also attempt to give the monument a 5000 year service.

Traditional historians never considered the astronomy of ancient sites, because observational astronomy was not considered other than a modern science. A similar ignorance and prejudice prevented analysis of the information available from the folklore and legend - that vast cauldron of the collective which holds the cultural past of the nation. Turning to folklore for source material presents many problems - whilst the nature of Sun and Moon astronomy lends itself to rational and objective analysis, the manner by which folklore is presented, through fairy tales, superstitions, legends and the oral traditions, cannot be understood in the same way, yet as a corpus of cultural baggage, the reader will see that it endures with the same tenacity as the megaliths themselves, and has much to inform us concerning Stonehenge. Perhaps even more astonishingly, this material will enable the reader to find a continuity from Stonehenge into the history of modern Britain. Because the geometry of ancient sites will be seen to be woven into the tapestry of this history, the folklore will be found a most reliable guide to how this history is to be interpreted and leaves no doubt that the legacy from Stonehenge is still forming an important part of our national psyche.

Sun, Moon & Stonehenge carries a most essential message: that it is not actually possible to destroy a cultural legacy, it is only possible to obscure it, deny it, avoid it, ignore it or malign it. Each of these tactics has been used on Stonehenge and on the cultural background from whence it emerged. Paradoxically, whilst this has certainly delayed the rediscovery of the full meaning of our national temple, it has continually drawn our attention back to its mysteries. Whilst some of those mysteries will be seen to have been solved, revealing a much grander importance for Stonehenge within the history of the British Isles, even bigger mysteries present themselves within these pages. To quote the final words of *Stonehenge*, by Richard Atkinson, 'to hope otherwise would be to deny the possibility of further progress, whether at Stonehenge or elsewhere.'

Robin Heath, St. Dogmaels, May 1998

Acknowledgements

A book such as this draws from many others, and their authors. In addition, I have received help from many quarters in preparing this book. Clarification and confirmation of certain points have been freely given by specialists to whom I am extremely grateful. Firstly, I would like to acknowledge John Michell for his great encouragement and friendship; similarly John Martineau for his selfless assistance with the production of the book. To archaeologist Aubrey Burl, for his assistance with diagrams and anecdotal material. To author Mike Postins, who makes wonderful models of Stonehenge, for his friendship and encouragement; to Danny Sullivan, editor of that unique magazine for earth mysteries, The Ley Hunter; author Chris Knight and Lionel Simms, of the University of East London; historian Tony Retallic in Cornwall, author and Celtic scholar Peter Berresford Ellis for tireless and willing help with the historical and mythological material relating to the early Celtic Church; once Lundy lighthouseman Robert Farrah for assistance and interesting correspondence; astrologer, author and historian Nicholas Campion for his experience, enthusiastic friendship and advice; authors Mike Poynder, Charlie Sharp, David Furlong, Miranda Lundy, John Ivimy, Palden Jenkins, David Elkington, Evelyn Francis, Hamish Miller and Paul Broadhurst for their enthusiasm and encouragement. To Helena Francis of the Hermes Centre, for her faith in my work; to calligrapher Mark Mills, for the fine planetary glyphs used on some of the diagrams. To the staff at Wooden Books I would like to express gratitude for the useful discussions on the text. Finally, to all my student groups and megalithic tour groups I wish to acknowledge my own growth through watching their learning processes taking place.

Sadly, the late Dr. Archie Thom will not see the results of his generosity in supplying photographs and accurate survey diagrams from the Thom archives and offering his encouragement to this project.

Finally, I would like to especially thank Janet Lloyd Davies for her beautiful cover artwork; and Tricia, for her support, her helpful suggestions and for bearing the brunt of the proof-reading far into the night. It is to her that this book is dedicated.

Photographs

All the photographs in this book, unless otherwise indicated were taken by the author. I am most grateful to Paul Broadhurst for the photograph on page 186, Mr E. B. Johnson for the the photograph of Pentre Ifan on page 94, and the staff at the English Heritage Photographic Library for their help with the three fine photographs, on pages 20, 48 and 120.

A Note on Style

The reader will notice that I keep the Sun, Earth and Moon revered through capital letters and, where appropriate, maintain the conventions of upper and lower case adopted by earlier pioneers within this subject material - the Megalithic yard, neolithic, Station Stones and sarsen circle are examples. Phi' is the reciprocal of phi, 0.618033989. There is no bibliography - relevant texts and their authors are listed in the text where appropriate.

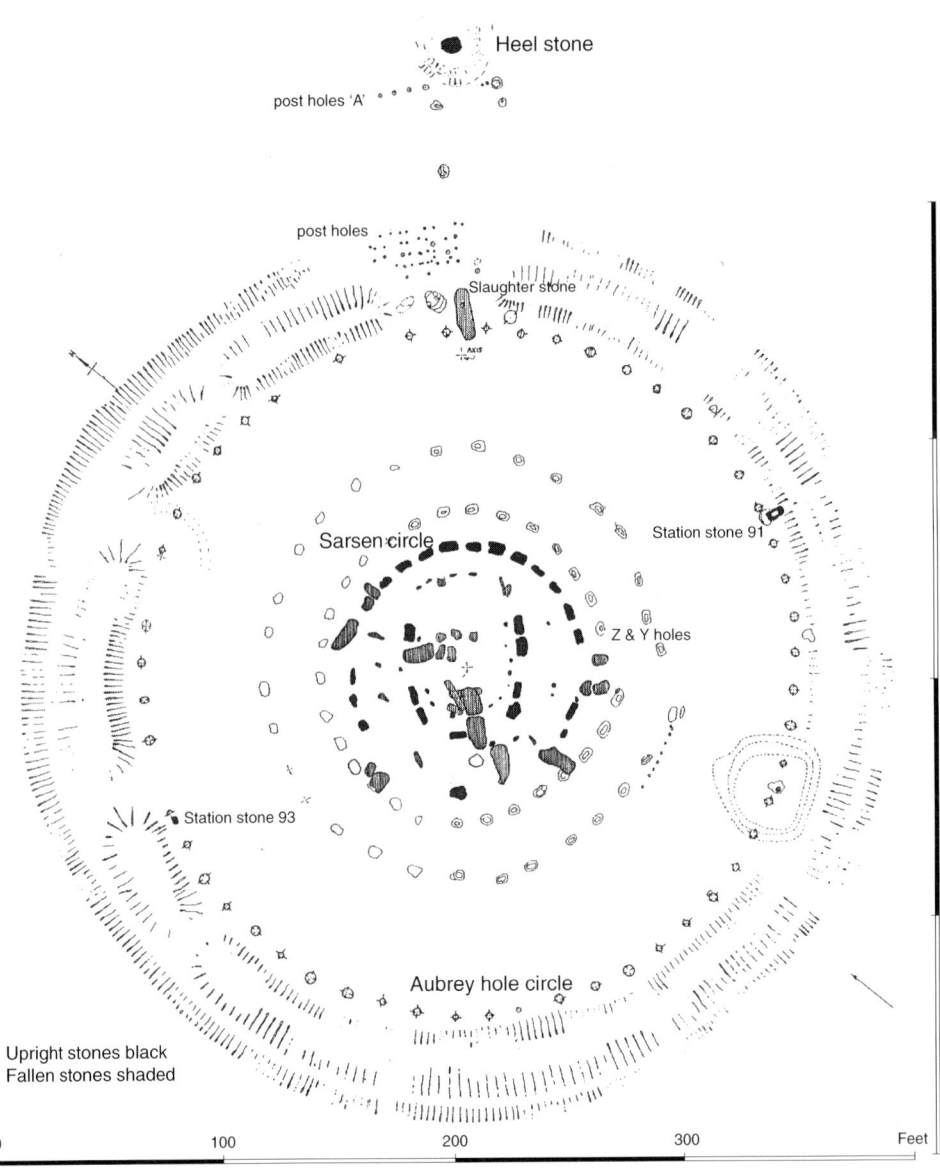

Heel stone

post holes 'A'

post holes

Slaughter stone

Sarsen circle

Station stone 91

Z & Y holes

Station stone 93

Aubrey hole circle

Upright stones black
Fallen stones shaded

| 0 | 100 | 200 | 300 | Feet |

Above: The Thom survey of Stonehenge, undertaken in 1973. This is the most accurate plan of Stonehenge available and is a ground level survey from closed traverse surveying. The evolution of Stonehenge progresses inwards with time, the outer ditch and bank framing the Aubrey holes, the earliest construction. The later upright stones of the sarsen circle (shown in black) then framed the five trilithons and the bluestone circle and horseshoe. (*Taken from the original survey plan, courtesy of the late Dr A.S.Thom.*)

Chapter 1

- A FIRST VISIT TO STONEHENGE -

The collection of stones, mounds and ditches we collectively call Stonehenge evolved over a period of at least 1500 years, an unmatched period of evolution for any cultural artefact. Stonehenge is a *pastiche* of developments each spaced well apart in time yet which meet and focus at a single space on Salisbury Plain. Despite centuries of inquiry, no one has yet discovered why.

Five thousand years of wind, frost, rain, vandalism and the attentions of the early archaeologists have taken their toll on Stonehenge such that the casual visitor sees a ruinous hotch-potch of impressively sized stones, some regularly spaced along curved arcs and with curved lintels placed on their tops. The word *Stonehenge* originally derived from *hanging stones* although *henge* has subsequently come to mean a circular ditch and bank.

In this opening chapter we will take each stage or phase of Stonehenge's construction, commencing with the earliest known developments, and, using illustrations and photographs, follow the likely sequence of building. This will enable comparison of the original condition of each stage of the monument with the reality of what is visible on site today. To begin with, some general statements can usefully be made about the monument and its site:

> *- Stonehenge consists of mainly concentric circular or elliptical constructions.*
> *- Two main kinds of stone are used - granite* bluestone, *a type of dolerite, for the earlier phases, and* sarsen *sandstone for the later constructions. Many of these stones were shaped and dressed, some jointed together with mortice and tenon and half-round 'jigsaw' joints.*
> *- The site is not level - sloping 0.4m across the diameter of the sarsen circle.*
> *- Three large aligned post-holes adjacent to the site date back over 8000 years.*
> *- There is evidence for an earlier smaller bluestone henge structure at the site before the sarsen circle was built. This may originate from elsewhere.*
> *- The axis is closely although not exactly aligned to the midsummer sunrise.*

There is little or no chance of separating each of the phases of construction when approaching the monument on the ground. Indeed, the only effective way of making sense of the monument's design is to study a plan or bird's-eye view (*opposite and on page 60*). Without such a plan, visiting Stonehenge is like going to the National Gallery without a programme guide and where none of the paintings are labelled, yet nearly a million people do just that each year.

Orthodoxy at Stonehenge

Despite all the analyses undertaken over the past centuries by archaeologists, astronomers and cranks alike, Stonehenge remains largely enigmatic and mysterious.

Absolute facts about Stonehenge are surprisingly few and far between. The dating of Stonehenge I has been pushed back nearly 1000 years since 1960, as accurate radiocarbon dating techniques and improvements in understanding this period in British prehistory have placed the various phases of Stonehenge within older timeframes. The dates given throughout this text may be subject to further changes and should be regarded as approximate. The same caution applies to the order of building operations.

The units of length used at Stonehenge were, amongst others, the *Megalithic yard* (MY) and the *foot*, and these are used throughout this text. The Megalithic yard is 2.72 feet in length (0.83 m), whilst the foot is 0.3m in length. Later chapters will confirm the wisdom of adopting these and other ancient units of length.

The Circular Ditch and Bank

Stonehenge I began as an outer ditch and bank, built around 3150 BC. The bank was originally about six feet high and its diameter about 300 feet. As such, it would have provided a level horizon to an observer in the centre of the circle, a considerable astronomical advantage. A wide gap in the bank, roughly aligned to the solstice sunrise provided a horizon vista from which the extreme risings of the Sun and Moon could be observed. Later, this gap was widened further and a long causeway or processional walkway - *the Avenue* - was constructed. Two large stones now flanked the axis site line from the centre of the circle to the dawning midsummer sun. The left hand stone (no 97 on the HMSO plan) has long since vanished whilst the other, now recumbent, has regrettably become known as the *Slaughterstone*, once part of the right hand flank of the axis-entrance and in line with the *Heelstone*[1].

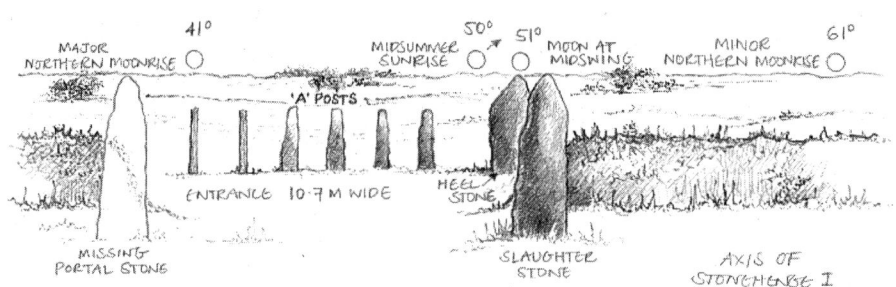

Figure 1.2 (a) The original axis entrance, looking from the centre of the henge with the solsticial and extreme lunar risings for 3000 BC shown.

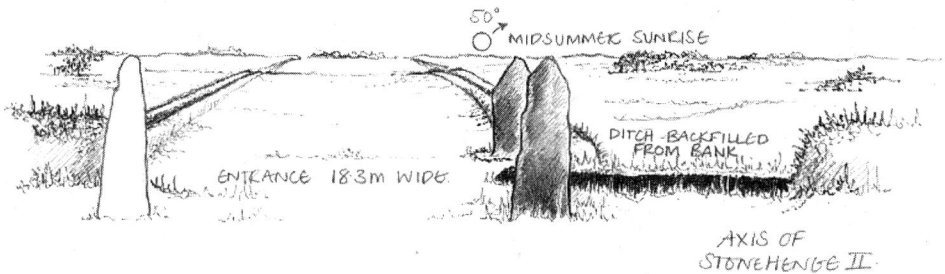

Fig. 1.2 *(b)* The later modifications to the entrance. The *Avenu*e runs for over 1800 feet, before turning sharply right down to the Avon river. *(After diagrams kindly supplied by Dr Aubrey Burl)*

Archaeologically, this gap was very 'busy' during the earliest times at Stonehenge. A great number of post-holes have been discovered around the entrance, these almost certainly being the socket holes for posts marking extreme lunar risings, which vary each month over a cycle which takes 18 years and 7 months to complete. The suspected layout of the entrance is shown in figure 1.2, and even in this first look at Stonehenge, we discover an astronomical purpose - the earliest known stage of the monument involved observations of the 18.61 year cycle of the Moon. Indeed, the monument was originally far more about *lunar* than *solar* astronomy.

The Aubrey Circle

Almost contemporary with the ditch and bank, the circular pattern of fifty-six Aubrey holes was dug. Each hole was accurately spaced around the perimeter of a circle 282 feet in diameter and each hole was originally about forty inches across and

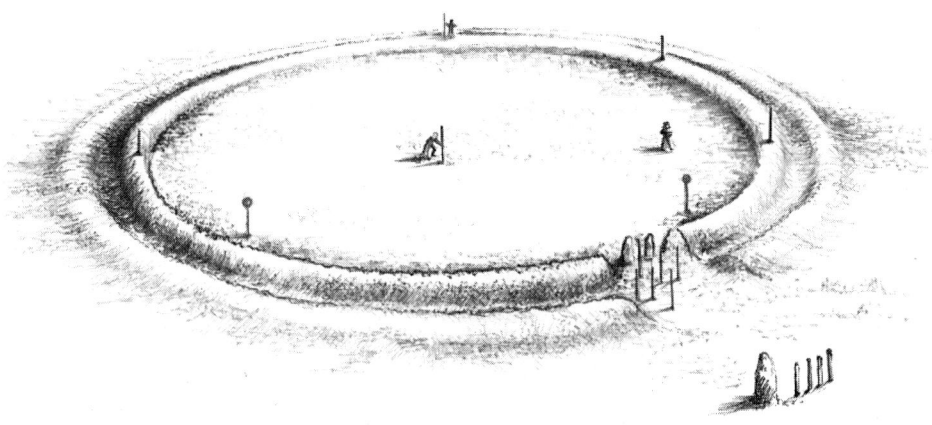

Figure 1.3.*(a)* Stonehenge: the ditch and bank - first known constructions

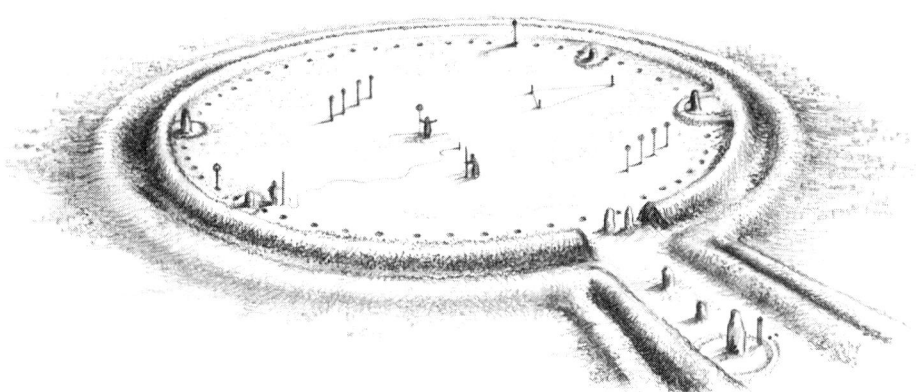

Figure 1.3 (b) Stonehenge I, showing the Aubrey hole circle.

32 inches deep. They were apparently filled in after a curiously short time and excavations have exposed bluestone chippings, remains of cremations, bones and ash. Figures 1.3(a) and (b) show the evolution of this first phase.

The choice of 56 holes for the Aubrey circle was no accident. Indeed, the very nature of the construction and the precision with which it was originally laid out show an intent which invites study: why 56 holes and why not sixty or fifty? The choice of 56 is in fact a numerical message, as valid as any heiroglyph inscribed on an Egyptian temple wall or a cuniform clay tablet from Babylon. We will discover its message later on, after this initial survey.

Some archaeologists suggest that these large holes once held huge posts, perhaps posts which supported a circular platform of wooden lintels.[2] Like so many other theories about Stonehenge, this is unlikely to be 'proved'. However, pursuing the 'artificial horizon' concept, the arrangement shown in figure 1.4 would have provided a level wooden horizon onto which the risings and settings of Sun, Moon, planets and stars could all have been accurately marked and recorded.

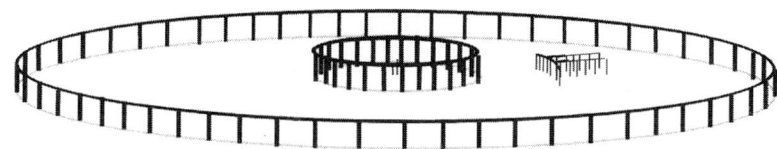

Figure 1.4 An artist's impression of a wooden 'Aubrey henge', where the 56 holes housed posts to support lintels 16 feet in length. The internal constructions are speculative, based on post holes found during excavations.

There is some evidence that a 78 foot diameter central wooden structure was associated with these early stages of Stonehenge. Its dimensions fit with other so-called 'calendar buildings'; the Sanctuary, near Avebury, and Woodhenge, within a mile of Stonehenge. Archaeologists have speculated that it may have been a roofed ceremonial dwelling-house, though with little consensus. However, it does seem likely, from evidence given, that this phase relied extensively on wooden construction techniques.

The Bluestone 'Q-R' circles and the four Station Stones

Following the initial activity on the Stonehenge site, a period of at least three centuries appears to have elapsed before substantial new building developments were deemed necessary, this time in stone rather than wood. It is now thought that, sometime after 2700 BC, three major additions were made to the site. The first was the placement of the four large *station stones* to form the corners of an accurate rectangle

Figure 1.5. Stonehenge, phase II, showing the station stone rectangle, the somewhat speculative central bluestone circles, and the axis 'avenue'.[4]

around the circumference of the Aubrey circle; the second was the arrival of some kind of central stone circle, using Welsh bluestone, with its entrance aligned to the existing axis. About 78 foot in diameter, it replaced any original building, although it is difficult to know quite where wooden post-holes end and stone holes begin. If this circle had ever been finished, it would have consisted of two concentric circles, each of 38 stones, with diameters 74 and 85 feet. Atkinson named their placement holes the *Q-R-hole system*. Finally, the *Avenue,* from the site along the midsummer sunrise axis, was constructed. The layout of these structures is shown in figure 1.5 above.

The two surviving station stones are *sarsens*, from the same source that was used, half a millenium later, to build most of the subsequent constructions. The sarsens come from the Marlborough Downs, near Avebury, some 24 miles to the north from Stonehenge. The missing stones were both originally set on mounds, the remains of which are still visible today on the plan. The rectangle formed by the four station stones is accurately rectangular[3] and has dimensions 96 MY by 40 MY. The diagonals of this rectangle coincide with the diameter of the Aubrey circle at 104 MY. Although the Aubrey holes had apparently been filled in by this time, sufficient evidence of their existence must still have been present in order to site the four station stones, an important point. A cursory inspection of the Thom survey plan (*facing page one*) reveals that the stations are almost but not exactly on the perimeter of the Aubrey circle and also that the rectangle they form lies perpendicular to the first 'posthole A' - the monument's *earlier* axis.

The Preseli Bluestones

The bluestones originated from the Preseli Mountains of West Wales, in the County of Pembrokeshire. The 'quarry' is a natural outcrop called *Carn Menyn*, and is 135 miles from Stonehenge. As some of the bluestones weigh in at over four tons, the removal and transport of these stones must engender a deep respect for the engineers responsible and informs us of an important quality attached to these stones - a *reason* for their use. We shall discover in a later chapter convincing evidence that *the original site* of the bluestones appears to have been an essential criterion for their importance and subsequent transportation to Stonehenge.

Bluestone is an extremely hard type of granite, called *dolerite*, with a blue-green colour flecked with white quartz, a combination which does resemble, with a little imagination and especially when wet, a starry night sky. The bluestone at Stonehenge was shown to originate from *Carn Menyn* in 1923, by petrologist Dr H.H.Thomas. It is certain that many of the stones were dressed *after* their long journey from Wales, for bluestone chippings have been found throughout the site; in Aubrey holes, along the nearby cursus and along the Avenue. Some of the bluestones are finely grooved (*figure 1.9*) and mortice holes may be seen on one bluestone, evidently once a lintel, near to the 'midsummer axis'.

The Sarsen Circle and Trilithon Ellipse

The next major phase of Stonehenge took place perhaps 600 years after the original ditch was completed. It required the transport and placement of the largest stones used in the entire development of Stonehenge, the heaviest weighing in at well over 50 tonnes, and all dragged 24 miles from Fyfield Down, near Avebury. It is these later massive engineering projects which people immediately associate with Stonehenge and to which they flock in their millions from all over the world.

It is perhaps too easily forgotten that the original henge-bank of Stonehenge 1 was over 320 feet in diameter and six feet high and that, within it, the 56 evenly spaced Aubrey holes - with or without posts/lintels - positioned around an 280 foot diameter circle must once have been a most impressive sight. The white chalk of the bank would have further enhanced the majesty of the site. The chalk is now grassed over, as are the Aubrey holes, and these earlier aspects of the monument are eclipsed by the remains of the massive sarsen circle and those of the five even more massive trilithons which once formed a complete inner 'horseshoe'. The bluestones, which were moved backwards and forwards several times before finally being put to rest as circles and ellipses within the sarsen circle and trilithon ellipse, also appear dwarfed by the sarsen circle and trilithon ellipse, yet placed anywhere else, such large and beautifully shaped stones would command enormous attention.

From 3100 BC to 2500 BC is a very long period of time, and yet, prior to this latter date, the only imposing stones erected at the monument were the bluestone concentric semi-circles, Atkinson's Q-R-system, the Slaughterstone, the Heelstone and the four station stones. In other words, *for over half a millenium*, the vast majority of stones used to build Stonehenge were Preseli bluestones. They are therefore associated with the earlier building phases of Stonehenge, that of the Aubrey hole circle and the four station stones. There is, however, a curious continuity between this circle and the much later sarsen circle, which will be explored later.

The Sarsen Circle

The sarsen circle was constructed around 2500 BC and is therefore contemporary with the current (and disputed) dating for the building of the Great Pyramid. It is a quite remarkable structure, unique and enigmatic, once comprising of 30 huge upright stones, towering five meters above the ground, arranged in a perfect circle, 100 feet in mean diameter, with 30 curved lintels accurately interlocked and jointed to form a circular and *almost perfectly level* circular platform six metres above the ground.[5]

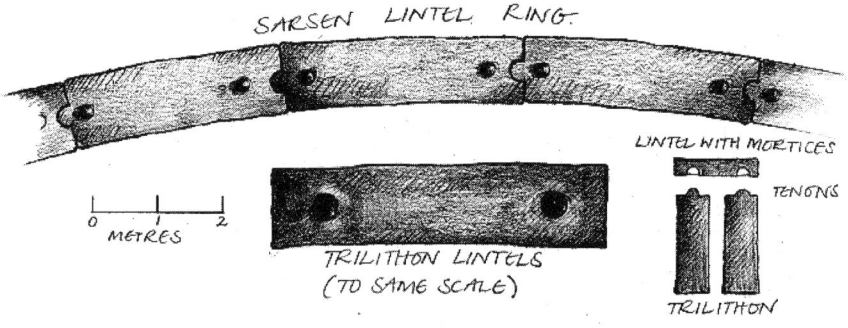

Figure 1.6 The Stonehenge lintels, showing mortice and tenon joints and, in the case of the sarsen circle, half-round 'jigsaw' joints.

Figure 1.7 Stonehenge - viewed from the eastern side. The tall single trilithon with its tenon joint rises above the other stones. To its right, a smaller sloping stone from the bluestone ellipse may be seen. The axis lintels remain from the once complete sarsen circle and the erosion of 5000 years may be seen by the concave appearance of the extreme right sarsen stone.

There are widespread theories concerning its original meaning, these range from stating that Stonehenge is a model of a UFO to the more probable theory that it formed a place of worship. Perhaps this just confirms to us that when mankind meets something apparently beyond understanding, something which is also awesome, then fantasies and fears are projected onto it. The sarsen circle remains the main feature people want to see when visiting the monument.

The sarsen lintels are locked into position onto their uprights in two dimensions, using half round 'jigsaw' joints and mortice holes (*see figure 1.6*), whilst the five trilithons used just mortice and tenon joints. The final results, in either case, were immensely strong structures 'henging' above the monument, and enough lintels have survived in place to enable the visitor to visualise how Stonehenge must have appeared when the sarsen circle was completed.

One of the upright stones (no.11 on the HMSO plan) forming the sarsen circle, the southernmost one, is half the width of the rest, a most odd feature. Archaeological orthodoxy suggested that the evolution of Stonehenge progressed inward with time with the conclusion that the trilithon ellipse was built *after* the sarsen circle. An engineer might be tempted to suggest that the resulting larger gap between this single thin stone and its neighbour was essential to allow the later and huge central trilithon blocks entrance into the central area - the gaps between all the other sarsen uprights are certainly insufficient to allow passage of those enormous inner stones. However, the difficulties of passing each of the huge trilithon stones through the gap between the half-width stone surely weighs against the trilithon ellipse being built after the sarsen ring. If the trilithons did come later, we must ask if the builders of the sarsen circle anticipated their building as part of the same building project and provided a single and barely adequate entrance through which to squeeze the inner 'monsters'.

To an astronomer, the half width stone provides a 'count' of twenty-nine and a half stone widths around the sarsen circle, suggesting that these upright stones could be used used to monitor full and new Moons - the lunation cycle is $29^{1/2}$ days long. Finally, a mathematician might assume the thin stone was untypical, count a total of 30 upright stones, and note that this was suggestive of a 12 month, 30-day calendar year of 360 days. Both these final points will be the subject of an in-depth treatment in later chapters. It would, however, be inaccurate to suggest that the thinner stone was the result of inaccuracy on the part of the architects or builders. The marking out of the sarsen circle involved dividing its circle perimeter into thirty equal segments, as an inspection of modern survey plans will reveal. This is no simple geometric construction.

The sarsen circle stones and lintels are carefully and precisely dressed on their inner surfaces, whilst the outer facing stones and their lintels remain much rougher. Clearly the interior circular space within the sarsen circle was important enough to

Figure 1.8 The Midsummer Axis. From the centre of Stonehenge, looking north-east, the main sarsen circle portals, with their lintels, frame the Heelstone (background). Between these features may be seen the recumbent and misnamed 'Slaughter stone', lying near the edge of the Aubrey circle. The ditch and bank are just visible. Two flanking bluestones, part of the bluestone circle, may be seen in the foreground. Note how differently these are shaped, the left hand one angular; the right hand one rounded. This juxta-positioning of 'male' and 'female' stones is typical of many stone circles, best seen at Avebury and the Hurlers, in Cornwall. The author is 5' 10" tall.

Figure 1.9 (a) The sole surviving upright (no 56) from the central trilithon. Note the tenon joint on the top face. Its one-time mate (55) has long since fallen and now lies in two pieces, whilst the lintel lies on its side, exposing its two mortice holes. On the upper side of this same stone, small dished mortices suggest either a dreadful mistake in the building supervision or the possibility of a raised structure once having existed on top of the central trilithon.

In front of the trilithon may be seen the grooved bluestone from the bluestone ellipse. This grooved bluestone may be one of a pair, as a tongued bluestone may be seen on site.

Figure 1.9 (b) The 'bum-stone' demonstrates the precision by which the grooved bluestone was shaped.

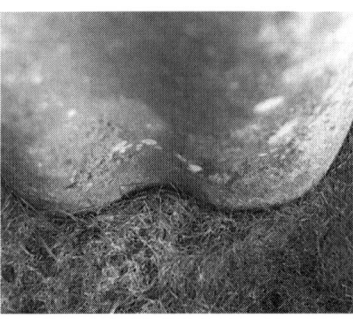

warrant such laborious attention by the stone masons. The sarsen circle is a true circle, some 97 feet across its inner diameter and 104 feet across its outer diameter. As we shall see, these dimensions can yield a great deal of information about the cultural landscape of the builders and an ancient 'canon of measure' by which they appear to have designed Stonehenge. For now, the resulting curvatures, jointing and surface finish of the sarsen circle is cause for sufficient admiration in itself, particularly in a structure built over 4000 years ago and which has survived adequately well to reveal its original form.

The Trilithon Ellipse

The largest and tallest stones at Stonehenge belong to a curious construction which broke the tradition of concentric circles, substituting five pairs of stones, each over 16 feet tall and capped with lintels, laid out on the circumference of an ellipse, with its major axis aligned to the 'midsummer axis' of Stonehenge. There is dispute over whether the shape is a pure ellipse or a horse-shoe; Alex Thom suggesting an ellipse proper with major axis 82 feet and minor axis 54 feet. The centre of this ellipse strays from the centre of the original monument by well over 3 feet, a further departure from convention (*figure 1.10*).

The largest, though not the heaviest stones, in the central trilithon weighed in at around 50 tons. One still stands, elegantly tapered and rising over 22 feet above the ground, showing off the tenon on its top face. Its one-time mate, and the curved lintel which once joined the pair, have fallen; the former split into two by the impact and the latter displaying the two splendid mortice holes gouged from its lower face. Curiously, its opposite side also contains dished mortices - either an embarrassing mistake or perhaps an indication that a stone structure once stood on top of the highest trilithon?

The height of the other trilithons progressively lessens - no level platform was intended here and their construction would also have lessened the usefulness of the level sarsen circle of lintels as an observing platform, or artificial horizon. These

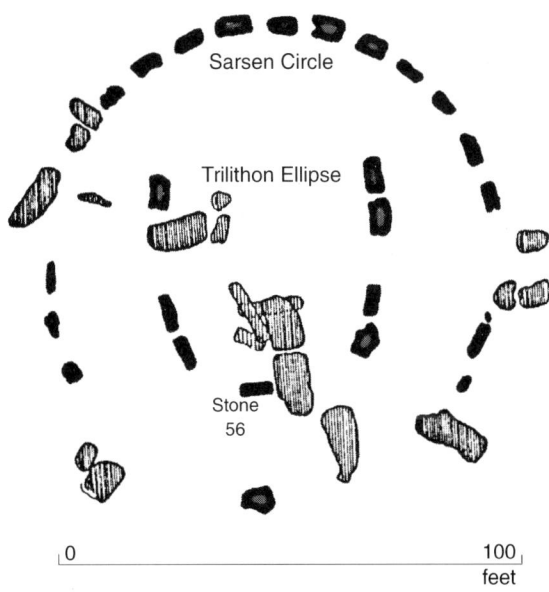

Figure 1.10 The trilithon ellipse in relationship to the sarsen circle.

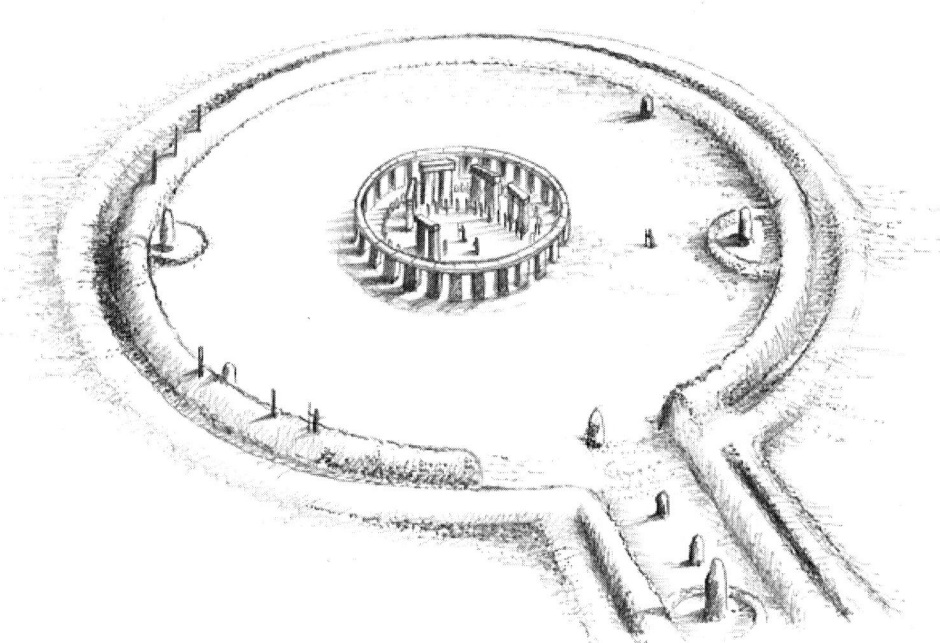

Figure 1.11 Stonehenge - the final temple / observatory. The addition of all the various stages of construction sums to show a diagram which, whilst perhaps unrealistic, assists our understanding of the relative dimensions of each phase and their inter-relationships. The final constructions, the bluestone circle and ellipse, may be seen within the sarsen circle and were probably placed there around 2000 BC. History leaves almost no clues as to why Stonehenge then became much less important to the culture which built it.

most massive stones remain perhaps the most enigmatic of all, despite being thought to have been erected almost at the end of Stonehenge's development, after 2400 BC.[6] Five huge portals once towered above a monument already over 500 years into its evolution, and we still don't really know why.

Compared to the sarsen circle, the trilithon ellipse has fared rather better, perhaps due to the sheer bulk of these stones making vandalism or removal proportionately more difficult. Three of these massive stone trilithons survive, whilst two are now represented by singletons, obviously minus lintels. These biggest stones at the monument have tempted hundreds of visitors throughout history to seek immortality by carving their initials and other *graffiti* on the first two metres of their height. A facsimile of a Mycean dagger and axe-heads, possibly even a 'goddess figure', may be seen and the high standard of ancient graffiti lettering ('JOHANNES DEFERRE' is the best example) makes the more recent examples appear to be the work of barbarians.

Only a 'special access' tour will enable the modern visitor to Stonehenge to experience these secondary features directly, although the nearby shop stocks a wide range of books and post-cards which display these features.

The Bluestone Circle

The use of bluestones within the earliest phases of Stonehenge links the monument to their source, the Preseli mountains of West Wales, some 135 miles to the northwest as the crow flies. An immediate question which springs from this connection is: *why was this stone or its location so important to the designers of Stonehenge?* A surprising amount can be done to answer this question, and later chapters provide much new material on the enigmatic bluestones. First we might look at the existing orthodoxy about these beautiful stones and also an odd-ball stone found at Stonehenge.

Atkinson felt that the bluestones were recycled and probably stored for periods of time during Stonehenge's earlier evolution. More modern work suggests that the bluestone circle now found within the sarsen circle was placed there within a century of 2200 BC, with the bluestone ellipse following before 2000 BC. They are thus late constructions, and only those rough half-hearted Y- and Z- holes came after, perhaps between 2000 BC and 1600 BC. From this we can conclude that Stonehenge's most magnificent building phase was over by 2400 BC.

There is a view that the bluestones arrived on Salisbury Plain courtesy of glacial flow during the last Ice Age[7], an accident of geological and climatic fortune rather than of any intent on the part of megalithic Man. Two factors weigh in heavily against this opinion. Firstly, why did no other monument in the Wessex culture utilise large bluestones? Secondly, we might ask why this huge glacier apparently only transported a few dozen bluestones and then only around Stonehenge and *environs*? In West Wales, the farming and building community have traditionally recognised the great strength of this material, gate-posts and lintels galore may be found throughout the region to suggest that bluestones found littered on a landscape become incorporated into human artefacts. No such artefacts are found in the Wessex region.

One of the stones at Stonehenge, the 'Altar Stone', is made of Cosheton Beds sandstone, a sparkling micaceous stone found only at a single lowland location near Milford Haven and the *Cleddau* river estuary - the same spot where the bluestones are assumed to have have embarked on their journey to Stonehenge on rafts. It is a very large stone, bigger than any of the bluestones, once being some 16 feet long and over three wide, with a thickness of 1.8 feet. It is now broken into two. Did this singleton also get to Stonehenge by glaciation and, if so, why did only one stone, albeit a most important one, make this trip? The southern limit of the last Ice Age glaciation (Devensian) apparently never reached the *Cleddau*.[8]

Four stones at Stonehenge are made from *rhyolite*. These are identical in colouring, mode of weathering and all structural and minerological details with rhyolite boulders found at *Carn Alw*[9], in the Preseli range about a mile from the bluestone site. Thus, all the foreign stones (discounting the sarsen stones as 'foreign') at Stonehenge originated from the Preseli region of West Wales.

In 1985, divers found what appears to be a large dressed bluestone similar in size and shape to those at Stonehenge, in the waters off Burton, in the Haven. If the bluestones were transported to Stonehenge via the *Cleddau* estuary, as the author

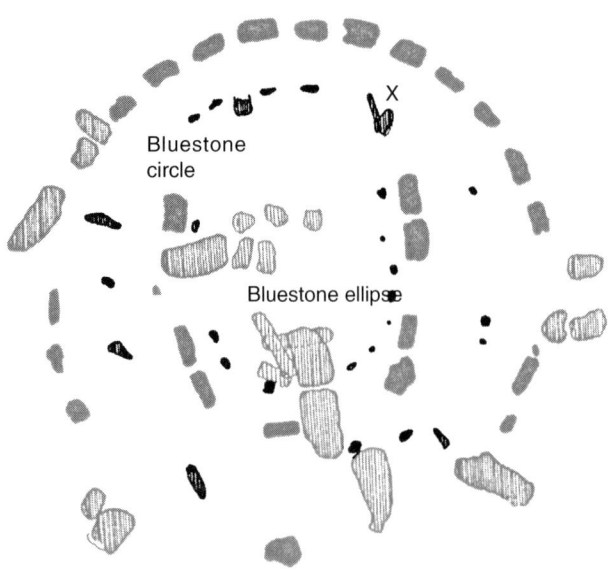

Figure 1.12 The bluestone ellipse, sitting inside the trilithon ellipse, is probably a rag-bag collection of stones made up from an earlier structure. Elegant in shape they contrast sharply with the stones in the rougher bluestone circle, which lies between the sarsen circle and the trilithon ellipse. The recumbent stone marked 'X' was once a lintel, the mortice holes still clearly visible.

believes they were, then the link with the adjacent Cosheton source of stone is obvious. However, if glaciation flow picked up the Altar Stone, together with bluestones from *Carn Menyn* (mysteriously found nearby) at Cosheton, then the flow to Stonehenge was almost directly east *and* from a lowland source, whilst other geological evidence points to a southeasterly flow for the glacial ice-sheet, with stones being gouged off outcrops on the summits of mountains, thence carried along with the flow and ultimately dumped as the ice melted. Whatever, we shall discover that *how* the stones arrived at Stonehenge is less important than *why* the Preseli site is so vital to understanding certain aspects of Stonehenge's architectural design.

If we still cannot answer for sure how the bluestones arrived at Stonehenge, we can at least recognise their importance. They were apparently used and re-used throughout the active life of the monument. Because one stone is grooved along its entire side, another tongued, and a bluestone lintel with mortice holes is still visible on site, we are safe in assuming that some kind of henge structure in bluestone once existed, perhaps from elsewhere. This supports the concept of an early prototype henge circle at Stonehenge - an original 'Stonehenge' about which we know very little - might it have come ready dressed from Wales?[10].

Today, the bluestones may be found in two distinct constructions. The first group consists of lightly dressed stones placed in a circle halfway between the sarsen circle and the trilithon ellipse. Once there may have been 59 stones[11], a figure based on the average spacing of the surviving stones around the circumference of the circle. The eleven standing survivors form a rather motley collection, five of them leaning, and the circle does not appear to have been laid out with much aesthetic sense, although the size of stones increases as the circle meets the axis. Some stones are squared off, others rounded, but with none of the order one can find at other sites, Avebury for example. Two stones were tooled as curved lintels. If this circle is the remains of previous constructions re-cycled for purposes unclear, then the builders failed to create the elegant symmetry and juxtapositioning of stones so typical of other stone rings.

A circle of 59 stones would have made good sense within a monument like Stonehenge - two lunar months take almost an exact 59 days to complete and the fractional '$^1/_2$' of the twenty-nine *and a half* day period of the lunar month disappears within just two months.

The Bluestone Ellipse

The other bluestone construction is a part ellipse inboard of the trilithon ellipse and more or less concentric to it. There is dispute over its geometry, as there is over nearly every other feature at Stonehenge. Its radius, in the rear half of the construction is 5.8 metres, which is almost exactly seven of Alex Thom's Megalithic yards - more on this unit of length later on. There were once 19 tall and slender finely tooled stones within this innermost construction, whilst only about half that number remain today, including the grooved bluestone. A further stone was tongued, and may have formed a pair with the grooved stone. Some of the stones once held lintels; other henge-like structures once occupied the site. Nineteen is another number very significant in a monument which is intended to be used to understand solar and lunar cycles. From any start time, nineteen years finds the Sun and Moon returned to precisely the same positions in the sky; it is the closest synchronicity between years (19) and lunar months (235) and is called the Metonic cycle.

Both these bluestone constructions thus appear to have been assembled from the remains of an earlier building. Whether this was built inside the present trilithon ellipse, at the centre of Stonehenge, or off-site, as Atkinson suggested, will be hard to prove. The student of this enigmatic monument is left with these few but significant facts: the bluestones formed a vitally important role at Stonehenge, some were shaped to form a henge-like construction, the original source of these stones is known and they were used and re-used at least once throughout the life of the monument.

The Y and Z Holes

Outboard of the sarsen circle are the remains of two rather ill-defined circles of holes. Compared to the earlier Aubrey holes (called the X holes by Aubrey, hence the nomenclature for these two later circles), they are each very roughly contained near to a given radius, 59 feet for the Y holes and 84 feet for the Z holes, some opinion even suggesting they took a spiral geometry. They were dug later than the sarsen circle, for one of these holes (Z7) cuts through the ramp once used for erecting a sarsen upright. There are 30 Y holes and 29 Z holes (although there is a space for the thirtieth hole). This totals 59 holes, interestingly, the same number as stones in the bluestone circle. They are illustrated in figure 1.13..

There is evidence that stones were never placed in these 3 foot deep holes; no compression or resistivity changes have been detected. Z8 was never dug and Atkinson postulated that this, plus the late dating for the feature (c.1700 - 1600 BC), may suggest that the Stonehenge community faced some cataclysmic change of circumstances. By 1600 BC, the era of stone ring building was almost ready for the history books, and we know that climatic changes from volcanic eruptions in Iceland, circa 1640 BC, caused the rapid human evacuation from huge tracts of land in Scotland together with the need to adapt to a weather system change which took southern Britain from a climate similar to modern northern Spain into one much like our present wet and cloudy climate.

Britain is today not an ideal place to take regular astronomical observations. Evidently it was once the ideal place to build megalithic monuments and we will discover that astronomy and megaliths are very closely connected. Perhaps the Stonehenge project came to an end simply because it was no longer possible to maintain the same enthusiasm and vigour for skywatching - the culture moved on to other things, other priorities. Perhaps survival needs stole back all the manpower hours needed to build and maintain Stonehenge, estimated by Hawkins[12] at 1,500,000 man-days. The Wessex culture evolved such that this astonishing amount of labour

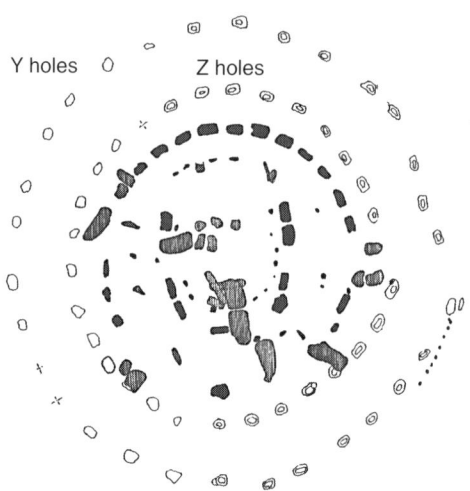

Figure 1.13 The Y and Z holes. Not visible on site at Stonehenge, these remain perhaps the most enigmatic feature of the monument.

was evidently left over from furnishing the primary needs of the society and diverted into labour intensive cultural pursuits such as megalithic building and programmes of long-term astronomical observation. We must marvel that so much of it has survived and has begun to reveal some of its secrets to our modern culture.

Summary

In these first pages we have built up a picture of Stonehenge's evolution in time and location. This, like the building of the monument itself, is a *pastiche* of the painstaking work of many great men over many centuries through at least two major cultural shifts. It may not be a completely accurate picture, the culture was pre-literate, at least in our modern sense, and left no plans nor written records. Instead they left their massive civil engineering projects, together with burials and cremations at auspicious places within their monuments. We shall discover that death and the treatment of the dead is to be found linked with megaliths and hence the sky throughout the megalithic culture, as it was in so many other ancient cultures.

Making sense of Stonehenge must begin by understanding the legacy left on the ground today. As far as is possible we must let the stones speak for themselves, without projecting our twentieth century cultural gloss onto the culture that erected them. The megalithic monuments themselves are our most reliable guides to the quality of ancient thought, from which an exploration of hypotheses and speculation can more safely begin. Hopefully the reader now has a better perspective on the hardware to enable a useful astronomical and geometrical study of the monument to be undertaken. Both these subjects are ultimately to do with *measurement*, the former of the sky and the latter the Earth. The ancient adage, *as above, so below*, is endorsed completely by analysis of the geometry and the units of length used in the construction of Stonehenge.

Footnotes to Chapter One

1. The name of the Heelstone may derive from *Heol* = *Sun* and also *Way* or *Road* in Welsh, the oldest European language. The portal structure of the axis-entrance is hinted at by the original illustration, *figure 9.1,* on page 159.

2. By several authors, but recently and most notably by Professor John North in his book, '*Stonehenge - Neolithic Man and the Cosmos*', Harper Collins (1996). North gives the average hole size as 1.06m dia. and 0.8m deep (3.478 feet dia. and 2.62 feet deep).

3. Certainly better right-angles than the corners of most modern buildings.

4. The *phases* of Stonehenge derive from the late professor Richard Atkinson's work on the monument, as described within his book, *Stonehenge* (1956). Although chronologically defunct, they describe a useful order of construction.

5. Within 7 inches over 100 feet, a slope of less than 0.34 degrees. Billiard tables are acceptable to this degree of levelling. The site is rather unusual in that the original henge is not level - sloping from north to south.

6. *Stonehenge*. R.J.C. Atkinson (Penguin Books), 1979, sets the chronology of the trilithons before 2000 BC.

7. G.A.Kellaway, *Glaciation and the Stones of Stonehenge*, Nature 232, no 5314, 30 - 35pp (1971).

8. D.Q.Bowen. *The Llanelli Landscape*. LBC (1980).

9. Dr H.H.Thomas. *The Sources of the Stones at Stonehenge*, Antiquaries Journal, Vol 3 (1923). 239-264pp.

10. *The First Stonehenge* by Gaynor Francis. C. Davies (1986) ISBN 0 7154 0666 3

11. Stukely (1723) claimed forty, Wood (1740) twenty-nine, whilst Atkinson claimed between 59 and 61 stones.

12. Gerald S. Hawkins. *Stonehenge Decoded*. Fontana, 1972, p101.

Above: Stukeley's Stonehenge. The familiar English Heritage photograph of Stonehenge taken under light snow. Modern computer techniques have allowed removal of the roads, fences, tarmac paths, security shelters and modern forestation. The snow brings the *Avenue* at Stonehenge into clear relief.

Chapter Two

- CALENDARS OF STONE -

Sunwatching at Stonehenge

At the latitude of Stonehenge, a little over 51° north, the seasonal cycle of the Sun's risings and settings moving along the horizon is remarkable, obvious and blatantly evident to anyone living an outdoor existence. Thus begins our first obstacle in understanding the *astronomy* of Stonehenge and the megalithic culture that built it, for our modern world has replaced the night sky with street-lights and today only a few souls think it important to observe sunrises and sunsets. In comparison to our forebears, we are mostly barbarians when it comes to basic astronomy.

The annual cycle of changes in the rising and setting positions of the Sun against the horizon are a direct consequence of the $23^{1/2}°$ tilt angle of the Earth's axis. The seasons are directly caused by this tilt of the Earth as are the changes in the length of day and night throughout the year. All these things have changed very little since megalithic times, the angular range of sunrises (and sunsets) along the horizon at Stonehenge being about 80°.

Many megalithic monuments have their axis or entrance shaft aligned to one of the key sunrise or sunset positions, and evidently neolithic folk well understood this yearly rhythm of the Sun's risings and settings. Figure 2.2 (a) shows a photograph of

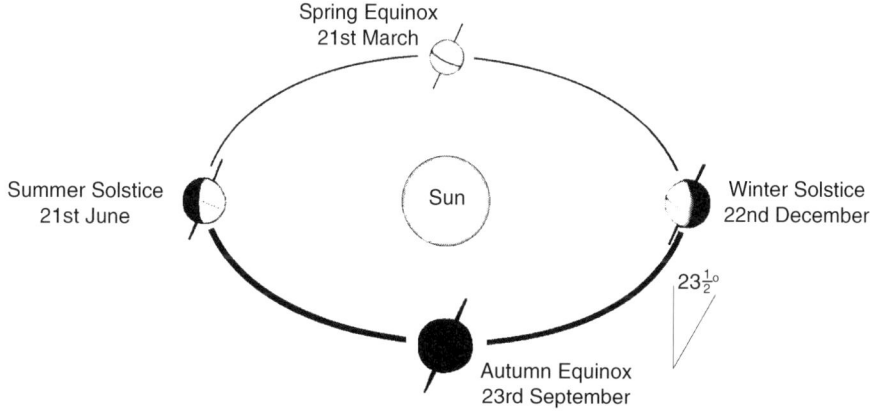

Figure 2.1(a). The Earth's axial tilt causes the seasons and the annual range of sunrise and sunset positions on the horizon.

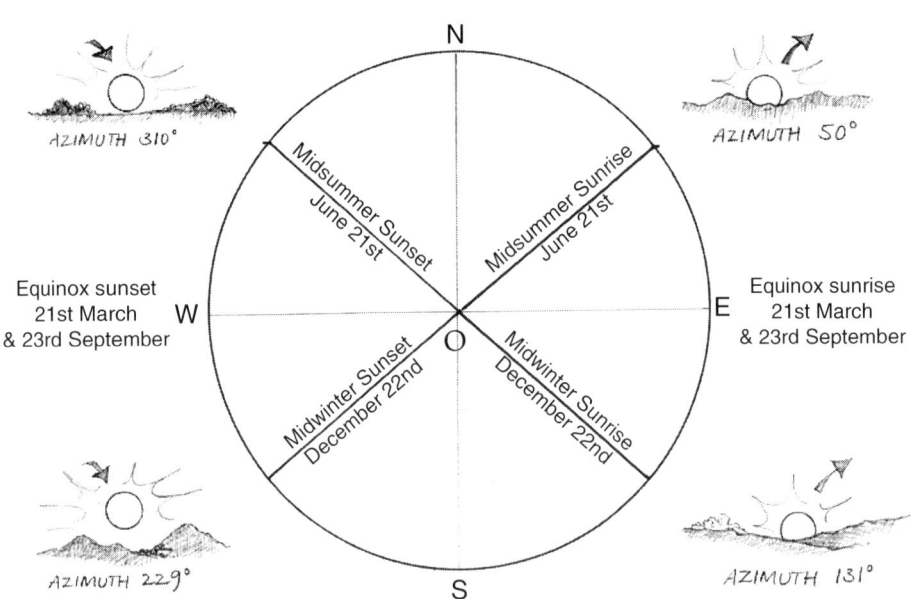

Figure 2.1 (b) At the latitude of Stonehenge an observer at point '0' sees, in one year, sunrises and sunsets travel along the horizon about 40° either side of the East-West equinoctial sunrise and sunset position. (*Azimuth = angle measured clockwise from true north*). The Moon's extreme risings and settings occur ten degrees either side of these four positions, taking 230 lunar months or 18.62 years to complete their cycle.

a monument erected to face the midsummer sunset; the small triangular spaces formed between the front support stone and the two rear support stones allows the setting Sun to shine through the monument only during the week of the solstice. Newgrange, that showpiece of ancient Irish megalithic achievement, was built so that its axis allowed the rays of the dawning midwinter Sun to penetrate right into the central chamber of the monument [*figure 2.2(b)*]. So elaborate and well engineered is the so-called 'roof-box' to enable this phenomenon to occur, once a year, that initial doubts about it being a coincidence have long since evaporated.

Stonehenge was constructed, from the earliest phase of its evolving design, with its axis more or less aligned to the midsummer sunrise. The Rev. William Stukeley opened our eyes to this alignment, in 1740, and thus single-handedly began what has since become the specialist subject of astro-archaeology, also called archaeo-astronomy.[1] Although the alignment is now only approximate, (due to the gradual decrease in the Earth's axial tilt since neolithic times), it is not possible to dismiss or ignore the fact that the axis of symmetry of Stonehenge is closely aligned to the Sun's most northerly rising - at the summer solstice. It remains a signature of the design - a message for our times about the cultural importance of astronomical cycles in the distant past.

Wheels within Wheels - The Whirling Sky

Each and every day, the entire sky appears to rotate once. Within this revolving sky, a given star may be observed to always rise and set at the same relative positions on the horizon at a given latitude; at least during a human lifetime.[2] The latitude of the observing site will determine where these positions will occur. The times of rising and setting will also rotate once around the clock-face during the year, because the solar day is slightly longer than the *sidereal* or star day.[3] Some stars never rise and set - the *circumpolar stars* are always revolving above us in the northern skies[4], although they are only visible at night.

The Sun, Moon and planets move relative to the fixed stars and each other, and this movement can be seen after only a few nights observation, as can the changes in their rise and set azimuths. This is why the planets are so-called, for the word *planet* means 'wanderer' in Greek, and we must certainly include the Sun and Moon within this category, for wander they both do.

Figure 2. 2. Solstitial Alignments, (a) Llech y Drybedd, Cardigan; summer solstice sunset, and (b) Newgrange, Boyne Valley, Ireland; winter solsticesunrise

The megalithic culture undertook the necessary observations and building techniques required to understand *where* in the sky these objects might be at any given time, and *when* and *where* they might rise and set. Implied within this task was a need to understand time and space and we have incontrovertible evidence that this understanding evolved through the *accurate* measurement of rising and setting angles against the horizon.

An Angle for all Seasons

Let us briefly look at how this technique was applied by neolithic astronomers. Throughout northwestern Europe, the culture that produced Stonehenge was also identifying and then using distant mountain peaks as *foresights* to mark the key turning points of the rising and setting Sun at the solstices. The observer's position is crucial to obtaining the utmost accuracy and at a few of these sites, one may find a marker stone, or a stone platform, termed a *backsight*, to indicate the precise spot from where the observation must be taken. The arrangement is rather akin to a rifle's sight - the longer the barrel, the greater the potential resolution accuracy. At some sites, the foresight is many tens of miles from the backsight, enabling an astonishing angular resolution to be established - certainly down to a few minutes of arc. The author has been able to resolve 3 minutes of arc during Sun and Moonset observations whilst David Furlong, whose book *The Keys to the Temple* (Piatkus 1997) claims an accuracy of less than 2 minutes of arc is possible for linear alignments - suggests less than 50 metres error in 19 kilometres. These figures agree well with Alex Thom's claims in various publications and letters.

Sometimes, a large stone will be found drawing the eye towards the direction of the distant foresight, such being the case at the Kintraw site, where extensive investigation by Alex Thom and Prof. Euan MacKie found and subsequently excavated an 'observing platform' which was apparently artificially constructed. From this *place* the distant mountain peaks of the *Paps of Jura* showed the actual moment of the winter solstice on one day alone [*figure 2.3(a)*]. At sunset, the Sun was seen to slip

Figure 2.3 (a) The Kintraw winter solstice alignment (after Thom and MacKie).

Figure 2.3 (b) The Ballochroy summer solstice marker.

down the right-hand slope of the mountain, its last flash confirming the *time* of the solstice. Three standing stones at nearby Ballachroy perform exactly the same function at the summer solstice [*figure 2.3 (b)*] .

At the Merrivale stone rows, on Dartmoor, the end of the longer row is blocked by a four-square dressed granite stone from which the summer solstice sunset could be observed slipping into an 'enhanced' natural rock outcrop on Middle Staple Tor, about two miles away [*figure 2.3(c)*][5].

Figure 2.3(c). Merrivale summer solstice and 18.61 year 'lunstice' lunar alignment (major standstill). Both foresights show evidence of having been 'enhanced' to suit their task.

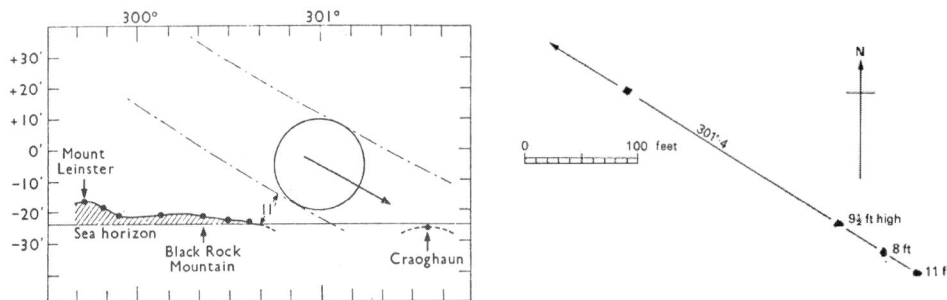

Figure 2.3(d). Parc yr Meirw 'lunstice' alignment (minor standstill).

The Sun is not the only body to have commanded this kind of attention - the Moon's risings and settings were similarly monitored. Although the Moon is dealt with later, the following demonstrations of megalithic interest in the 18.6 year cycle of the Moon's maximum rising and setting points against the horizon are shown below. At Merrivale, the end of the shorter row serves as the backsight for a lunar alignment - it allows the *major standstill*[6] of the Moon to be seen as the midwinter full Moon sets at its maximum azimuth, once every 18.6 years, into a natural feature further along Staple Tor [*figure 2.3(c)*].

Parc yr Meirw, near Fishguard, aligns to the *minor standstill*, which was observed (January 1997) by the writer as the full Moon set by slipping down the side of Mount Leinster, nearly 80 miles away in Ireland, an event only observable once every 18.6 years (*see figure 2.3(d) above*). The reader may be assured from these sites and many others, that ancient astronomers were marking the key positions of the Sun and Moon.

Measuring the Year

It is one thing to observe and measure the angles of sunrises and sunsets at the summer and winter solstices, but quite another to assume that in 3000 BC the number of days in the solar year was accurately known and recorded. The mathematical tables impressed into clay tablets in Babylon suggest otherwise[7], as do the fundamental dimensions of certain Egyptian buildings[8], but these artefacts from the Middle Eastern cultures are dated from a *later period* than the earlier phases of Stonehenge. What evidence do we have that might suggest that ancient Europeans were actually counting the days in the year?

The famed *Venus of Laussal* sculpture shows a pregnant women or 'goddess' figure holding a crescent or lunar shaped horn inscribed with fourteen notches, these dating way back into mesolithic times. This seems to indicate a knowledge of the menstrual cycle and/or the monthly ovulation period which occurs about fourteen days after each period. Bones have also been discovered with ordered number patterns which also may correspond to lunar cycles, these dating back to 30,000 BC.

There would not appear to be a giant intellectual gap between carving 13 or 14 notches on a stick or bone and the enlarged process of recording the 365 day solar cycle. Indeed, 'artistic' solar and lunar designs incorporating relevant astronomical or even planetary data are quite widespread, even if unrecognised by conventional archaeology[10]. Even today, there are cultures around the globe which use a 'sun-stick' for calendrical purposes; structuring time is still and probably always has been, a vital aspect of human life. The additional ability to accurately date the solstices or equinoxes, using horizon markers, inevitably would have slotted this routine day/night counting into regular number patterns and sequences from whence our first astronomy and mathematics evolved. The date of this giant leap for mankind is lost forever in the mists of antiquity, but we shall begin to amass firm evidence that it first took place and was developed in neolithic Britain[11].

Because the Earth's orbit is not perfectly circular, the equinoxes and solstices do not occur with an equal number of days between them - they do not divide the year into four equal parts. This may be checked today with any modern calendar or diary - currently the summer half of the year is about 10 days longer than the winter half. Therefore, for an alignment to act for *both* the spring and autumn 'solar equinox', equally dividing the year into two, counting *must* have been employed and therefore the number of days in the year were known. Such alignments are found throughout northwestern Europe. Repeated division by two then gave the dates for the quarter days - still celebrated today as Imbolc, Beltane, Lammas and Samhain; whilst one further division gave sixteen 'months' varying between 22 and 24 days each in duration. Alex Thom produced much statistical evidence that ancient man succeeded in making single sets of horizon markers cover both halves of the year - multiple division by two then offering a 16 month neolithic calendar.

Recording the Length of the Year

At the latitude of northern Europe, it is extremely easy to establish that 365 sunrises occur during the annual cycle of the Sun. Confirmation requires only the ability to differentiate between day and night, and two cloud free sunrises (or sets) during the equinoctial periods (March 21st and September 23rd). At the equinoxes, the Sun rises almost exactly due east of an observer placed anywhere on the globe. In addition, at the latitude of southern Britain, each successive sunrise finds the Sun more than its own diameter further along the horizon, which makes identification of the date a very easy matter. The author has made these solar observations many times, using nothing more than a telegraph pole used as a foresight and positioned about half a mile from an observing platform, appropriately provided by a neolithic burial chamber.

From the top of West Wales' most famous peak, *Carn Ingli*, two distant mountain peaks, *Penberi* and *Carn Llidi*, form a natural 'egg-cup' into which the Sun sets on February 18th each year (*figure 2.4.(a)*). This perfectly arranged site allows the length of the solar year to be ascertained to an accuracy well within one day. In fact, the set up allows an observer to recognise that the solar year is 365 *plus about a quarter of a day* long.[12] 365 days, not 364 nor 366, is the number of days one observes for the year and would surely have been the number of notches on a neolithic astronomer's tally stick. The Welsh Bard Taliesin reminds us[13] that he knows who it was '*who emptied the bowl, where the dawn terminates*'; all within a poem filled with soli-lunar allegory. The origins of the glyph of the zodiacal sign Libra, probably from ancient Egypt, are a round Sun placed in a bowl-shaped foresight, either setting or rising, and this remains the sign of the autumn equinox. [⊖]

Figure 2.4(b) shows how the Sun rises around an equinoctial marker at the latitude of Stonehenge at successive sunrises. The size of the solar disc is about 0.6°, whilst the next sunrise in springtime occurs at about 0.8° further northwards against the horizon, an angle which is easily measured using the most rudimentary of foresight markers.[14]

If the reader requires further proof of neolithic strivings to understand the patterns of the Sun and Moon in Europe, a visit to the Newgrange and Knowth complex in the Boyne Valley, Ireland is recommended. Repeated solar and lunar numbers predominate as patterns and linear markings on hundreds of large kerbstones.

Figure 2.4(a) A natural landscape feature used to measure the solar year to within a day. Although the foresight alignment is 22 miles from the observer's position on the peak of *Carn Ingli*, a cairn about half a mile away and visible under the right hand peak, marks the alignment, just as does the cairn at Kintraw (*see fig.2.3.(a)*).

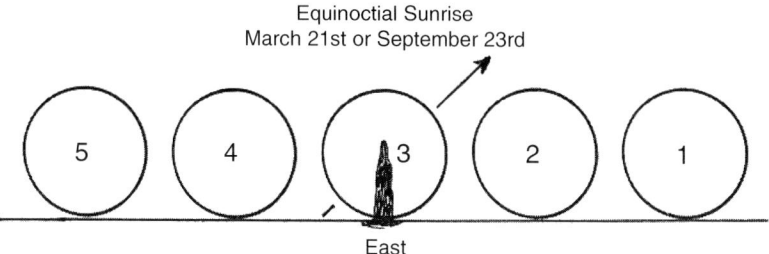

Figure 2.4 *(b)* Successive equinoctial sunrises at the latitude of Stonehenge.

Because we now look in reference books in order to 'know' that the true length of the tropical solar year is 365.2422 days long, it does not follow that there are 365.2422 sunrises in the year! A moment's thought will indicate the absurdity of such a statement. In truth, there are almost exactly 1461 sunrises in four years, division by 4 yielding (almost) the exact period taken by the Earth to orbit the Sun. It is the Earth's orbital period around the Sun which takes 365.2422 days to complete and this has not measurably changed since Stonehenge was constructed. 365 days is the nearest whole number observed for the length of any single year and, we are stuck with this number - it is *immutable*. Unfortunately, as we shall now discover, it is rather difficult to produce a sensible calendar system using this number.

365 : A Mathematical Inconvenience

365 is not a terribly easy number of days for the length of the year. Purely on a practical level, the year naturally divides into *two* halves - winter and summer. The seasons, framed by the two solstices and two equinoxes, suggest a natural division of the year by *four*. If we include months, then it would be ever so convenient if our calendar year divided by *twelve* (or perhaps *thirteen*, as we will suggest later). Finally, if we retain the worldwide adoption of seven days in a week, based on the Sun, Moon and five visible planets and enshrined in the creation story of Genesis, then we require our calendar year to divide by *seven*.

> *The choice of 365 days for the year within our present calendar system fails to meet every single one of the above requirements.*

To a mathematician or calendar maker, the factors of 365 (1 x 5 x 73) are dismally few and wholly inconvenient. This makes our present calendar, based on 365 days, a complete folly. Whilst astronomically correct, this number is a veritable 'pig' when it comes to designing a calendar structure and we must dwell on this a little further, for it has a lot to tell us about calendars and about Stonehenge.

29

364 : The Calendrical Wonder Number

The nearest number to 365 which has a range of suitable factors is 364. The factors of this number are 2, 2, 7 and 13, and they are indeed very suitable[15]. It is therefore not too surprising that we find that they lurk within our present 365-based calendar system. Despite the present choice of a twelve month year, we all think that there are 52 weeks in the year (4 seasons x 13 weeks), we use a seven day week and often make the assumption that there are 4 weeks in the month (4 x 7 = 28 days). We are taught as young children that there are 12 months in the year. This 'knowledge' takes us into dangerous waters, for the consequences of these assumptions lead to an implied year length, formed by multiplying 4 x 7 x 12, of 336 days. We are therefore missing one lunar month (29 days) by making these erroneous assumptions. The numbers here are shouting out that *we need a thirteenth month* and bright ten year olds with cheap calculators can work all this out. So did someone else many, many years ago, enshrining this wisdom in the world's most popular game.

A Year of Cards

If you pick up a pack of ordinary playing cards you will discover four suites, each of thirteen cards; two black suites and two red ones. The counting of the 'pips' is very revealing, taking the Jack (knave) as 11, the Queen as 12 and the King as 13, they total 91 within each suite, the complete pack totalling 364 'pips' (*figure 2.5*). A pack of cards actually represents the ancient calendar system based on 364 days. Furthermore, the symbolism found within the pack has a great deal to tell us about our myths and legends. Twelve and thirteen are juxtaposed within each suite as the Queen and King - there is a gender allocated to each number - and numerical supremacy goes to the King, as perhaps we might have suspected in our present culture. The King is taken to be the 'highest' value card, and is surrounded by twelve lesser cards - 'disciples'. We can all still immediately identify here with our own cultural 'solar heroes' - King Arthur and Jesus, both of whom took the enigmatic thirteenth position amongst twelve disciples or knights. A similar mythology may be found in Mayan American culture, where there were thirteen gods until their leader *Kukulcan*, vanished withour trace, leaving twelve. This left the Aztecs constantly alert for the re-appearance of their own equivalent thirteenth god *Quetzalcoatl*, which cost them dearly, for one day they mistook the arrival of a Spanish galleon with the god's expected return - with horrendous consequences which cost them no less than their civilisation.

A thinly veiled but easily accessible calendraic information lurks within every pack of cards as it does within our myths, folkstories, religious codices and legends. The pack of cards is a very ancient artefact but clearly it is shown to be related to a 364 day calendar year structure.

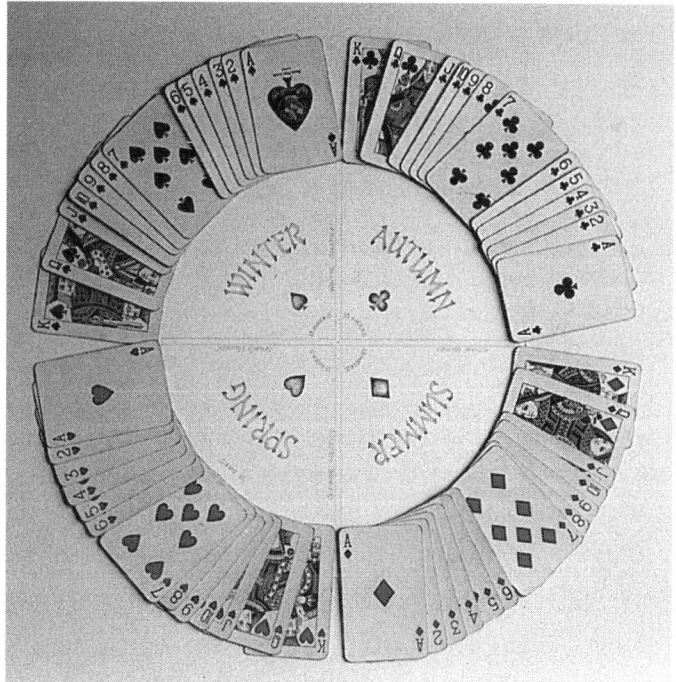

Figure 2.5. A pack of cards seen as a 364 day calendar analogy. Black and red on a white background, these are the three colours traditionally associated with the Moon. The four suites of 13 cards has seven as the central card.

An Irrational Legacy : 365 into 364 won't go

Cramming the 365-day Roman 'Julian' (later 'Gregorian') calendar into a 364-day based structure automatically spills out irrational numbers all over the place. For example, within our present calendar, there are 52.142857+[16] weeks in the year, 4.34523+ weeks in an 'average' month and month lengths which vary from 28 to 31 days - average 30.41666+ days - and which require the repetition of a crazy little rhyme in order to remember which months have 30 and which 31 days. Hardly a logical system, but then Roman mathematics and their numeral set held back mathematics in Europe until well after 1100 AD, when our present arabic numerals were introduced. Try multiplying XVII by IX if you need more proof of Roman mathematical ineptness[17].

It is the ubiquitous seven day week which is responsible for many of the absurdities in our Roman calendar, seven being a factor of 364 but not of 365. The Egyptians adopted a 360 day calendar system and then rejected the seven day week in favour of a ten day week[18]. So, how else do you suppose they got those pyramids built?

'A Year and a Day'

A 364 day Calendar, whilst in error to astronomical realities, involves only a single day to be added each year (and two days every fourth year) for the calendar to align or 'track' with the seasonal cycle. In calendar language, this is called an *intercalary* day. We are all familiar with this concept, for we presently add a 'leap year day' to our modern calendar every fourth year[19]. We might surmise that the Joker in the pack of cards provided the intercalary day needed to make the required 365; to be played once a year, whilst the second Joker represented the leap year day, to be played once every four years. One cannot imagine a better way to preserve this calendar structure than by inventing the plain pack of cards!

The expression 'a year and a day' is so commonly met with as a *mnemonic* appended to fairy tales and other folklore stories originating in Europe that we might profitably investigate its origins a little further with regard to the 364 day calendar.

The origins of the 364 day calendar are obscured by the mists of time. Although *'The Song of Amergin'* and other pre-Celtic folklore, such as the various 'Tree Calendars' and the Ogham alphabet-calendar are perhaps fanciful, a thirteen month year is a logical choice numerically and astronomically, for the Moon *does make thirteen circuits of the zodiac each year*. There is evidence that, until the Middle Ages, the 13 month, 364 day calendar was in popular use in Europe. The number system inherent within a pack of cards demonstrates some antiquity for this calendar system. Although it finally faded from use around the seventeenth century, this calendar's remains are still lurking within the hapless Roman calendar for anyone to discover.

When a 364 day calendar is used, 52 weeks fall *exactly* in the year, there are *precisely* thirteen months all of the same length - 28 days, a season becomes *exactly* 91 days (or 13 weeks in length). There are four seasons to the year (4 x 91 days = 364 days) and each week can have the traditional seven days described in the creation story of Genesis. And the Moon does orbit the Earth thirteen times a year. So, why do we not use this calendar today?

Re-adoption of the 364 day calendar would allow the numbers which infuse the present calendar to integrate harmoniously - the seven day week; four week month; four seasons each of 91 days; thirteen weeks to the season and 52 week year. These things are already implied within the ludicrous 365 day calendar we inherit from the Romans; *only the thirteen month year is missing*. Why? Almost certainly because the number 13 is very much connected with the Moon and hence to matters matriarchal and the old Goddess religions. The advent of Patriarchy, around 2000 BC, saw to it that all matters relating to lunar worship, and hence the Moon, were systematically and thoroughly to be eliminated from the new culture, a process which, even despite the horrors of the medieval witch-hunts, still permeates throughout western society. Our present calendar reflects this decision, as does our modern ignorance over matters lunar.

To ascertain just how much more 'solar' our culture has become, and how dimished is the 'lunar' element, try asking people to state the period of the solar year and then the lunar month. The former question will be answered correctly by nineteen out of twenty people, whilst only 3 out of twenty will correctly give either of the two main monthly lunar periods. In school textbooks, the year is always 365.242 or 365.25 days whilst the lunar month is given as 28, 29, 29.5 or 30 days, depending on the book chosen. The cultural imbalance between 'solar' and 'lunar' is evident from the number of decimals given after the correct period and no degree in psychology or mathematics is needed to conclude that our culture is predominantly 'solar'.

Precession, Patriarchy and Flawed Mathematics

There are much longer cyclic periods of time than the annual solar year and the lunation and sidereal months, and these, too, have been known about since very ancient times. We shall be meeting longer term solar and lunar cycles later on, but immediately we need to ponder the numerical properties of the Earth's 26,000 year precessional cycle. The astronomy of precession is complex but in simple terms the effect, after one human lifetime, is that on a particular date, the Sun appears to have moved backwards just over one degree with respect to the fixed stars. Assuming we live 72 years, it takes roughly 360 lifetimes for the Sun to make a precessional trip around the zodiac, a little under 26,000 years. This is one historical cycle based in astronomic reality, the Sun rising at the spring equinox in a particular sign of the zodiac for approximately 2160 years. Today we are living at the end of the *Age of Pisces*, the age linked with Jesus, *Ichthus*, the fish. The precessional *Age of Taurus* came to an end around 2000 BC and gave way to the new *Age of Aries*. This was the time of Abraham and the rise of the Jewish Patriarchs. The story of Abraham's substituted sacrifice of a ram in place of his only son demonstrates the cultural identification with these precessional 'months' for the Jews were collectively known as 'The Ram' and the astrological coincidences between Aries' ruler, Mars, and the Iron Age are well established.

The stolid megalith building so typical of the Taurean Age - ruled by Venus and with the Moon exalted - gradually dissipated as the Arien Iron Age replaced it. The Patriarchs threw out the Goddess religions, and anything lunar automatically went out with the package. Lunar calendars began to fade from the cultural landscape. The number thirteen became 'unlucky', and a corpus of superstitions was appended to this number in order to deter would-be witches and calendar makers from rediscovering their old cultural heritage, including the 364 day calendar and other matters lunar. Thirteen months were replaced by twelve, courtesy of the 360 day Egyptian and Greek calendars and with this, around 45 AD, coincidental with the advent of the Age of Pisces, came the enforced arrival in Europe of the totally solar, astronomically 'politically correct' and yet totally irrational and 'user-unfriendly' 365 day calendar we use today.

Unfortunately, the precessional cycle does not divide by twelve to give nice, neatly packaged precessional 'months' of 2000 years each, yet our culture believes that it does and adheres to 2000 year 'Ages'. The 26000 precessional cycle is, surprise,

surprise, divisible by 13 to yield *exact* 2000 year periods, and again we must face the misalignment of our own cultural heritage with cosmic truths, for as long as we adopt 2000 year periods for precessional 'months' (Ages), we are ignoring the mathematical realities which inform us that there should be thirteen 'Ages'. *The message from our treatment of 'Ages' is that the zodiac should be divided into thirteen signs rather than twelve.*

Thirteen is a very lunar number. The Moon moves just over thirteen degrees a day around the Earth. It makes just over thirteen orbits in a year. Rejecting the Moon and therefore the number thirteen sounded the death knell of the 364 day calendar - and there was no longer any meaning in having a factor 13 within a calendar. However, a few minutes playing with a pocket calculator - or a pack of cards - should convince anyone that no number other than 364 is practical or factorisable into numbers which allow some reasonable measure of integration between the apparently incompatible solar and lunar cycles. It is also apparent that our social history over the past few millenia is reflected in our choice of calendar. I believe this to be a natural evolutionary law - life on Earth evolved because of the complex movements of the Sun and the Moon. The seasons, the day/night cycle, the tides, menstrual rhythms and weather patterns are all caused by, or depend on, the actions of the Sun *and* the Moon. To ignore either one brings imbalance and we can turn to that vast repository of knowledge preserved within our folk-lore to confirm this.

The ever popular and charming fairy story *Briar Rose*, otherwise known as *The Sleeping Beauty*, has encrusted within its plot the dangers of tampering with the calendar and the dynamic balance of solar/lunar qualities. For those not familiar with the story, the trouble all starts when the king plans to invite the thirteen wise women of his kingdom to a banquet to celebrate the belated birth of his daughter and to confer their blessings on the child. Unfortunately, he cannot invite the thirteenth and final wise woman of the land because he only has twelve golden plates. Inevitably, she bursts in anyway, and places a predictable curse on both princess and the kingdom, sending both to sleep for a very long time.

Briar Rose is a classic example of arcane wisdom preserved within a popular format. Here is a theme of unification between the male and female aspects of life following a period of disregard of the feminine component - the kiss representing a renewed acceptance of the truths of evolutionary law and a subsequent awakening. It deals with the mathematics of the twelve versus thirteen conflict head on, relating this to a prophetic warning concerning what *automatically* will happen when the feminine, and hence lunar, qualities of life are neglected. Like all good fairy tales, the awakening of the sleeping princess by the kiss of the charming prince heralds a 'happy ever after' marriage and restoration of the decayed kingdom. A lot of briars and brambles have to be hacked through in order for the prince to reach the princess and for the marriage to become possible.

The 364 day calendar system probably has its roots way back beyond the development of writing, but it might surprise even the more open-minded reader that there is a working model of just such a calendar system installed in the turf on Salisbury Plain. It is called the Aubrey Circle, and we know this to be over 5000 years old. To understand why Stonehenge is constructed like it is, we must first consider what the Moon does in the skies each day.

Moonwatching at Stonehenge

To a casual observer, the Moon's movements in the sky, particular the daily changes in where it rises and sets, appear wayward and even chaotic, yet a few month's more diligent observation reveals a simple underlying pattern. Observations of the Sun's rising and setting place along the horizon take a year to complete their pattern. The Moon follows, more or less, the same pattern, except that it completes *the same cycle of risings and settings in just one sidereal month.*[20]

We have seen something of the types of building and the astronomic techniques utilised by megalithic man in order to time the solar year; perhaps it is no surprise that all over western Europe may be found megalithic remains which were once used for equally accurate, systematic observations of the Moon. The work of the late Professor Alexander Thom furnished ample evidence of various sophisticated geometric and mathematical techniques whereby the observers at such sites were able to ascertain accurately the lunation period, the sidereal month and the extreme positions of the rising and setting Moon against the horizon during its 18.61 year cycle. We have already met one of these sites, *Parc y Meirw*, near Fishguard, Wales[21]. It even appears that the tiny 9' 'wobble' or *variation* of the Moon's orbital inclination was recorded in order to perfect the prediction of eclipses[22].

The 18.61 year cycle of the Moon's nodes enables moonrises and sets to occur *outside* the annual range of azimuths of sunrise and set - at Stonehenge this extra range amounts to ten degrees. The extreme positions of moonrise and set 'breathe' in and out by over ten degrees either side of the four solar stations shown in figure

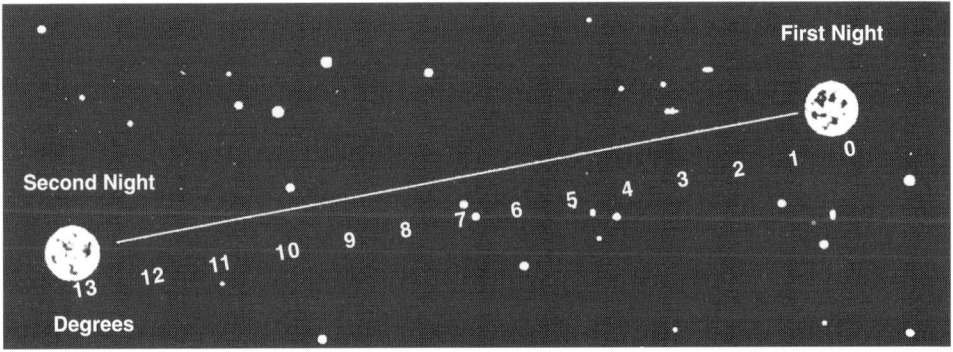

Figure 2.6 The Moon's daily motion against the stars. Every 24 hour period, the Moon moves an average of 13.176 degrees along the ecliptic. In just over one hour the Moon has moved by its own diameter against the fixed stars.

2.1(b) (*page 22*), taking 18.62 years to complete their cycle. There are *two* major monthly lunar cycles, the time taken for the Moon to pass past a selected star, 27.3 days; and the lunation period (the phases of the Moon) which takes 29.53 days. Each of these cycles are easily observed and recorded with little more than a sharp eye and the ability to count or keep a tally. Both measurements demand a little ingenuity: the exact moment of full Moon cannot be determined unless there is a lunar eclipse and for two months of the year, the Moon's passage past a chosen fixed star will be obscured because the Sun conjuncts both of them - near to the time of the new Moon.

I believe that neolithic and bronze age astronomers faced these difficulties and found effective ways around both problems. Their monuments will be seen to provide proof of this. The fact that the two inner circles at Avebury originally contained 27 and 29 equally spaced huge stones is strongly suggesting that neolithic man was familiar with the numbers of both 'monthly' lunar cycles.

The Moon moves an average angular distance of just over thirteen degrees a day *anticlockwise* relative to the stars, about twenty-two of its own diameters. Its motion past a chosen star approximately every 27 days can be seen and easily measured, whence the sidereal lunar month may be found, as described in the text.

' Moonths ' - Slicing up the Year Circle

Convenient and globally observable subdivisions of time between the day/night rhythm of the Earth's daily rotation and the much longer annual cycle of the Earth's orbital period around the Sun - the year - are naturally provided by the phases of the Moon. The month (or 'Moonth') reflects this useful rhythm. Although from month to month the time between each full Moon can vary somewhat, this period, called the *lunation period*, takes about 29.5 days to complete.

The oldest surviving religious texts originate from India, these showing that ancient cultures recognised and applied this natural subdivision of time within their calendars - the *Rig Veda* containing some solid and practical advice to would-be calendar makers:

> *"The Moon is that which shapes the years"*
>
> *R.V.10.85.5*

These most ancient cosmologists, who fortunately left written records, had acquired just enough number theory and, interestingly, just enough musical theory to harmonize the heavens with the calendar and the musical scale[23]. But a price had to be paid - astronomical realities were sacrificed to enable their 'unified theory' to work. This culture chose the one other possible contender for the length of the calendar year - 360 days - in order to achieve their apparent 'harmonisation'. There are strong mathematical reasons for so doing, but the Moon's importance becomes much reduced and the sky becomes abstracted - removed from the immutable numbers derived from direct observation.

Although the Moon's motion is highly complex[24], no great ability is needed to understand the two highly significant rhythms associated with the Moon which become evident whenever one makes observations of its motion. About every thirty days, the Moon disappears for nearly three days - hidden in the light of the Sun at each new Moon or *lunation*. The lunation period is 29.53059 days in length as a long term average figure. It can vary by plus or minus 6.5 hours (a thirteen hour range) due to many complex factors.

The Moon's passage past a preselected star re-occurs about every 27 days - the sidereal period or lunar orbital period. The long term average figure is 27.32166 days. So much about the basic astronomy of the Moon is misunderstood, even by astronomers and astrologers, that it is not surprising that we have been able to make little sense out of megalithic monuments erected to study the Moon.

- THE TWO MONTHLY LUNAR RHYTHMS -

The Lunar Orbital Period of 27.322 days

The time taken between the Moon's periodic transit past a fixed star is called the lunar orbital period, or *sidereal lunar month*. It averages at 27.322 days in length, and is thus over 2 days shorter than the lunation period. Figure 2.7 shows how the two motions relate to each other.

The Moon makes 13.368 orbits of the Earth in one solar year.

The Lunation Period of 29.53059 days

The most observable feature of the Moon's motion is that its phases change [*figure 2.8*]. From new Moon to full Moon and back again to new Moon takes about 29 and a half days, and this cycle is readily observable to even the most bleary-eyed modern city dweller. Each of the four phases (quarters) of the Moon thus lasts about seven and a half days, a number which supports the universal adoption of a seven day week. The lunation cycle is also referred to as the *synodic period* of the Moon.

There are 12.368 lunations in one solar year of 365.242 days.

Figure 2.7 also tells us that lunations - and thus the phases of the Moon - depend on the motions of both the Sun *and* the Moon, as seen from the Earth, to manifest. The reflected light from the Sun increases over a fourteen day period as the Moon

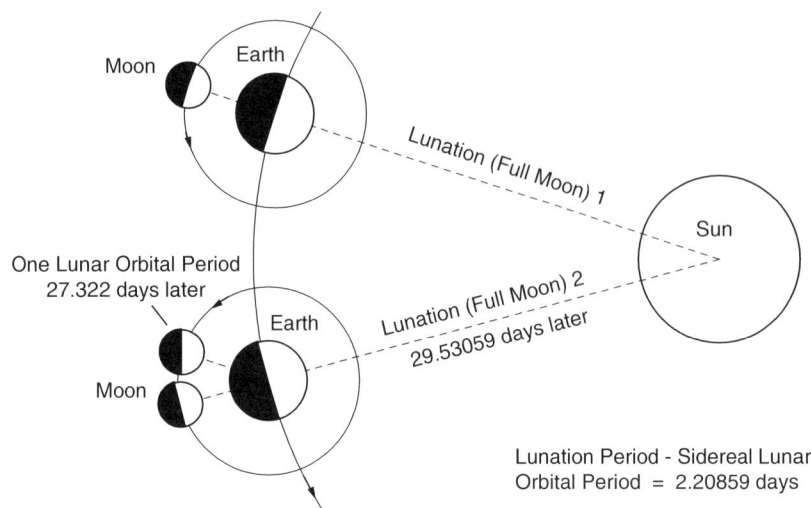

Figure 2.7 Why the lunar orbital period and lunation period differ. *Not to scale.*

waxes from new to full; the waning Moon then takes around fourteen days for the reflected light to diminish to zero as the Moon passes once again in front of the Sun's face. During this 29.5 day cycle, the Earth has moved on about one twelfth of its orbit around the Sun - we earthlings experience this as the Sun having moved from one zodiac sign to another - and the Moon thus has to over-run or catch up with the Sun each month, over and above its own circuit of the Earth, in order to complete the lunation cycle. Thus, we can now see that figure 2.8 is incorrect, yet it may be found in countless astronomy books, helping their readers confuse lunations with sidereal months.

Which month to choose?

Which 'Moonth' do we adopt for the division of the year - the lunation or sidereal month? The *Rig Veda* citation quoted earlier evidently made one choice - the lunation month was chosen. For calendar makers and mathematicians, the lunation cycle seemed to take the cake. The lunar sidereal cycle was more hidden, less obvious and needed dedicated observation of the fixed stars to confirm its rhythm; furthermore, it appeared independent of the Sun - a dangerous blasphemy in a world becoming increasingly 'solar'; a Sun worshipping world of Apollo and other 'solar heroes'. The sidereal month is an observation of the astronomer and therefore of a culture where careful observation of the skies is elevated to an art. It certainly isn't for the casual observer of the night sky.

> *If the Moon is to be included within a calendar structure, a fundamental choice has to be made between lunation or sidereal month lengths.*

Our culture deserted the Moon a long, long time ago, our 'moonth' lengths now have nothing to do with either cycle of the Moon, and the consequences of this choice of month length still resonate through our social fabric today.

Design-a-Calendar

Let us now look at the basis for the design of a calendar. This may appear unrelated to a study of Stonehenge and yet the reader will discover that such a excursion is essential to understanding what underpins the design of the monument. It will also impress upon the reader the limited number of numerical choices available for a calendar system on Planet Earth. These calendar structures are shown overleaf [*Table 2.1*], and show the number theory underpinning the three main choices.

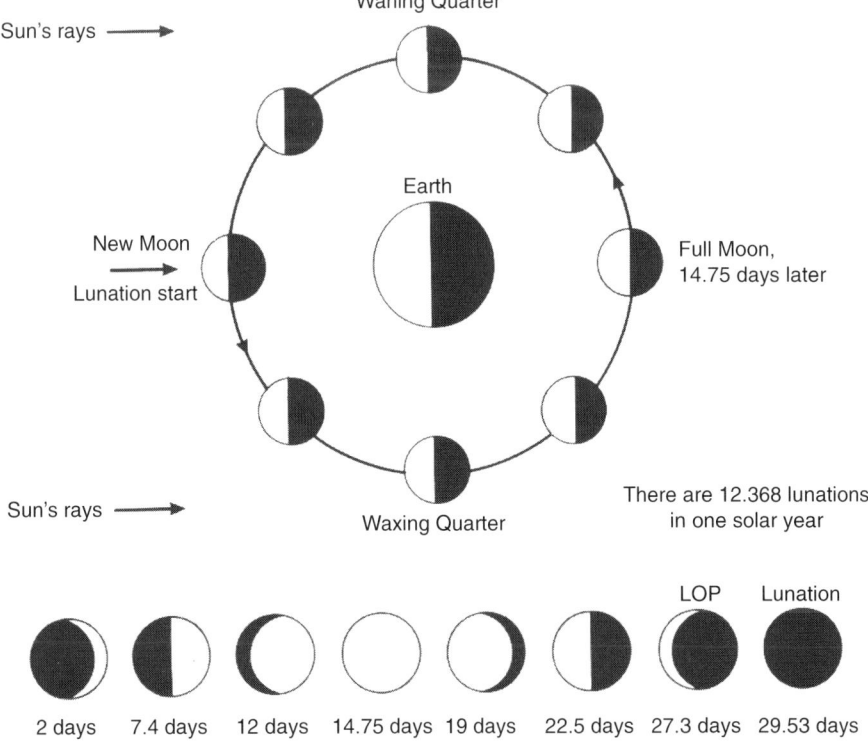

Figure 2.8 The 'Age' of the Moon. The standard, although incorrect, lunation diagram beloved of school textbooks, showing lunar phases. The sidereal lunar orbital period (marked LOP) takes 27.322 days to complete, and is independent of the phase of the Moon.

TABLE 2.1

The three main calendar structures which emerge naturally from the numbers of solar and lunar cycles.

- 360 days -

Main advantage: - Numerical structure allows division by 2,3,4,5,6,8,9,10 and 12 amongst the lower numbers. Month lengths closely fit lunation period.

Main disadvantage:- Astronomically remote from true solar year. Complex intercalary day ritual which, if not observed, rotates calendar quickly out of line with the seasons.

Ritual procedure:- 5 intercalary days added each year - six every four years.

Structure:- Arranged as 12 months of 30 days each, 3 months per quarter year followed by an intercalary day, followed by the next quarter etc. The Egyptians had 'weeks' of ten days, thus 36 'weeks' in the year. These were called 'decans'.

- 364 days -

Main advantage:- Divisable by 2, 4, 7 and 13, thus offering the most natural calendar structure possible for soli-lunar integration. No fractional numbers. Astronomically close to solar year length and sidereal lunar month length.

Main disadvantage: - The 13 month year is culturally remote. Unlucky!

Ritual procedure:- 1 intercalary day added each year - two every four years.

Structure:- Arranged as 13 months of 28 days each. Four quarters, each of thirteen weeks duration total 52 weeks in the year. Four weeks, each of seven days make up a month.

- 365 days -

Advantage: - Astronomically closest to solar year length of 365.242 days.

Main disadvantage:- Irrational numbers! Does not divide by any factors other than 5 and 73. Calendar structure is thereby very awkward and rotates days of the week around the calendar each year.

Ritual procedure:- 1 intercalary day added every four years

Structure:- Arranged as 12 months of variable length, averaging 30.1466 days each. 52.142857.. weeks to the year. 91.25 days to a quarter (a season), corresponding to an irrational 13.0357.. weeks.

The solar year is immutable at 365.242 days. A calendar system cannot use a number greater than 365 to define the year - one cannot subtract days already lived (although many of us would perhaps like to), only allow an over-run of *intercalary* days. Similarly the lunar year of twelve lunations is immutable at just over 354 days - and thus nearly eleven days short of the solar year.

Purely lunar calendars are not, and cannot be, synchronised to the seasons. A modern example is the Islamic religious calendar where one finds *Ramadan* occuring eleven days earlier each year, due to the difference in length between lunar year and solar year. Solar calendars track or synchronise to the seasons, being based on the solar tropical year of 365.242 days.

The ultimate goal for a calendar designer is to produce a *soli-lunar* calendar - where the two cycles of the Sun and Moon can be completely integrated. The culture which produced the earliest constructions at Stonehenge, around 3000 BC, solved this task better than anyone else has since, leaving a legacy of calendraic excellence and soli-lunar wisdom for later generations to decode.

The 360 day Calendar : A Mathematical Convenience

A 360 day calendar year aligns well to lunation and phase timings and allows halves, quarters, fifths, sixths, eighths, tenths, twelfths and so on. 360 is a wonderfully factorisable number - for 360 is 1 x 2 x 2 x 2 x 3 x 3 x 5 and thus divides by all numbers up to twelve with the exception of 7 and 11.

To adopt a 360 day calendar implies twelve months of thirty days. Thirty is also wonderfully divisable - the first number containing the factors 2, 3 and 5. The choice of 360 days for the calendar year abstracted the true length of the solar year into a calendar system which was mathematically easier and which, in an era without decimals, enabled a huge range of fractions to be utilised in subdividing time. The obvious choice of a month length of 30 days provided similar mathematical facility and aligned to within half a day of the lunation period. 360 days was, for several millenia, the chosen numerological basis for the calendar systems of the Indians, Babylonians, Egyptians and, rather latterly, the Greeks. Our circles are still divided into 360 degrees as a consequence.

To align a 360 day calendar year to the solar year and hence the seasons, *five* intercalary days must be added each year. The Egyptians added these *neter days* at the four cardinal points of the solar year - equinoxes and solstices - with the extra fifth one announcing the annual inundation of the Nile Delta. We are also informed that the Egyptians accurately timed the year through observation of the heliacal rising of Sirius[25], the Dog Star. Setting aside the practical problems of the extinction angle of Sirius, parallax and refraction, the date of the heliacal rising changed from the 16th to the 20th July over the period of the Egyptian civilisation[26]. The annual Nile flood is more or less fixed, based as it is on the *tropical year.*

No calendar will ever fully integrate the difficult numbers which exist between the Sun and the Moon, just as no musical scale is perfectly harmonious. The Hindu-

Greek musical scale derived from 'fitting' the thirteen note chromatic scale (twelve notes plus octave) into the number range 360 to 720, whilst the eight note (seven note plus octave) diatonic scale ran from 30 to 60, with no fractional or nasty irrational numbers appearing. Musical proportions were thus made to align to events in heaven and, in an age before pocket calculators, this must have appeared in some way like a minor miracle - the alignment of heaven and earth made possible by a minor fudge of the immutable numbers of the Sun and Moon.

Perhaps this abstracted numerical calendrical system 'harmonised' too well - certainly it discouraged if not obviated the need to make direct observations of the Sun and Moon with quite the same diligence as our megalithic ancestors thought fit, cutting man off from the sky, into a world of increasing abstraction.

The nearest whole number to the lunation cycle of 29.5 days is 30, and 12 months of 30 days results in a 360 day *calendar year*. However, no ancient culture would ever have believed that the actual year was 360 days in length, as the writer (and others) have already demonstrated[27]. The idea that 360 was the measured number of days in the year observed by 'primitive cultures' who were incapable of more accurate measurement, is a historian's blunder *par excellence*. The choice of 360 days for a *calendar* year demonstrates a level of *mathematical* sophistication which can hardly be termed 'primitive'. It demonstrates the existence of minds capable of grappling with the problems of alignment between astronomic truths and mathematical convenience.

By alternating month lengths of 29 and then 30 days, the months can actually follow the lunation cycle adequately well, and many calendars in the ancient world adopted such a system. Calendar makers preferred to use a calendar system which fitted into the lunation period of 29.5 days. By alternating 30 and 29 day months they achieved this to a reasonable accuracy.[28] Two months thus take 59 days to complete, a number to be found in two separate constructions at Stonehenge - the bluestone ellipse and the Y- and Z-holes.

The lunation was a natural cycle to follow - for the Moon's phases offer a world-wide visual indication of the passage of time - the weeks are shown, approximately, as the Moon's 'quarters' and these, together with the (lunation) month's 'age', can be seen and hence 'read' in the sky each day by anyone. *The problem is that the number of lunations in a solar year is not a whole number*.

The 364 day Calendar : A Natural Choice

364 days aligns well to lunar motion through the zodiac and provides the most integrated and practical soli-lunar calendar possible. Numerically, its factors are somewhat of a mathematical problem, yet the factors *two* and *four* suit the way the year divides astronomically whilst *seven* fits our convention that there shall be seven days in the week. Prime numbers like 7 and 13 are mathematically awkward as factors, leading to irrational fractional divisions even though, astronomically, the Moon orbits the Earth thirteen times a year. A 13 month year connects a calendar straight away to a 28 day month (28 x 13 = 364), which follows closely what is observed in the

sky. Direct observation allows the lunar zodiacal position and the position of the Sun against the circular zodiac girdle of constellations to be ascertained. The relationship between these two positions immediately allows the lunar phase (lunation stage) to also be seen. In effect this is what one sees on an astrological birthchart, which records the zodiacal positions of the Sun and Moon and thereby allows the Moon's phase to be seen at a glance, like the hands of a watch allow the time to be seen instantly. *The problem is that the number of sidereal lunar months in a solar year is also not a whole number.*

The 365 day Calendar - A Beast of a Number[29]

Unfortunately, in the modern world, we have adopted a rather less useful calendar based on 365 days - a solar dominated calendar originally imposed on the growing Empire by the Romans. The imposition of this calendar - the most astronomically close to the actual seasonal year - was in order to prevent the keepers of the calendar throughout outposts of the Roman Empire from forgetting to account for the intercalary days. So chaotic had this vital timekeeping process become that, in 45 AD, Sosigenes designed the Roman calendar, with one important departure from the calendar we still use today. He originally alternated 30 and 31 day months, apart from February which had an interesting 28 days.

Later, Caesar Augustus (August), in order to not appear any less than Julius Caesar (July), added an extra day to the month named after him, thus breaking the sequence and providing the necessity for remembering the rhyme we all learn at school to learn the individual month lengths. Thus it is true that the random egoism of a megalomaniac Roman nearly two thousand years ago still determines just one of the many irrational aspects of modern timekeeping in the Space Age!

In Britain, this calendar is an imported cultural artefact, but not the only one. We all still continue to use angular measurements imported from alleged Babylonian origins and based on the number 360, a time structuring system for clocks based on 12, 24 and 60, all divisors of that same number. Meanwhile, the only calendar system which appears to be indigenous, soli-lunar and also uniquely fitting in with the universally-adopted-since-year-dot seven day week, has sunk without trace - or very nearly.

The Incompatibility between Sun and Moon Cycles

Unfortunately, no calendar or human committee can resolve the fact that there are not a whole number of lunar months nor sidereal months in the solar year, an interesting fact we shall be returning to throughout this book, for it holds enormous implications for understanding human social development. Twelve lunations take 354.37 days to complete, another immutable number and this leaves an over-run of 10.875 days between the end of the 'lunar year' and the end of each solar year. This amounts to just over a third of a lunation cycle.[30] The prophet Enoch, perhaps our most well known ancient calender-maker, referred to this approximate 11 days period as the 'overplus'.[31] Enoch holds fast to a 364 day calendar structure, but arranged as 360 day calendar plus four intercalary days. This 'fudge' allows a twelve month year (of 30 days per month) and Enoch to appear to have had his cake and eaten it. The later translation (Enoch II) goes entirely to 365 days and is filled with mathematical errors, demonstrating the mathematically flawed attempts to adapt the calendar systems of the ancient world to the new Roman calendar by the time-hallowed method of fudging the numbers to fit their brave new and increasingly abstracted world-view. The two translations taken together, side by side, illuminate beautifully the calendraic and social ferment going on within the world culture of 2000 years ago. The path which leads to calendrical *nirvana* is strewn with numerical traps, intercalary days, intercalary months and that most fundamental choice - does one pick lunation or sidereal month lengths for the calendar?

Summary

This chapter has clarified the way in which time may be structured on our planet using the immutable cycles of the Sun and Moon. In so doing, I have exposed an irrational and hotch-potch collection of cultural oddities which, in our self-professed learned and oh-so-logical civilisation, now lumber us with horribly irrational calendar numbers, mathematics that doesn't work, a time structure which uses number bases that do not fit at all within our decimal (or binary) world, and which uses clocks whose hour hands double the Sun's angular velocity in the sky.

All of these things are imports which originated *after* the European neolithic culture was established. No history book I have ever read makes this important point - *that the megalithic culture in Britain and Ireland preceded the known flowerings of mathematics, geometry and astronomy elsewhere*, and I think our children at least should now be told this important fact during their education.

We have also discovered in this chapter just how much emphasis is placed on the solar numbers over the lunar numbers, these latter lying largely beyone our cultural horizon. I have shown that the classic astronomical diagram displayed in most school textbooks and not a few astronomy texts is actually misleading, if not downright incorrect, confusing sidereal with lunation months and thus making the point quite well that we have lost touch with the Moon. The fundamental choice of which lunar cycle to adopt for the calendar has been presented as a inescapable dilemma for calendar makers modern or ancient, and some examples of the cultural legacy left by such a dilemma have been presented.

The two numbers twelve and thirteen, juxtaposed wherever our culture seeks to identify a superhero figure, such as Jesus, King Arthur or the Mayan Kukulcan, point to a cultural legacy which appears to be calendraic in origin, naturally fundamental to the immutable numbers of the Sun and Moon. In later chapters we will look much further into the social, religious and political legacy of this historical theme of the enigmatic thirteenth saviour figure, always with twelve Knights, disciples or kings, and always sacrificed to be then resurrected in order to save the culture.

Any person who begins to seriously observe the two luminaries and ponder the numbers which result from their observations will arrive at the same apparent conflict between 12 and 13, between sidereal and lunation months. Our civilisation is so cut off from these processes that it is no longer even aware of the conflict, and thus fails to understand its legends, folklore and megaliths, never mind the solar and lunar cycles from which they derive.

The roots of northwestern European culture are presently thought to be irrelevant and their contribution to the modern world a mere curiosity; this attitude blocking our efforts to understand the minds and motives of the megalith builders. Superficially, the roots of our modern culture appear as a left-over from the Roman Empire and the Greeks, although, under the surface, a much older tap-root may still be found - if you dig deep enough. The full extent of this tap root is exposed in chapter ten. The story of *Briar Rose,* the basis for the precessional *'Ages'* and the calendrical structure of a pack of cards offer firm evidence for the existence of this earlier legacy. From such cultural artefacts we can glimpse the struggle that was going on in men's minds as they wrestled with understanding the mechanisms of Sun and Moon. The earliest phase of Stonehenge is another such artefact, even more ancient, which perhaps accounts for why it still fascinates so many folk and which, despite its ruinous state, still has the power to draw nearly a million visitors each year. If marrying the Sun and Moon appears from this chapter to be *numerically* impossible, we will now go on to discover that neolithic astronomers found a *geometric* solution at Stonehenge.

Footnotes to Chapter Two.

1. *A little history of Astro-archaeology - stages in the transformation of a heresy.* John Michell. Published By Thames and Hudson, London (1977). ISBN 0 500 27097X.

2. The Earth's precessional cycle causes these positions to change very slowly with time - more on this later.

3. Each day, the Sun appears to move 1° anticlockwise with respect to the stars, taking a year to complete a revolution of the zodiac. Each day the zodiac stars are 3 minutes and 56.6 seconds earlier in their rising time.

4. For residents of the northern hemisphere.

5. *See Sun, Moon and Standing Stones*. J.E.Wood. OUP 1983.

6. The range of extreme lunar risings and settings over the 18.62 year cycle. The mechanism is covered later, page 56 and 57.

7. There are thousands of these tablets, dealing with astronomical and surveying techniques. They often run to ten decimal places of precision. Some are 4000 years old.

8. The Great Pyramid contains at least four references to the solar tropical year of 365.242 days, in two unit systems.

9. Dated at 18,000 BC. See *Goddess - Mother of Living Nature* by Adele Getty, page 43 (Thames and Hudson).

10. The Knowth complex, Boyne Valley, Ireland, and Gavrinas, Baie de Morbihan, Aurac region, Brittany,France.

11. I include Ireland and Brittany within this category.

12. This technique is described in *Culture and Cosmos*, Vol 1, No 1, by the author. See Appendix 1, page 227.

13. In *The Hostile Confederacy*. D.W.Nash's translation in *Taliesin, or the Bards and Druids of Britain*. [1858]

14. A neolithic astronomer would also see the sun slip each year by about a third of itsown diameter, the count would remain 365 days. On the fourth year, this slippage would have acrued to produce a count of 366 days. Thus, observations over four years produce a count arranged as 365 + 365 + 365 + 366, totalling 1461 days.

15. $1 \times 2 \times 2 \times 7 \times 13$ (= 364).

16. The '+' sign at the end of the number means the decimals continue *ad infinitum*.

17. CLIII.

18. Structured as 36 weeks of 10 days, a calendar year of 360 days. Each week occupied one *decan*, a third of one of the twelve zodiacal signs.

19. And a few minor nudges, like the addition of an extra second or two from time to time in order to keep the calendar tracking perfectly with the seasons.

20. *Sidereal = with reference to the stars*. The sidereal month is the time taken for the Moon to orbit the Earth and may be observed as the time taken for the Moon to return to the same star in the sky.

21. *Parc y Meirw* is Welsh for *"the enclosure of the dead."*

22. The variation in inclination of the Moon's orbital plane has an amplitude of only 18 minutes of degree and a period of about 173 days. Some sights appear to have used natural features to enable this wobble to be observed.

23. See *The Myth of Invariance* by Ernest G. McClain (Shambala 1978) for a fascinating look into the ancient links between cosmos, mathematical and musical theory.

24. E. W. Brown's tables are used in most almanacs and utilise no less than 1500

terms to arrive at the Moon's exact location and velocity.

25. Heliacal rising = rising simultaneously with the Sun.

26. From 3500 BC to 500 AD, precessional changes made little effect on the date of the heliacal rising. However, this is still a very poor way of accurately establishing the length of the solar year.

27. Sir Norman Lockyer: "Had ignorance led to the the establishment of a year of 360 days, yet experience would have led to its rejection in a few years. If observations of the Sun an solstice or equinox had been alone made use of, the true length of the year would have been determined in a few years" (245-246pp). *The Dawn of Astronomy* (1894). Reprinted by M.I.T.Press 1964.

28. An intercalary month every three years was added to account for the over-run of the solar year above the lunar year.

29. The Roman numeral set originally consisted of D,C,L,X,V and I, which sums to 666, the *Number of the Beast* in the Bible. To early Christians, suffering enormous persecution under Roman dictatorship, this encoded numerical identification of the Romans provided protection and was entirely appropriate to a numerate culture.

30. The annual over-run of the moon amounts to 0.368 of a revolution, which equals 10.875 days or 132.5 degrees of lunar angular motion.

31. *The Book of Enoch*, translated by Canon R.H.Charles. SPCK ISBN 0 281 01261 X. In old mathematics books, the word 'overplus' was used instead of 'remainder'.

Above: The Moon and the British Isles at the same scale. The Moon creates the highest tides in the world around the waters of Britain.

Above: The Heart of Stonehenge. This fine English Heritage photograph taken from the north-east of the sarsen circle shows two trilithons to the left. The remains of a third (stone 56), with its fallen partner to the left, may be seen to the right. The clear height difference between each trilithon is evident. Stone 11, the half width sarsen upright, is visible between the two left trilithons.

Chapter Three

- THE STONEHENGE -
SOLI-LUNAR CALENDAR

Drawing down the Sun and the Moon

The design of an integrated soli-lunar calendar needs to incorporate the following basic specifications:

(i). It should correspond as closely as possible with what the Sun and Moon are actually doing in the sky.

The calendar should be as true an *analogue* model of the heavens as possible. Any abstraction will detract from this mirroring of the skies.

(ii). Its accuracy should be adequate enough to enable the design to be 'fast-forwarded' in order to forecast future calendraic and astronomic events of significance.

The calendar needs to be able to furnish information regarding solstices, equinoxes, the actual point in the seasonal round at a given moment, lunations (full and new Moons), lunar position against the stars and, if possible, eclipse information. All of these things need to be estimated from the calendar in advance.

(iii). The operator's instructions need to be simple in order to avoid errors of omission.

An overly complicated instruction set will lead to human error and failure of the calendar. For example, failure to add in any intercalary days introduces a rotation of the seasons around the calendar. This was the precise situation facing Caesar when he asked the Alexandrian astronomer Sosigenes to reform the calendar. Throughout the Roman Empire timekeeping had become chaotic due to failure to account for the intercalary days and messengers were returning from distant lands before they had set out!

To replicate what is going on in the skies within a calendar, systematic *observations* of the basic movements of the Sun, Moon and stars have to be undertaken over a minimum of several years. We have already discussed how the length of the seasonal (tropical) solar year was measured by ancient man, and we have also discussed the nature of the two basic lunar cycles and how they may be measured. Now we need to find practical ways of procuring the observational lunar data needed to design and build the best possible integrated soli-lunar calendar.

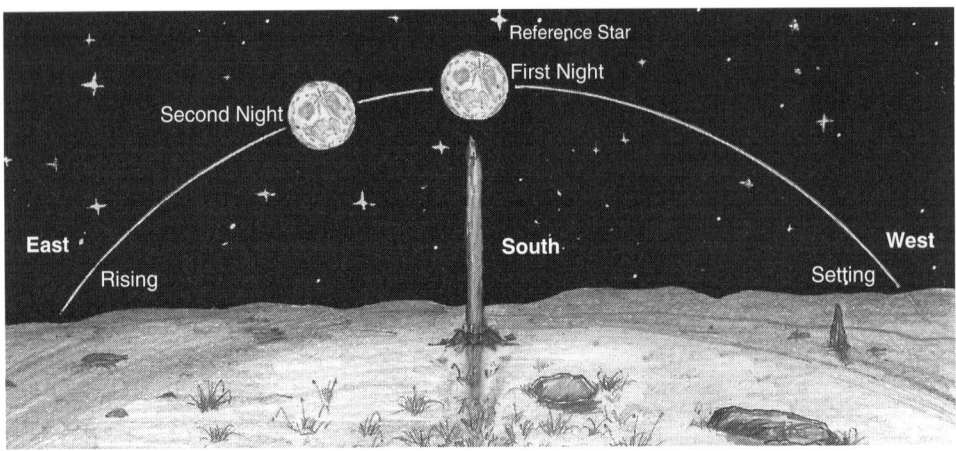

Figure 3.1 A 'transit' stake marks the culmination of all objects in the heavens and therefore lies exactly south of the observer. The line from the stake to the observation point thus lies exactly north-south. This is how true north and south are defined; standard geometric construction can enable the builder to add the east-west line, thus dividing the circle into four quadrants or 'seasons'.

Drawing down the Moon

The Moon, like all other astral bodies, culminates exactly due south of an observer. Once every few days, the Moon culminates whilst passing directly next to a bright star. If an observer can count or record days on a tally, then even after a few months an understanding will be reached that it has taken the Moon between 27 and 28 days to return by the same chosen star. Every day, the Moon moves anticlockwise relative to the stars - by about twenty-two of its own diameters - more or less by a constant daily angle as seen from the Earth[1]. After just a few years of committed observation, an observer would come to understand that the Moon's path always follows and lies within the ecliptic star patterns of the zodiac. In our epoch the Moon's daily rising is always furthest north each month when the Moon passes through the region of the sky below the Twins, *Castor* and *Pollux*; the most southerly rise occurs when near the fixed star *Antares*. Ancient astronomers could not fail to rapidly come to the understanding that the zodiac stars are a girdle encircling the Earth, nor that the Moon is a monthly traveller around and through this band of stars. We have already seen that the Moon takes an average 27 and one third days, (7 hours, 43 minutes and 11.51 seconds in modern chronology) to complete this sidereal journey, corresponding to an average daily motion of just over 13°.

1. A long stake some distance from the observer suffices to accurately mark this north-south line, termed *the prime meridian* by astronomers. The distance from the observer to the first stake will define the radius of the finished calendar. The

observation point becomes the centre of this circular replica of the heavens. The following construction is made much easier by having two people involved.

2. On the following night, at the same time (i.e. when the same star passes directly in line with the stake once again), a second stake is placed to the left of the first, at the same distance from the observer, to mark the Moon's new position - and thus the distance across the sky it has moved during the previous twenty-four hours. The angle made between the observer and the two stakes will be found to be about 13°, although it is not necessary to actually measure this angle.

3. Once these two stakes plus the central point have been placed accurately, then they may first be used to construct a 'Moon clock' on the ground.

4. Taking a rope pegged at the observer, walk to the first stake.

5. Trace the perimeter of the complete circle which results from this defined radius (observer to first stake) and then measure the distance between the two stakes at the circumference (on grass these techniques can be facilitated by using white flour or quartz pebbles to mark the perimeter; chalk is useful on a hard surface. Replication of this same distance around the perimeter of the 'sky-circle' will then produce a perimeter having 28 points marked around it (*figure 3.2*).

6. Moving a 'Moon marker' anticlockwise one hole each day will now emulate what is going on in the heavens. However, the Moon is quite variable in the daily angle which it moves; full or new Moons do not allow easy observation of the stars needed for the observation (there is too much light in the sky to see them clearly). This encourages measurements to be taken at or near the time of the waxing quarter Moon - near to sunset.

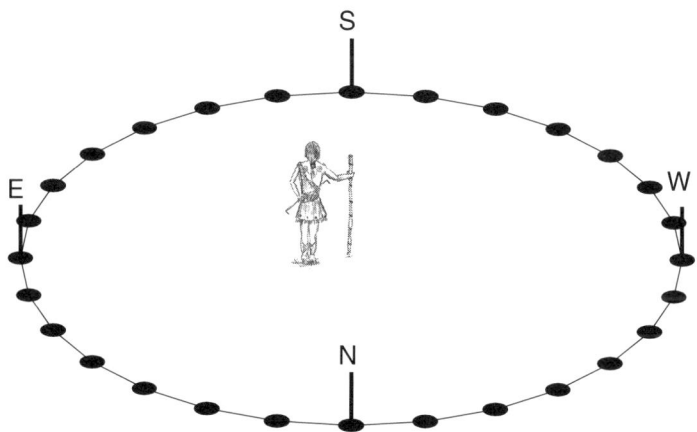

Figure 3.2 Completion of the daily Moon motion to produce a circle of 28 markers. This is the closest whole number to the Moon's orbital period that also allows the cardinal points (North, South, East and West) to become integrated with the calendar.

7. If the first stake is erected directly south of the observer then the cardinal points can become integral with the circle, and one always ends up with a total of 28 markers around the circle. Within each of the four quadrant markers, as shown opposite and below, six and only six markers can be placed, whatever the variation from 13° in the daily movement of the Moon.

8. As a final step, each quadrant of six markers can be evenly spaced. A stake at the middle of the circle - the observation point representing the Earth in this model - can assist in this process, as stakes on opposite sides of the circle may then be sighted using the central stake to align their placement. Undergraduate students take under two hours to erect a moderately accurate 150 foot diameter circle using 28 six foot lengths of 3 inch square timber to define the 28 *lunar mansions* of vedic astronomy - the daily residences of the Moon in her journey around the zodiac.

This simple circle of twenty-eight equally spaced markers is now immediately able to provide a fairly accurate analogue of the Moon's motion. A 'Moon-marker' is simply moved one marker per day anticlockwise around the circle in order to emulate the Moon's position in the sky. The starting position may be found by watching the Moon move past a significant star or group of stars, or from other techniques to be described shortly.

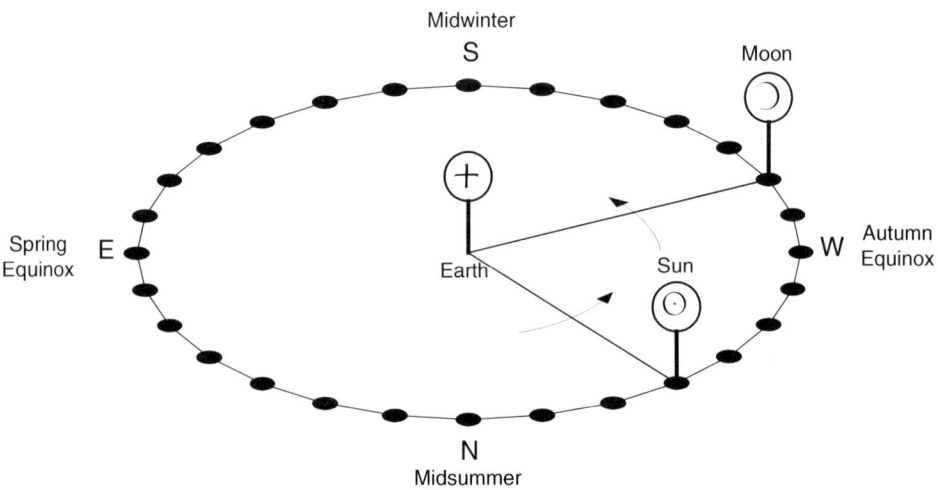

Figure 3.3 The Basic Sidereal Sun/Moon Calendar. 28 markers derived from a simple observation of the Moon's motion. The Moon marker is moved anticlockwise one marker per day, the Sun similarly moved every 13 days. This model is surprisingly accurate, predicting the dates of lunations months in advance.

Integrating the Sun with the Moon

However roughly the initial measurement is made, the practical outcome within a cardinal point circle is always that one ends up with 28 markers around its perimeter. Thus, 28 markers define a lunar 'month-circle'. But this same circle is also the 'year-circle' of the Sun's annual journey around the zodiac stars. Inherently, the message we receive through building the circle is that *there are thirteen months in the year* and that *the Moon moves thirteen times faster than the Sun*. Clearly, if we now wish to include the Sun within our model of the heavens, we must move a 'Sun marker' at the rate of *one marker stake every thirteen days* - it will then complete its 'round' of the circle, after 28 moves, in 364 days (*figure 3,3*).

The accuracy of this basic 28-marker model of the motions of the two luminaries seen from the Earth is entirely creditable: 97.5% for the Moon and 99.66% for the Sun. The accuracy of the Moon's motion could be improved (to 98.82%) by reducing the marker hole count to twenty-seven, but then the Sun's accuracy would be reduced dramatically to 96.1%. Twenty-nine markers would incur similar penalties. *The number twenty-eight thus forms a resonance, it is the lowest whole number which allows soli-lunar integration to take place.*

The accuracy may be improved for the Sun by making the last move after fourteen and not thirteen days - the Sun then completes its round after 365 days. A leap year could be included every four years by waiting fifteen days for the final move. For the Moon we could skip forward a marker every two months to achieve an accuracy of 99.4%, but these are 'fudge factors' hardly necessary to a culture who could determine the exact dates of the four key positions of the Sun and had constructed alignments to the minor and major standstills of the Moon. From these, they could thereby reset the 'clock' they had built, just as we do today from the Greenwich 'pips' on the radio. Further, by marking the positions of the main fixed stars around the perimeter of the circle, the Moon marker can be reset any time the Moon is visible by noticing which stars in the sky the Moon is currently passing, and aligning the Moon to the facsimile 'stars' around the circle - a neolithic planetarium, in fact.

> *An integrated model of the motions of the Sun and Moon must therefore be circular and must have a minimum of 28 separate circumference markers.*

Even with this simple model, we have realised most of the design criteria outlined at the beginning of the chapter.

Near-perfect Integration

This first model shows the current zodiacal position of the Sun (season and date) and the Moon at a glance. It also shows, automatically by default, the current phase of the Moon - the place within the lunation cycle. It provides a very elegant and simple solution to the problem of furnishing a useful calendar, showing *both* lunar rhythms and the annual solar cycle simultaneously.

The more observant reader will have noticed that the motion of the Moon with this model integrates with the diurnal rhythm of the Sun - one marker *per day* - and that the Sun marker is moved every 13 days, the lunar number *par excellence*. Thus, every thirteen days the Sun is moved thirteen degrees. By following the less obvious and more hidden lunar orbital period (the sidereal month), we have achieved the optimum possible measure of harmony between the 'difficult' numbers which connect the Sun, Moon and Earth in their cosmic dance.

Let us now take this information to our first attempts to make astronomical and numerical sense of Stonehenge.

The Aubrey Circle Revisited

The design layout of 56 evenly spaced holes around the Aubrey Circle, indeed, the very nature of the construction of the Aubrey circle within the ditch and bank at Stonehenge connects with the numerical pattern of 28 markers needed to construct an analogue model of just where the Moon (and Sun) may be located each day within the zodiac.

The Aubrey Circle possesses 56 holes, twice 28, and we should investigate why. An obvious response would be that, having seen how easily observations of the Moon produce a 28 marker circle, the builders decided to place an extra hole between each of the originals. The advantages of *'Mark Two'* are better resolution accuracy and the possibility of 'hole-skipping' the Moon marker in order to sustain higher accuracies over long periods of time. For example, skipping the Moon marker stake over the Sun marker stake each and every new Moon - i.e. never allowing the Sun and Moon markers to alight in the same marker hole - would improve the Moon's accuracy to 99.4%.

This emulates a lunar orbital period of 27.5 days and the Moon marker is then only slow by about 4 hours each month - two days error (four holes 'out') after a year's operation. To further improve accuracy, if the Moon marker is made to 'skip' a further hole each time the Sun marker passes one of the four cardinal points of the year - the equinoxes and the solstices - then the error becomes better than one hole a year (0.14%). This is equivalent to a clock which gains a minute every twelve hours and, just as one can reset a clock to the Greenwich 'pips', the Moon pole can always be precisely reset by placing the Moon marker opposite the Sun marker every time there is a lunar eclipse - a fairly regular occurence at Stonehenge. *Operating this model reveals the pattern of eclipses, and therefore invites curiosity to discover more about their capricious nature.*

Figure 3.4 shows the Aubrey Circle set up to run as an accurate calendar. The operator's instructions hardly change from the basic 28 marker circle - the Moon marker is now moved *twice* a day, once at dawn and again at twilight; the Sun marker is moved one hole after 7 days and another after 6 days[2]. Two 7 day moves must occur at some point in the year in order to make the day count per year equal to 365. The 'leap year day', every four years, must also be accounted for. The Sun marker

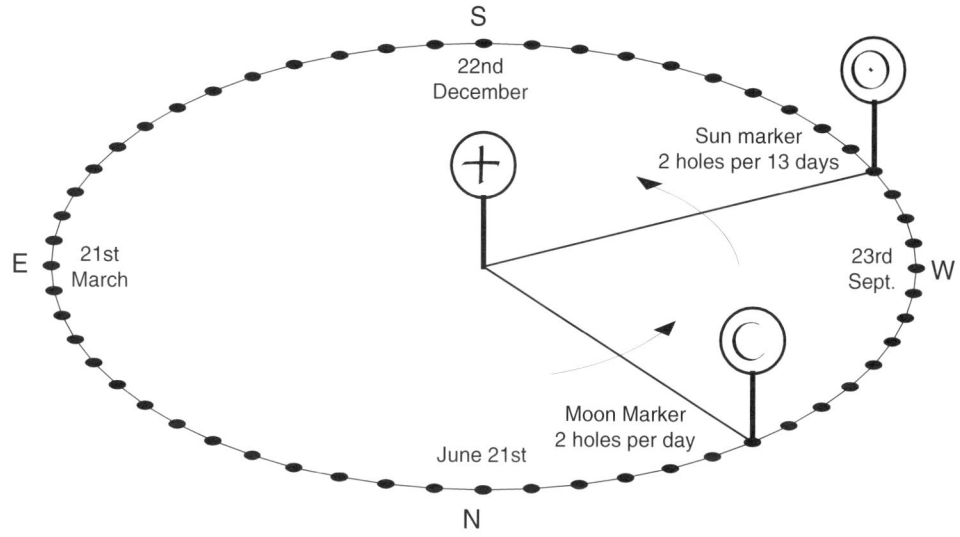

Figure 3.4 The 56-hole Aubrey Calendar. The Moon is moved to the diurnal rhythm of the day / night cycle; one hole at dawn, another at dusk. The Sun marker is moved two holes every thirteen days, thus copying the Moon's daily angular motion. The calendar is therefore an *integrated* soli-lunar calendar, and if the Moon marker is made to skip over the Sun marker at every new Moon, and a further skip forwards is made at the four key points in the year. equinoxes and solstices, an accuracy of 99.9% may be achieved for the Moon, whilst the Sun's accuracy remains at 99.8%.

could be moved sequentially through twelve lesser markers placed between each pair of holes, one degree (more accurately, one day) each day around the year-circle.

Whatever technique is employed, the Sun completes his round in 364 days and for the longer term accuracy of the calendar, a ritual or routine must be invoked in order to slow the Sun marker down to 365.25 days/rev if the seasons are to track with the calendar and the Sun is to correspond with the skies. The equinox and solstitial foresight observatories discussed in chapter two enable this tracking to be maintained to the highest levels of accuracy and, theoretically, such a calendar can be reset every three months.

The Aubrey Calendar shows at a glance the current phase of the Moon, the current season and the position of the Sun and Moon in the zodiac. It is elegant, potentially very accurate and, perhaps astonishingly, it still exists and could still be made to operate after 5000 years of disuse. Presently filled with white concrete and often overgrown with grass, the present custodians of the monument, English Heritage, could readily incorporate this oldest known calendar within any future educational provision to be made at Stonehenge, enabling our children and not a few adults to understand so much more about Britain's national temple - and the skies above their heads.

The Inevitable 56 holes

We might suggest a stronger reason why 56 holes were dug, this bringing in a fascinating numerical relationship between the Moon's orbital period and the times in the year when eclipses are most likely to occur. We need to first understand the mechanism of eclipses before we can understand the importance of placing 56 marker holes around the Aubrey Circle.

It is impossible to determine visually the exact moment of a full or new Moon. The former event lasts for a day or two and the latter is indeterminate because the Moon disappears within the glare of the Sun. However, during an eclipse the timing can be exact - the Sun, Moon and Earth align perfectly and the moment is known exactly. Total and partial lunar eclipses are not uncommon anywhere and occur, on average, at least once a year.

If the Moon's orbital plane was perfectly in line to that of the Sun and Earth, then there would be a solar *and* lunar eclipse each and every month at new and full Moon. Because the Moon's orbital plane is tilted at a little over five degrees to that of the Earth, only when a full or new Moon occurs near to the intersection of these two planes can this alignment take place (*figure 3.5*). This event occurs about every 173 days. Then, any full or new Moon within about 17 days of the Sun passing one of the intersection points, which are called the *lunar nodes*, will produce an eclipse of some kind, although not necessarily visible from Stonehenge.

Even with no knowledge of the Moon's nodes or their complex behaviour over an 18.6 year cycle, both the 28 and 56 marker models will show that eclipses only ever

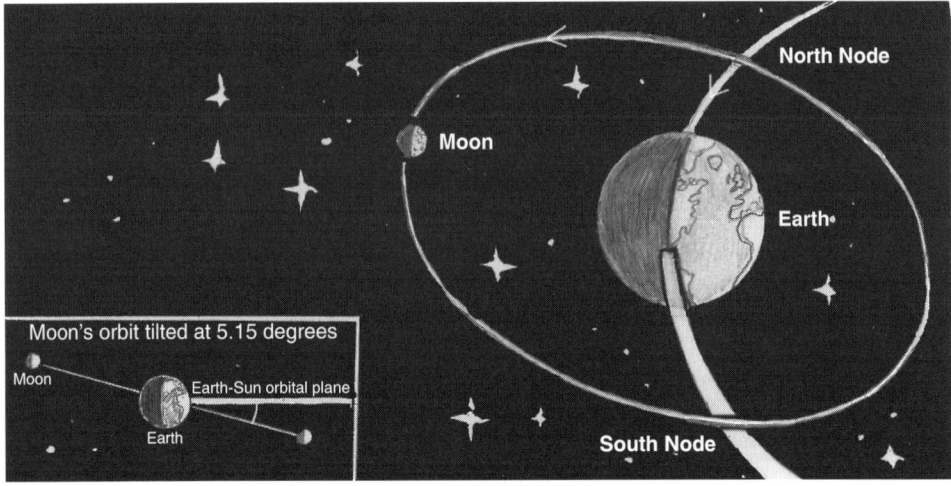

Figure 3.5. The intersection or nodal points of the Moon's orbit with the orbital plane of the Sun and Earth. Only when the Moon is full or new *and* crossing the nodal points does an eclipse occur, the Sun, Moon and Earth making an exact alignment.

occur when the Sun and Moon markers are adjacent or opposite each other, and this invites curiosity to discover more about eclipse cycles. Even within a couple of years, an operator would also discover the following:

(i). *That eclipses can only occur at full or new Moon.*

(ii). *Eclipses are seen only to occur at two places in the calendar year, and even at these places, they are not reliably predictable in advance.*

(iii). *After a few years, it is seen that the dates of eclipses move backwards around the calendar by about 19 days every year.*

(iv). *Eclipses can only occur during two months of each year (each 'month' being 34 days long, separated by about 173 days).*

(v). *An 'Eclipse Year' - eclipses occuring at about the same time of year from a previous eclipse - takes about 346 days to complete.*

The two points where the Moon's path cuts the ecliptic (the imaginary line which the Sun follows through the 'year-circle' of the zodiac) are termed the *Moon's nodes*; the passage of the Moon into the northern hemisphere is called the *north node* whilst that into the southern hemisphere is called the *south node*. In ancient astronomy texts, these become the Dragon's Head and Dragon's Tail respectively and they were given tremendous importance. A full or new Moon occuring when the Moon passes near to these intersection points will inevitably produce an eclipse, for the Sun, Earth and Moon are then in alignment.

The two intersection or nodal points revolve too, moving backwards (clockwise) around the zodiac and therefore the calendar, taking 18.62 years to complete a circuit (*figure 3.5*). If this is found too complicated to comprehend heliocentrically, then this is where a *geocentric* model scores, enabling anyone to grasp the principle of the eclipse mechanism and thus the way in which the intersection points between the plane of the Moon's orbit, and that of the Earth's, change.

Using the Aubrey calendar, for example, one cannot fail to notice that when there is a lunar eclipse, it occurs about three holes in a clockwise direction from the previous eclipse on one particular side of the circle. Three holes corresponds to 19 days.

After several years of use, it would become evident that 'eclipse markers' placed opposite each other around a 56 marker circle should be moved *one hole clockwise three times each year* - thus taking 18.618 years to complete a circuit. The mathematical elegance of this unlikely coincidence is astonishing, for 18.618 multiplied by three equals 55.854, a figure extremely close to 56 and one which enables the Aubrey calendar to readily predict eclipses. Two extra poles, which represent 'Danger! Likelihood of an eclipse', are placed opposite each other and moved clockwise three times each year. Figure 3.6 shows the complete Aubrey calendar/eclipse predictor; the most elegant, minimal and accurate practical solution for understanding the motions of the Sun and the Moon.

Fifty-six is therefore the *inevitable* choice for the number of markers around a solar/ lunar analogue model intended for eclipse prediction. To find such a number at

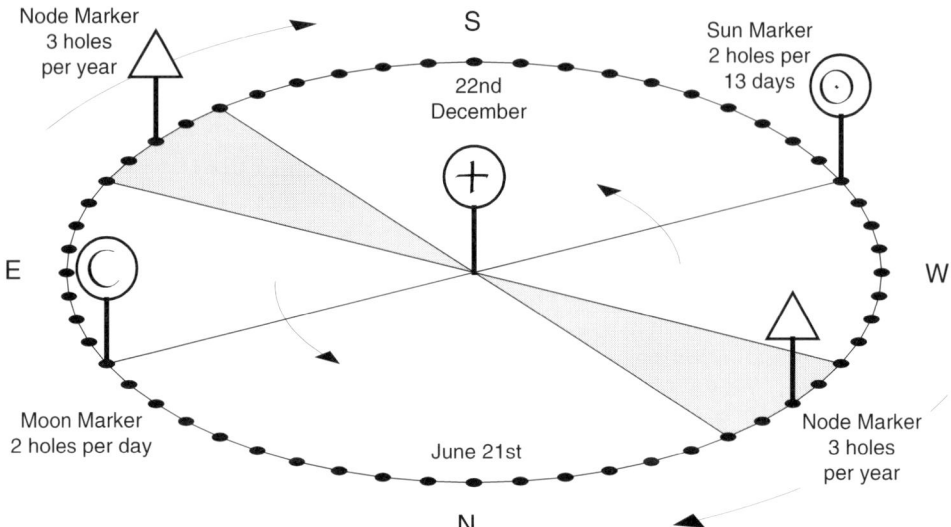

Node Marker
3 holes
per year

S

Sun Marker
2 holes per
13 days

22nd
December

E

W

Moon Marker
2 holes per day

Node Marker
3 holes
per year

June 21st

N

Figure 3.6 The Aubrey Calendar adapted for Eclipse Prediction. Two node markers define two eclipse zones (shaded) in the year when full or new Moons will produce an eclipse. They are moved clockwise one hole three times a year. The full Moon shown above (October 20th) would *not* produce an eclipse - it lies outside of the eclipse zone. The eclipse zones rotate backwards around the calendar over an 18.6 year cycle.

Stonehenge reveals an important implied purpose for the Aubrey holes. Interestingly, it was only the later and impressively massive developments at Stonehenge which drew John Aubrey's attention to this rather unimpressive collection of minor hollows in the ground which now bear his name. But for the later constructions at Stonehenge, we may never have been privileged to know of the existence of this testimony to astronomic and design expertise in late Stone Age Britain. The Aubrey holes are thus named after this early 'magotie headed' explorer of the mysteries of Stonehenge, whose discovery was made whilst 'out fox-hunting' in 1649, and whose first sketch plan of Stonehenge was drawn up in the year of the Plague - 1666.[3]

Perhaps the remnants of other 28 or 56 hole circles lie waiting to be discovered at less impressive megalithic sites. Large Indian medicine wheels exist with 28 sectors clearly visible and present-day Vedic astrologers divide the sky into 28 lunar 'mansions'. Orthodox history contains some evidence for the association of the number 56 with eclipses, for Plutarch writes, "There are some who give the name Typhon to the shadow of the Earth into which they believe the Moon falls and so suffers eclipse." And, "The 56-sided polygon is said to belong to Typhon." That one superb 56-marker circle survived at Stonehenge has been enough for many hundreds of replicas of the Aubrey Circle to have been constructed throughout the world, these accurately emulating the soli-lunar astronomy unfolding in the sky above.[4]

Summary

Whether one feels that all of this was beyond the wit of neolithic Europeans would be a subjective and unscientific opinion because the necessary hardware evidently still exists from 5000 years ago. Furthermore, it could so easily be made to operate once again - it would be very easy to restore the Aubrey calendar to its task of tracking the physical realities of solar and lunar motion. Whilst it may never be proved that men built and used the Aubrey circle in the above described manner, it would have been even stranger for them to have laboured to produce a mindless monument - with 56 holes accurately placed and equally spaced around the perimeter of an accurate circle - this number which just happens to be perfectly suited to the task of accurate solar, lunar and eclipse timekeeping and which is described as such in classical Greek texts. Certainly, the monument is perfectly set up to perform this task, and no number of holes other than 56 (or multiples) would suffice to replicate soli-lunar astronomy.

The Aubrey Circle is a cultural artefact which has been hopelessly played down in terms of its likely function. The cosmologist Sir Fred Hoyle appears to have been the first soul to have recognised its purpose in recent times.[5] He writes of the builders that they were "... meticulous observers of the night sky, ... (they) calculated with numbers, and communicated sophisticated astronomical knowledge from generation from generation."

The quality of ancient thought in these lands was such that the word *primitive* cannot be applied to this, nor, as we shall discover, any of the other designs built by the megalithic culture. This was high culture, in prehistoric Europe.

Footnotes to Chapter Three.

1 During the lunation month, the Moon's daily motion varies from 11 to 14 degrees a day, this being caused by it falling away from and then accelerating towards the Sun during each circuit of the Earth.

2 It is curious that the expression, 'all at sixes and sevens' describes a confusion over a routine procedure, exactly as when operating this calendar and using the same numbers. The basic ritual is that, for every 13 'Moon marker' movements, the 'Sun marker' is moved just once.

3 The Aubrey holes owe their rediscovery and their name to R.S. Newall, who collaborated with Colonel Hawley in his excavations and persuaded him to search for Aubrey's 'cavities' observed just inside the bank. John Aubrey lived from 1626 to 1697 and was described as 'shiftless, roving and magotie headed.'

4 An early monogram, *Building and Operating Stone Circles and other Calendar Devices*, by the author, was first available in 1992. Many people, schools, colleges and universities have built facsimiles of the Aubrey calendar.

5 *'Stonehenge as an Eclipse Predictor'*, Antiquity, 1966. Quote from Fred Hoyle's, *On Stonehenge*, published by Heinemann Educational Books Ltd, in 1977.

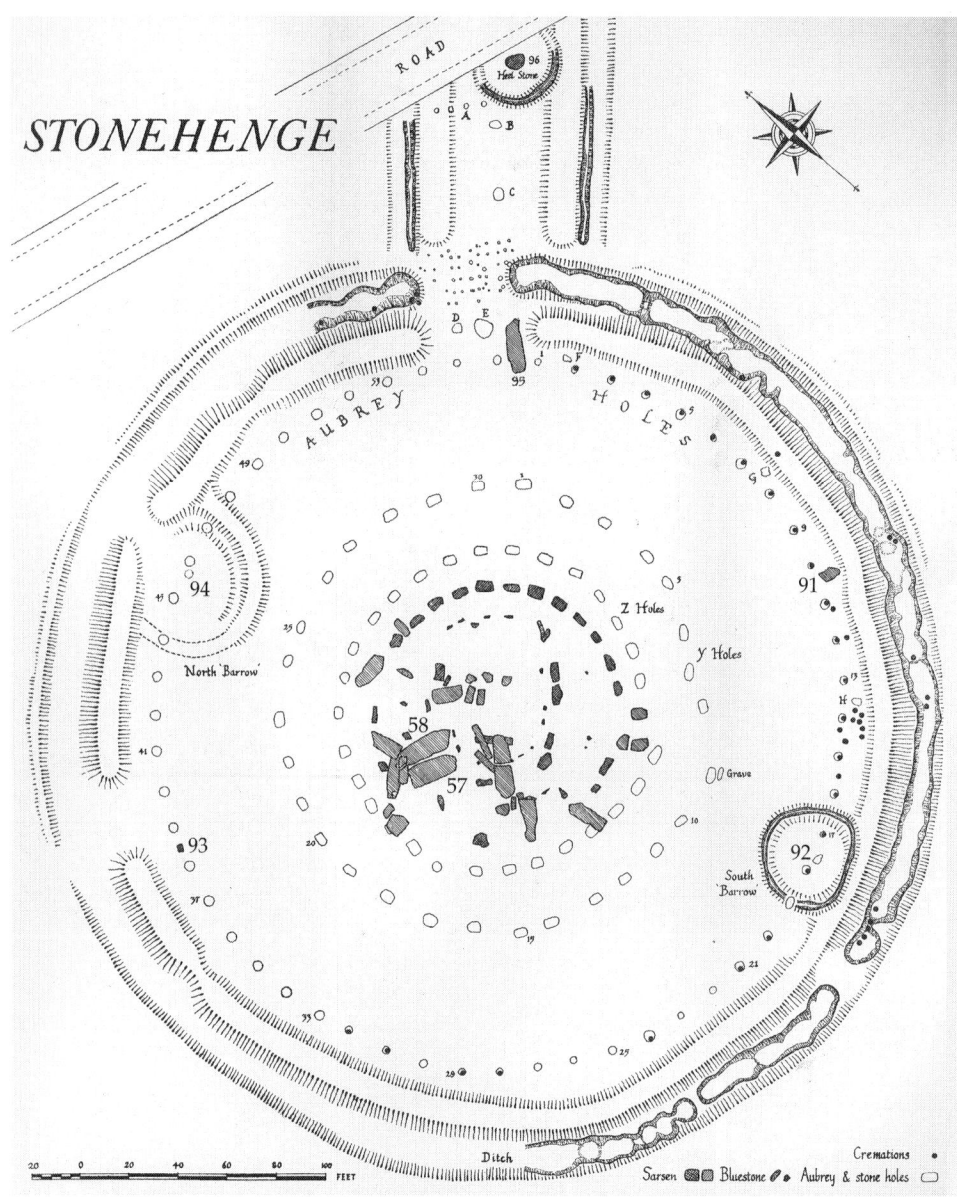

Above: Atkinson's Stonehenge. Trilithons 57 and 58 with their lintel (157) fell in 1797, and were re-erected after Atkinson's plan was drawn, in 1958 (compare with Alex Thom's survey facing page 1). The four station stones, numbered 91 - 94, are clearly visible forming a rectangular construction which contains the sarsen circle.

Chapter Four

- THE EIGHTH WONDER -
OF THE WORLD

Stonehenge as a model of the Earth

The earliest constructions at Stonehenge furnish a remarkably accurate model of the motions of the Sun and Moon as seen from the Earth. The Aubrey circle provides evidence of an intended *geocentric* framework for Stonehenge, implying that the inner parts of the monument are to be understood as a representation of the Earth itself. This is neither esoteric nor unrealistic - if the circular ditch and bank are taken to represent the zodiac or year-circle, and the Aubrey circle understood to be an analogue model of the Sun and Moon in the skies around the Earth, then the inner constructions of Stonehenge must represent the Earth itself in some way and the centre of the monument represents the immediate present - the here and now.

Perhaps the most immediate and pleasing visual confirmation that this is indeed the case may be made by an inspection of the original siting of four stones placed in a rectangle around the Aubrey circle and perpendicular to it during 'phase II' of the monument (c.2700 BC) - the so-called *station stone rectangle*. This construction linked the earlier Aubrey circle to the later sarsen circle, and its importance will become very clear in this and later chapters .

The Station Stone Rectangle

Four stones, numbered 91 to 94 on the HMSO plan, once formed an accurate rectangle whose side lengths held the numerical ratio 5:12. Two of the stones remain (91 and 93), but the sitings of the missing two (92 and 94) are still plainly visible because an elaborate ditch and mound structure remain around each site. Archaeologists have located the holes that once held these large (10 ft) sarsen stone upright. In addition, the accuracy of the rectangle has been investigated and confirmed by modern archaeologists and recent surveys.[1]

Straight away, one can find a parallel between this rectangle, the Aubrey circle and the realities the Earth holds with the Sun (*figure 4.1*), for the '12' sides of the rectangle emulate the position on the Earth of the tropics of Capricorn and Cancer.[2]

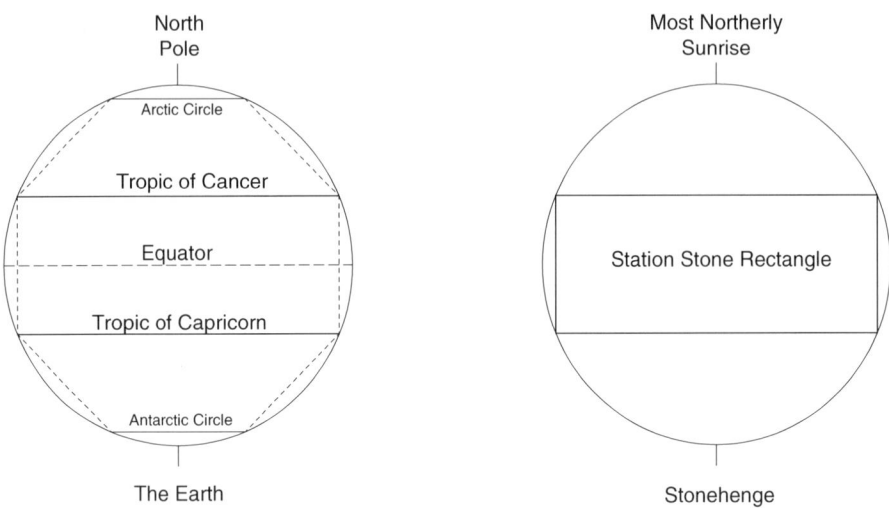

Figure 4.1 Stonehenge seen as a model of the Earth. The four stones of the station stone rectangle define, with the midsummer sunrise, an accurate analogue of the Earth's principle latitudes. These are defined by the axial tilt of about 23.5 degrees.

The octagonal shape implied from the axis of symmetry can be seen to represent our planet. The axis azimuth degree, which aligns closely with the latitude of Stonehenge, also marks the *most northerly* annual sunrise at this latitude - the same annual midsummer sunrise which still causes so much animosity between factions in our society at Stonehenge and warrants an incredible four mile exclusion zone being placed around the monument each and every summer.

The similarity between the Earth and Stonehenge is thus clearly seen - the monument mimics our planet in a quite astonishing manner. The apex angles formed by the diagonals of this rectangle copy closely the axial tilt of the Earth. Furthermore, an octagram 'star' can be drawn from the heelstone, and immediately there is seen a reinforcement of this octagonal motif (*see figure 4.2*). The Aubrey circle now defines the inner boundary of the eight 'star points' and this also allows us to see the two tropics and the arctic and antarctic circles[3].

North, in *Stonehenge* (p 477), confirms that, "..each of the shorter sides of the rectangle needed to be a chord of just an eighth part of the defining circle. ...such a geometric construction had already been used at the time of marking out the Aubrey circle..". The Earth takes on an octagonal motif by virtue of its axial tilt angle and Stonehenge emulates this same shape, which should interest us greatly, for the tropics of Cancer and Capricorn, like the arctic and antarctic circles, are *imaginary* circles devised by men who understand how the Earth moves in space and, perhaps more importantly, knew that our planet is *spherical* in shape.

Present orthodoxy prevents us from accepting that the architects of Stonehenge possessed such knowledge - instead we continue to applaud Greek or *renaissance* astronomers like Eratosthenes, Copernicus and Galileo for this discovery. Time for a rethink perhaps. Eratosthenes was director of the biggest ever repository of ancient wisdom - the ill-fated Alexandrian Library. Unlike him, we have lost contact totally with this knowledge and our history is written without it and therefore incomplete.

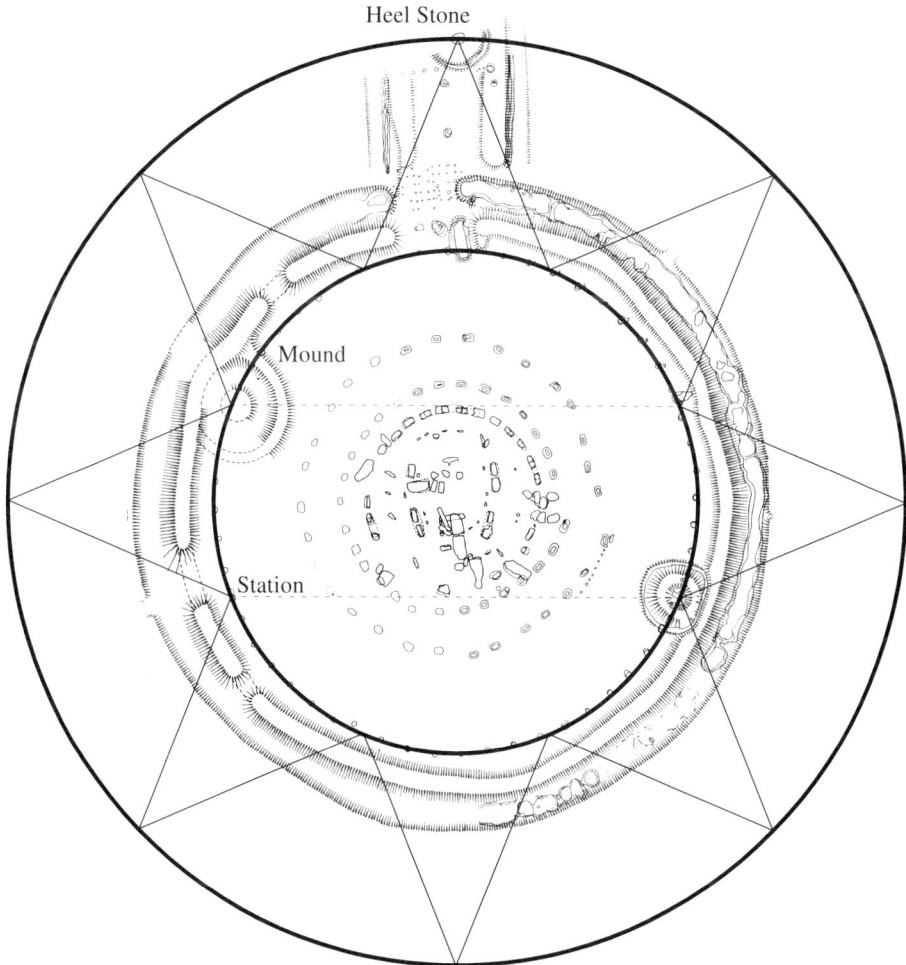

Figure 4.2 Octagonal geometry at Stonehenge. The diameter of the Aubrey circle compared to the circle formed from the Heelstone makes the ratio 1 : 1.848, the same ratio present in the octogram which defines the positions of the heelstone and the four station stones (*Courtesy John Martineau*).

The Station Stones and the Latitude of Stonehenge

Dr Gerald Hawkins' seminal work, *Stonehenge Decoded*, (Souvenir Press, 1966) opened up the importance of the Station Stone rectangle in terms of soli-lunar astronomy, showing that the solar and lunar alignments found within the rectangle could only occur within half a degree of the chosen latitude of Stonehenge. Astronomically, it is true that Stonehenge is sited in the middle of a very narrow band of latitude - less than 1° - where the astronomical alignments shown in the figure opposite permit these four stones to take a precise rectangular shape.

If Stonehenge had been built north of Oxford or on the Isle of Wight, the shape would have had to have taken the form of a parallelogram - and it could not then have been fitted around the perimeter of the Aubrey or any other circle. These alignments are shown in figure 4.3 - if they are intentional, then it confirms that the designers of Stonehenge attached great importance to the exact latitude of the site.

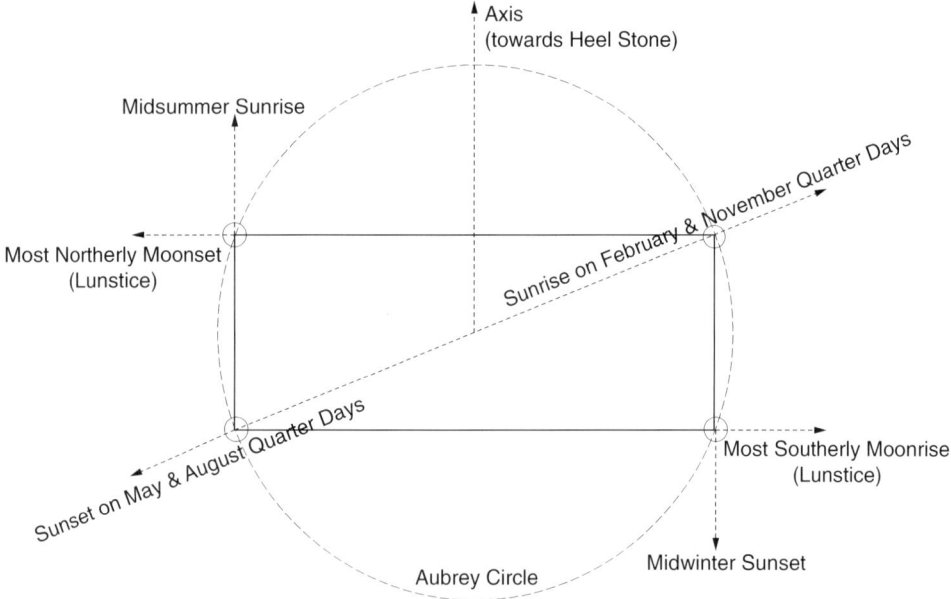

Figure 4.3 Solar and Lunar Alignments from the Station Stone Rectangle. Dr Gerald Hawkins' book *Stonehenge Decoded* was centred around these alignments, but Duke, Lockyer and Newham had noted them earlier. The unique combination of a right angle between midsummer sunrise and the most northerly moonset, and between midwinter sunset and most southerly moonrise, only occurs over a narrow band of latitude - less than a degree - with Stonehenge located in the middle third of this band. Above or below this latitude and the rectangle becomes a parallelogram and cannot be made to fit around the perimeter of the Aubrey circle. Extreme lunar rise and set occur every 18.62 years when the 5.15° tilt of the lunar plane adds to the Earth's tilt.

Because the Moon's orbital plane is angled at just over five degrees to that of the Sun and Earth, the Moon does not rise and set with the same annual angular range as the Sun. At the latitude of Stonehenge, the range of solar rising and settings is confined within two arcs of about 80° whilst the extremes of lunar rising and settings occur over a larger arc. The extreme midsummer full moonrise occurs at 90° to the midsummer sunrise and the midwinter sunrise occurs at 90° to the extreme winter full moonrise. Such a relationship connects Sun and Moon through right angles *only* at the latitude of Stonehenge, perhaps a reason for this single rectangular structure being built there and thereby a discovery of the uniqueness of the siting of the monument on our planet.

Hawkins used the then remarkable new IBM computers to analyse every possible alignment at Stonehenge - he was thorough, well qualified and presented his results in a proficient manner. His book was blasted by the establishment. *"Moonshine over Stonehenge"* was how Professor Richard Atkinson[10] headed his attack on Hawkins' theories. Whilst Atkinson's *Stonehenge*, written in 1955, remains the best source of archaeological information on the monument, it contains almost no astronomical analysis.

Hawkins' book became a classic alternative text on Stonehenge and it was widely popular. It was a major contribution to public awareness of the astronomical importance of Stonehenge and that of the megalithic culture. Today it is hard to imagine that, barely thirty years ago, so little astronomical meaning was being given to Stonehenge by academics.

Perhaps it was Hawkins' book which fuelled Atkinson to state that "shots in the dark may not always be accurate: but at least they serve to wake sleepers from their beds". And the alarm call was being given by both Hawkins and Thom - using 'a well constructed parcel bomb'. Both men were showing that there was much, much more to the megalithic culture than prescribed within the then current orthodoxy.

It is interesting in retrospect to study what Hawkins thought about Stonehenge. On page 150 of *Stonehenge Decoded*, he cites three reasons for the alignments and calendrical uses of Stonehenge. The first was to assist planting and other seasonal activities (a calendrical purpose), the second was to augment priestly power through the ability to predict cosmic events such as eclipses (shamanistic astronomy). His third reason was that the architects and the builders "enjoyed the mental exercise above and beyond the call of duty". Hawkins concludes by nominating the monument as the "Eighth wonder of the world" and the octagonal nature of Stonehenge numerically confirms this.

Right angled triangles whose sides have lengths which form whole number ratios are termed *Pythagorean* triangles or, less commonly, *Diaphantine* triangles - some examples are shown in figure 4.4. In truth, they were known about and their properties used millenia before the Greek philosopher was a twinkle in his father's eye. The station stone rectangle, with an added diagonal, forms two right angled triangles whose sides are in the ratio 5:12:13. Figure 4.5 shows the arrangement. They may be found inscribed on the walls of Egyptian temples and, as we shall see, are central to understanding Stonehenge and other megalithic designs. They also have the unique

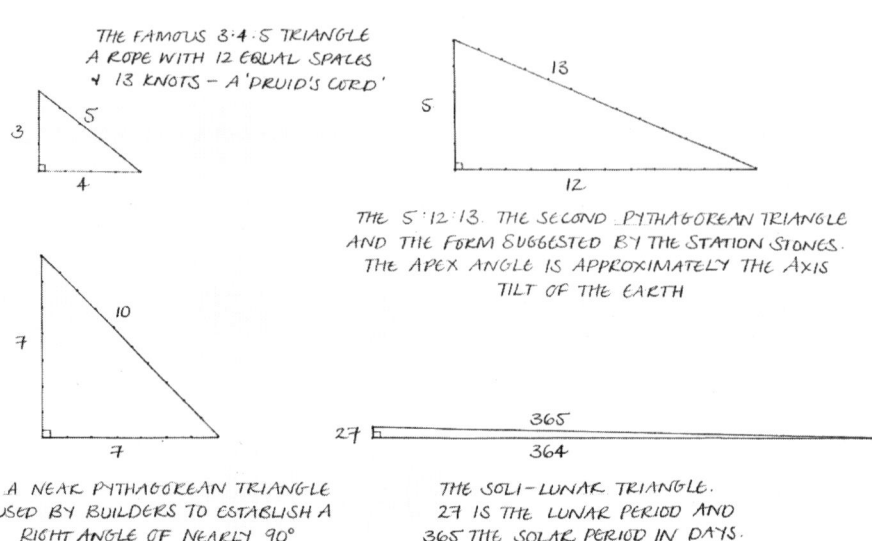

RIGHT ANGLED TRIANGLES ~ PYTHAGOREAN AND NEARLY.

THE FAMOUS 3·4·5 TRIANGLE
A ROPE WITH 12 EQUAL SPACES
+ 13 KNOTS ~ A 'DRUID'S CORD'

THE 5·12·13. THE SECOND PYTHAGOREAN TRIANGLE
AND THE FORM SUGGESTED BY THE STATION STONES.
THE APEX ANGLE IS APPROXIMATELY THE AXIS
TILT OF THE EARTH

A NEAR PYTHAGOREAN TRIANGLE
USED BY BUILDERS TO ESTABLISH A
RIGHT ANGLE OF NEARLY 90°

THE SOLI-LUNAR TRIANGLE.
27 IS THE LUNAR PERIOD AND
365 THE SOLAR PERIOD IN DAYS.

Figure 4.4 The first members of the Pythagorean Triangle set (with some 'near misses'). Builders have used the 3:4:5 for millenia to establish accurate right-angled corners for buildings and the 7:7:10 where accuracy is not as important. The 12:35:37 may be found at megalithic sites, and it is surely interesting to discover the 27:364:365 triangle, with the orbital periods of both Sun and Moon written into its dimensions.

property that the square on the hypotenuse (the length of the longest side squared) equals the sum of the squares on the other two sides of the triangle. Remember that from school?

The 5:12:13 triangle is the second Pythagorean triangle in the series. Thus, in the most commonly known 'Pythagorean' triangle, the so-called 3:4:5 triangle, five squared (25) equals three squared plus four squared (9 + 16), whilst for the 5:12:13 triangle, 169 = 144 + 25 and the apex angle of the triangle is 22.6°, which is less than one degree from the Earth's axial tilt angle (currently 23.45°, but this varies with a 41,000 year period from 21° to 24.5°). Sixteen 5:12:13 triangles form, approximately, an octagon.

Five, Twelve, Thirteen

The numbers twelve and thirteen should by now hold considerable meaning for the reader. They suggest something far more than just numbers and we may now suppose that they suggest the Sun (12) and the Moon (13) and thus the archetypal 'male' and 'female' qualities. But what about the number *five*, juxtaposed between them with this triangle? In many ancient cultures, alchemic texts, folklore and Pythagorean traditions, the number five represented generic Man, the unified being created "in the image and likeness of God, male and female created he(?) them" (Genesis, Chapter I, verse 26). Five was seen as the number of health, harmony and consciousness. It was the 'Number of Man' enshrined in the pentagonal drawings of *renaissance* artists Leonardo da Vinci and Fludd. The pentagon and its brother, the pentagram star form two of our most ancient 'occult' symbols. This shape links the number five with the Golden Section number *phi* to a remarkable extent.[4] Five also linked the integration of the male with the female qualities and thus became associated with marriage - Pythagorean numerology and Hindu-Greek musical theory identifying the number 2 as being the first female number, whilst 3 represented the first male number - two plus three equals five and symbolically represents marriage (integration of male and female qualities).[5] However strangely such ideas fall on modern ears, the ancient world built entire philosophies on such things, and we might do well to remember that the most harmonious interval in music remains the *tonic* or *keynote* played with the *fifth* or *dominant* note of the scale, and that the relative frequencies or string lengths of these two notes form the exact ratio 3:2.

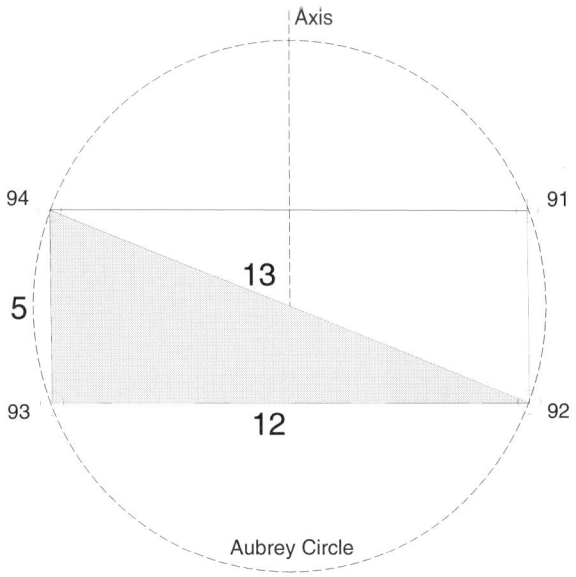

Figure 4.5 A 5:12:13 triangle formed from a diagonal of the Station Stone Rectangle. The '13' side interestingly defines the diameter of the Aubrey circle, which actually measures 104 Megalithic yards, from which the units above are 8 Megalithic yards each. Thus the dimensions of the triangle are 40:96:104 Megalithic yards, a strong indication of neolithic knowledge of both the triangle and its properties.

Man (5), is the highest evolving consciousness currently on the Earth, and stands as the end product of an evolutionary engine whose drivers are the Sun and Moon. As the mediator between the Sun (12) and the Moon (13) in the 5:12:13 triangle, Man (5), can solve the incompatibility between solar and lunar cycles. Working with plans of Stonehenge,the writer discovered a most interesting truth:- Dividing the '5' side of a 5:12:13 triangle into the ratio 3:2 produces a point from which can be drawn a new hypotenuse whose length is 12.369 - *the number of lunations in one solar year*. This number is the vital key to harmonising the calendar and understanding soli-lunar integration. The 'female 2' comes down from the feminine and lunar '13' side; the 'male 3' comes up from the masculine and solar '12' side of the triangle. Their point of meeting contains a profound truth concerning the astronomy of the Sun, Moon, Earth system, for here the number 5 is able to 'arrange' a geometrical 'marriage' of the Sun and the Moon, a marriage which integrates symbolic material and astronomical realities, numerology, astrology and musical science.

I have named this geometric construction *the lunation triangle* (see overleaf). Its pedigree is impeccable and I believe it was once a revered icon of the ancient world, particularly at Stonehenge.

Footnotes to Chapter Three.

[1] See *Sun, Moon and Standing Stones*. John E.Wood. (OUP). page 148.
[2] To within a degree of the present axial tilt, which varies over a 41,000 year cycle of variation of the axial tilt.
[3] Atkinson, in his survey of hole 94 in 1978, found the rectangle diagonal angles to be 45° 11'.4.
[4] *Phi* = 1.618 to three decimal places.
[5] The 'mother' framework for all music depends on multiples of 2 - the resulting octaves set the form within which the notes of the scale under construction are placed, this invoking the number 3 and other odd numbers.

Figure 4.6 (right) Station Stone 93. Dwarfed by the single and elegant trilithon 56 (*central*), the upright stump of station stone 93 may be seen to the left of the picture. The camera was placed at station stone 92, and the alignment of the trilithon and the sarsen circle stones to its right can be clearly seen. In the extreme left foreground, the huge 'foot' of the fallen trilithon 55 may be seen, as can various fallen stones from the sarsen circle.

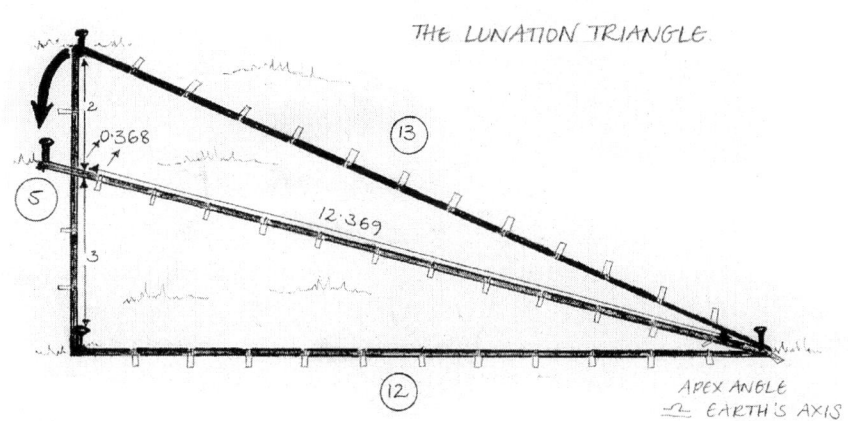

THE LUNATION TRIANGLE

(13)

0·368

(5)

12·369

2

3

(12)

APEX ANGLE
⌒ EARTH'S AXIS

THE '12' SIDE IS A DRUID'S CORD
THE WHOLE LUNATION TRIANGLE COMPRISES

    30 SPACES
    31 MARKERS
    IT'S AREA IS 30 UNITS²

IF THE CHOSEN UNITS ARE MEGALITHIC YARDS,
THE 0·368 'OVERPLUS' CORRESPONDS TO
      ONE FOOT AND THE REMAINDER IS
    ONE ROYAL CUBIT

ANNUAL LUNATIONS = 12·36826623
ERROR USING TRIANGLE = 0·0085%

GEOMETRIC SOLUTION
$3^2 + 12^2 = (\text{HYPOTENUSE})^2$
$9 + 144 = 153$
$\text{HYPOTENUSE} = \sqrt{153}$
$= 12·369$

Above: The Practical Use of a Lunation Triangle. An extended 'Druid's Cord' of thirty-one knots and thirty spaces is laid out on the ground as shown above. The '13' side is brought down as shown and pegged at the 3:2 point of the '5' side. Its internal length is then equal to the number of lunations in a solar year.

The '12' side, which consists of a traditional 'Druid's Cord' of thirteen knots enclosing twelve spaces, can then represent a twelve month solar year in calendrical work or eclipse prediction.

Chapter Five

- THE LUNATION TRIANGLE -

In this chapter we look at some compelling evidence which suggests that there was ancient knowledge of the lunation triangle as an artefact. It will become apparent that the ancient world's astronomers and mystics understood the usefulness of this geometric device whilst later cultures apparently lost sight of it, for unclear reasons. All that remains today are the numerological, musical and mythological crumbs. And Stonehenge.

In one of the display cabinets in the Alexander Keiller Museum, at Avebury, a large notice informs visitors, somewhat despairingly, that:

> *"These broken pieces of tools and utensils are like the pieces of a jig-saw puzzle. When complete, the puzzle should show us what Neolithic life was like. Unfortunately, we do not have the completed picture on the puzzle-box lid to tell us how the pieces should fit together. Worse still, many of the pieces have been lost."*

To anyone interested in megalithic culture, calendar production, or a better understanding of the order inherent in the cosmos, the lunation triangle supplies a long lost vital piece of the jigsaw, and will be seen to facilitate an astonishing glimpse of the completed puzzle-box lid picture. Once, in the ancient world, the discovery of the lunation triangle represented a scientific achievement on a par with the discovery of the calculus and it is not hard to see why:

> - *It reveals directly and with extreme precision the single most relevant astronomical constant - the average annual lunation figure - as a length to within 0.008% of the true figure.*[1]
>
> - *It is an easily memorised and simple geometric construction which uses only whole numbers. It can be transported and used anywhere using a single rope marked with 30 equal divisions.*
>
> - *It is not necessary to deal with fractions or decimals. The lunation rate is already correctly proportioned to either 12 or 13 month calendar years - the lunation triangle provides both.*

The lunation triangle begins life as a Pythagorean 5:12:13 triangle and this same construction may be found in the middle of Stonehenge. Both artefacts are about soli-lunar astronomy. In addition, the solar and lunar alignments made by the station stone rectangle are unique to the latitude of Stonehenge. I now suggest that the architect knew something else about life on Earth, something we have long since forgotten about. For a start, the required 5:12 ratio automatically allocates the number 13 to the Aubrey circle diameter - a singularly appropriate number whose validity appears further enhanced when we discover that the unit becomes exactly eight of Alex Thom's Megalithic yards. We can now let Stonehenge 'speak' for itself:

The Evidence at Stonehenge

(i). The station stone rectangle allows Stonehenge to resemble the planet Earth in cross-section.

(ii). The right-angle arrangement between the Sun's solstitial and the Moon's extreme (lunstitial?) risings is unique to the latitude of Stonehenge. If the architect knew this, then the siting of Stonehenge was equally as impressive as the building of the monument itself.

(iii). The rectangle has side ratios of 5:12, and a corresponding diagonal of 13 of these same units. These units turn out to be 8 MY each, and the Aubrey circle diameter is therefore taken to be 'read' as 13 units of 8 MY each, i.e. 104 MY, a whole number.

(iv). The same ratio, using the same units, may be found between the Heelstone and the centre of the monument compared with the Aubrey circle diameter. The accuracy of this ratio is better than a fifth of one percent[2].

(v). The 5:12:13 triangle, implied within a monument which appears to honour the motions of the Sun and Moon, is an astonishingly valuable tool for performing a range of astronomically precise tasks which enable forecasts to be made concerning solar and lunar positions and phases. A neolithic calendar maker would have given away his entire set of round-bottomed pots for such a technique.

It has been suggested that the station stone rectangle could have been a device used to provide, through the intersections of its diagonals, the precise centre of the Aubrey circle and thus the Stonehenge site. It is postulated that later work, i.e. the sarsen circle, could have then resumed where the original builders left off four centuries earlier, and the rectangle, or more relevantly, the crossing of its diagonals, would meet at the exact centre of the Stonehenge site. Several factors weigh against this argument, the first being that one normally does not employ stone megaliths weighing in tons nor build small mounds around two of these in order to locate a building centre using this technique - wooden pegs alone suffice. A second factor is that there is no need to incorporate a 5:12 rectangle to find the centre - *any* rectangle or square would do. Also, the stone corners were not placed exactly on the circumference of the Aubrey circle, suggesting that the objective was more about achieving accurate solar and lunar alignments than finding the monument's exact centre. Finally, the sarsen circle and all subsequent phases of the monument's evolution were based on a quite different centre to the Aubrey circle - more than 20 inches off the 'Aubrey' centre. The argument appears so seriously flawed as to be dismissed.

All five statements (*opposite*) are, of course, completely unacceptable within conventional archaeology, which has yet to agree that the Aubrey circle is other than 56 'ritual pits' arranged rather precisely along the perimeter of a circle. As the 'keepers of the keys' concerning our ancient past, nothing is going to change quickly here unless new evidence is brought to light. This evidence is, I believe, available in a number of forms which, when put together, vigorously confirm ancient knowledge of the lunation triangle. We can begin this forage by returning to folk-lore and a hoary old superstition.

Friday the Thirteenth

Even in modern and apparently sophisticated Europe, a remarkably persistent superstition tells us, succinctly, that *'Friday the thirteenth is unlucky'*. If the thirteenth day of the month happens to fall on a Friday, then all manner of ill-luck is believed to abound and things will go bump in the night. This kind of superstition is guaranteed to make certain folk, like the author, look deeper into matters, which may be the ultimate intention of such things. They hide esoteric information in a form which frightens people, who, in order to avoid such things, remember the information very well indeed, thus guaranteeing that it gets passed on to their children, whom they rightly want to protect above all else. The baton thus gets passed down through the generations and although the esoterics may become lost due to cultural changes, they remain recovereable once the original cultural context is understood.

We all know, in reality, that nothing terribly nasty is observed to happen on most Fridays which fall on the thirteenth, as well one might expect seeing that there is nothing particularly cosmic nor divinely authorised about having twelve months in the year nor about 'Friday' as a weekday. We might surmise, from what we have been looking at in chapter two, that the thirteenth month itself has been historically unlucky, having been dumped from our calendar. But what *really* underpins this superstition?

Friday is named after the Nordic goddess Freya, or Frigga, a direct counterpart of Venus, the goddess of love, whose number is five and whose day is the fifth day of our week.[3] The thirteenth day of one of the twelve calendar months then links 5, 12 and 13 together in an interesting calendrical combination. Certainly, it places these three numbers directly in front of our eyes as a calendrical puzzle. From which one might, given some knowledge of the Sun and Moon's behaviour, and an interest in matters calendrical, reconstruct the lunation triangle. *Just five words preserve all this information.* We might usefully ask from where this superstition sprang, who began it and why?

The Draught of Fishes

In the twenty first chapter of the Gospel of St John, the so-called *appendix* to the Gospel, will be found an accurate description of the symbolic, mathematical and geometrical functions and purpose of the lunation triangle.[4] Because the Bible is not found in every home these days, I give the story below, allowing the reader to fully comprehend the esoteric information hidden beneath the surface of a religious text. Despite translations through the ages, the story has survived intact and is completely transparent as to its astronomical meaning. I have omitted verses from the story which are not directly relevant.

> 1. *"After these things Jesus shewed himself again to the disciples at the sea of Tiberias; and on this wise he shewed himself.*
> 2. *There were together Simon Peter and Thomas called Didymus, and Nathanael of Cana in Galilee, and the sons of Zebedee, and two other of his disciples.*
> 3. *Simon Peter saith unto them, I go a fishing. They say unto him, We also go with thee. They went forth, and entered into a ship immediately; and that night they caught nothing.*
> 4. *But when the morning was now come, Jesus stood on the shore: but the disciples knew not that it was Jesus.*
> 5. *Then Jesus saith unto them, Children, have ye any meat? They answered him, No.*
> 6. *And he said unto them, Cast the net on the right side of the ship, and ye shall find. They cast therefore, and now they were not able to draw it for the multitude of fishes.*
> 8. *And the other disciples came in a little ship;(for they were not far from land, but as it were two hundred cubits), dragging the net with fishes.*
> 11. *Simon Peter went up and drew the net to land full of great fishes, an hundred and fifty and three: and for all there were so many, yet was not the net broken.*
> 14. *This is now the third time that Jesus shewed himself to his disciples, after that he was risen from the dead."*
>
> *St John's Gospel, Chapter 21*

Jesus, the thirteenth member and the saviour of the group of twelve disciples, admonishes three named disciples to cast their net on the right side of the ship. Which is the right side of a ship[5] - is this the right angle being described? The number 153, for the number of fishes caught, is unique to this chapter of the Bible and occurs only in the above passage. So what has the number 153 got to do with anything, you may ask?

153 is the square of 12.369, the number of lunations in the year. To find the numerical length of the hypotenuse of the lunation triangle one must use Pythagoras' theorem, then evaluate the square root, whence:

$$(\text{hypotenuse})^2 = 3^2 + 12^2$$
$$= 9 + 144$$
$$= 153$$
$$\text{hypotenuse} = \sqrt{153} = 12.369$$

Two hundred cubits[6] (a *Sacred Cubit* was 25 inches long) corresponds to 5000 inches. The numbers 2, 3 and 5 interplay throughout this story. It was the *third* time that Jesus appeared to his disciples. The number of disciples in the boat will be found to contain the numbers 3 and 2, albeit somewhat encrypted in the manner by which they are named.

This story is seen to be a remarkably coherent and well preserved account of the function of the lunation triangle embedded within another story - a metaphysical text. That it links a Pythagorean triangle at Stonehenge with the Christian message may, at first, seem very strange indeed and yet the message of the triangle is that same one of harmony and unity, the coming together of the male and female aspects into a 'marriage'. If the reader cares to look at the Gnostic or Nag Hammadi texts, the oldest original Christian texts known, this male/female theme will be found permeating within the more familiar Christian messages. The modern Bible has excluded these as spiritually irrelevant.[7] The 'appendixed' story at the end of St John's Gospel holds *both* the spiritual implications and carries the lunation triangle along as astronomical cargo, although, in fact, both are the same message.

If the reader reads the explanations mooted throughout various religious analyses of this passage in St John, he or she will be entreated to a vast range of waffle, complex explanation, spiritual gloss and wholly unconvincing argument. Without understanding the coded message, that's exactly what one would expect, whilst with the geometric origins revealed, this same passage reveals the secret of soli-lunar astronomy, the sacred marriage of the Sun and Moon, and symbolically explains what underpins the Christian story - the integration of the human soul. The lunation triangle is *the* symbol of this particular revelation and the story has another level once one becomes conscious of its meaning.

A further and most spectacular example may be found where both these messages again appear interlinked.

The Stonehenge-Preseli Lunation Triangle

The latitude of the Stonehenge site has been shown to be unique, but what about the longitude? If we could discover something that would 'lock' the placement of the monument in coordinates of both latitude and longitude, that would surely be a major step forward in understanding what the designer(s) were thinking about.

Consider the following unlikely statement:

> *The siting of Stonehenge is such that it forms, with the Preseli bluestone site and their respective lines of latitude and longitude, a huge lunation triangle across southern England and Wales.*

Using standard high-school geometry, it is readily shown that this huge triangle is accurately represented on the ground, emulating the one found within the Aubrey circle. Lundy Island contains the *exact* site of the right angle, and Caldey Island, three miles off the coast from Tenby harbour, contains the site where the 3:2 point is located. Lundy and Caldey thus form, with the Preseli bluestone site and Stonehenge, all the four points needed to define a huge lunation triangle. Only one of these points is man-made, Stonehenge (*figure 5.2*). As long as Stonehenge survived in some form, the triangle and its message were there to be 'read' from the environment, and dozens of forty and fifty ton stones can survive the rigours of time and human tampering rather well.

Thus it is that only two large islands in the Bristol Channel are linked to the Preseli site by distances in the ratio 3:2. All three points lie on an *exact* north-south line - the *prime meridian*. Stonehenge provided the final point in defining this giant triangle. This is very strange material indeed, especially when one further considers that both these islands and the Preseli bluestone site sport ancient remains dating back to at least 8000 BC. The ancient name for Tenby is *Dinbych y Pysgod*, Welsh for 'City of the Fish'. This is, indeed, an appropriate name for an ancient Christian settlement lying almost on the 3:2 point, the 'Christ-point' of unity, on this huge 5:12:13 triangle. The symbol of Christianity remains the fish, historically aligned to the precessional age of Pisces, which began synchronously with Jesus' birth. In addition, the letters of the Greek word for fish, *ichthus*, are made up of the initials, in Greek, of the words "Jesus Christ, Son of God, Saviour". *Christianity* and *fish* are inextricably linked together, through the astronomy of precession and gematric word-play.

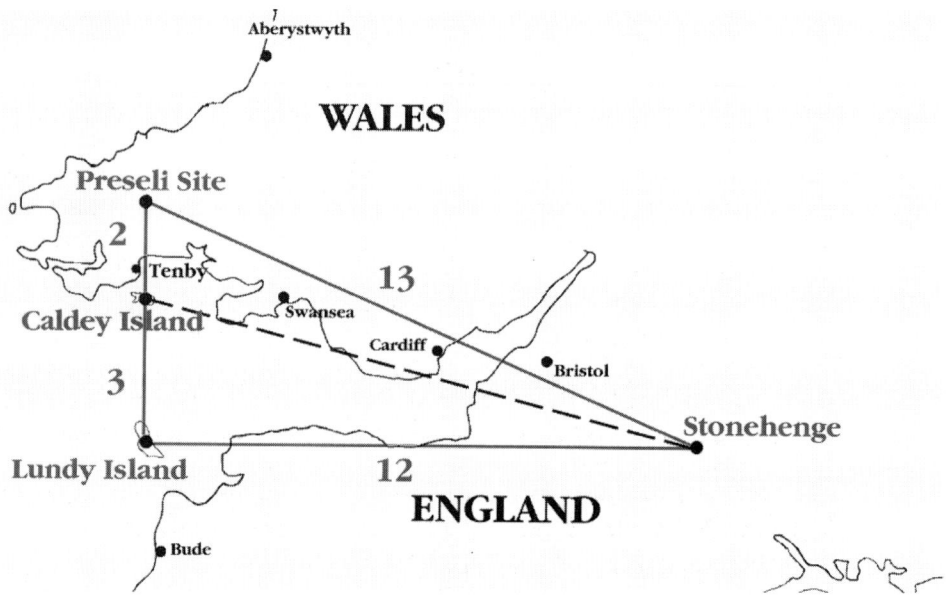

Figure 5.2 The Stonehenge - Preseli Lunation Triangle.

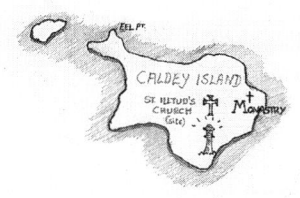

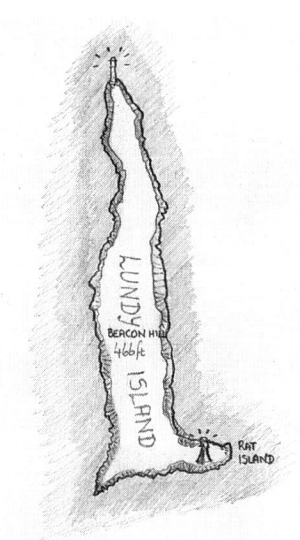

Figure 5.3 (a) Caldey Island, off the southern coast of Pembrokeshire. Prehistoric remains and artefacts show a long history of human occupation whilst the more recent history links Caldey with the very early Celtic Christian Church, via St Illtud and St Sampson.

Figure 5.3 (b) Lundy Island. Exactly west of Stonehenge, at a latitude of 51°10′ north, Lundy's shape suggests the right angle of the lunation triangle of which it is a component part. There are aligned megalithic stones and an original connection to Celtic Christianity, the church originally being dedicated to St Elen. The root word *elen* or *eli*, in a modern Welsh dictionary, is translated as *elbow, angle* or *corner*. These are the two largest islands in the Bristol Channel, and lie on a north-south line, longitude 4°41′ west.

Caldey island is known to have supported a monastry since at least the fifth century AD when the first Celtic monks from St Illtud's monastry arrived. There is a Christianised Ogham stone in St Illtud's church, originally discovered near to what was thought to have been a Celtic burial ground. Bronze age pottery has been excavated from Caldey, which was evidently a most important place in prehistoric Britain.

Lundy island was also a most revered place in ancient times. Although its name appears to suggest something lunar, the name is a derivative of the old Norse word for a puffin. Visited by Ptolemy, the Egyptian geographer, it was included on his maps, the land between the island and Hartland, Devon, being likened by him to the Pillars of Hercules, the name given to the mountains either side of the Straights of Gibraltar. The old name for Lundy was *Ynys Elen*, thought to mean *Elen's Island* and the original island church was dedicated to a certain St Elen of Luyddog, a 4th century Celtic saint, daughter of Eudas, King of Caernarfon. However, an argument runs that some of the place names which contain 'elen' and which have become attributed to St Elen are etymologically sourced from another word *eli* or *elen*, which a modern Welsh dictionary informs us means 'angle, elbow or corner'. The mistranslation is thought deliberate, due to 12th and 13th century writers anxious to claim St Elen as the progenitor of religious sites.[8]

Welsh is the oldest European language and the old Welsh name for Lundy was certainly *Ynys Elen*. The word *elen*, used in the sense of 'angle', 'corner' or 'elbow' is common to Welsh, Cornish and Breton. Perhaps more importantly, it is also found in anglo-saxon as *hele*, the dative form of *healh*, and the word has much more ancient Indo-European roots.[9] Whatever, it certainly augments the lunation triangle hypothesis - for Lundy is exactly where the right-angle bend, corner or elbow part of the form is located. *Ynys Elen* is just that - the island of the corner, angle or elbow.

The once lighthouse keeper on Lundy, Robert Farrah, has recorded midsummer alignments from megalithic standing stones on the island and kindly sent the writer photographs showing that the island's megalithic occupants were keenly aware of, and practising, exactly the kind of astronomy covered in chapter two.[10] At the *exact* same latitude of Stonehenge, at the second highest point on Lundy, Tibbett's Hill[11], one can find Knight Templar Rock, an interesting link with an ancient order.

It follows that if the Stonehenge-Preseli lunation triangle be embraced as other than a quite remarkable coincidence then Stonehenge was sited uniquely, in both latitude and longitude, *after* the builders discovered the north-south alignment of the two islands. That two sides of this triangle still align to the four cardinal points interestingly demonstrates that the Earth's polar axis has not changed during the past five millenia.

The surveyors who planned this construction would presumably have noted the north-south alignment of Lundy and Caldey, measured the 3:2 ratio to the Preseli region, discovering the various outcrops which litter the mountain tops there, finally taking the stones from the selected and thus venerated site all the way to Stonehenge in order to confirm the geometry. If this indeed was the case, then we have at last the reason why Stonehenge is sited exactly where it lies, locked in latitude and longitude lines each of which carry a profound meaning.

Stonehenge was built *exactly* east of Lundy Island and was the final and not the first stage in this geometric statement. It is therefore reasonable to conclude that knowledge of the triangle was incorporated into the monumental decision to build Stonehenge exactly where it is. This decision was taken prior to 3100 BC, perhaps a long time prior. We presently know very little about the site pre-ditch and bank, but the other three sites which form the triangle have yielded human artefacts dating back beyond 8000 BC.

Each of these three other sites, Lundy, Caldey and the Preseli bluestone outcrop, are visible one from the other, under good viewing conditions, and only Stonehenge is visually remote. Again, orthodoxy prevents acceptance of an indigenous megalithic culture in possession of the surveying and measuring skills necessary to conceive of such a project, yet alone having an understanding of Pythagorean triangles. Throughout this text I have produced evidence that both skills formed an integral and essential part of ancient culture, skills which were allied to astronomical aspirations.

How does it become the case that this triangle, which is so clearly used as the basis for an early Christian text, existed 3000 years before the time of Jesus and then descended beneath our cultural horizon until now? The Gospel of St John quoted above was thought to have been written before 100 AD, at least 3000 years after the the choice of site for Stonehenge and at least 2700 years before the placement of the Station Stone rectangle, which makes ourselves much nearer to St John than he was to the builders of Stonehenge. Where did the writer get his information from? Did the Christian story become appended onto another, much older realisation concerning the symbolic and astronomic secret held by the lunation triangle? Was this triangle common knowledge to several cultures? If so, then we can no longer say that Stonehenge is/was an independent cultural artifact. One way or another, the monument reflected something which is still written into an important religious text of our era, a text which we think originated in the Middle East, proving that some cultural interchange took place, although not necessarily during neolithic times and not necessarily from East to West.

I recognise that the large landscaped lunation triangle presents very strange material indeed to a mind weaned on twentieth century cultural values and its view of ancient history, but one cannot wriggle away from all the corroborative and peripheral information presented here. Too many factors integrate to confirm its use as an astronomic icon and a calendraic tool. Those two islands in the Bristol Channel have always been fixed points (even if once they were not surrounded by the sea they remained high peaks and both have features still named *Beacon Hill*). The ratios, lines of latitude and longitude, and certainly Stonehenge itself, are also fixed, immutable and there for all to see and measure on the ground. And together these things do form an accurate lunation triangle. Once our mental horizons are widened beyond the Stonehenge site itself, something of profound importance appears - an aspect of *Ancient Wisdom* and about the ancient world and its aspirations.

A Geomantic Station Stone Rectangle
(and a second lunation triangle)

If we can find the remains of a lunation triangle lying across England and Wales, emulating the form suggested within the Aubrey circle, is there evidence for the equivalent giant 5:12 rectangle? We need to locate only one remaining point, which shares the identical longitude as Stonehenge and which is located about 52 miles north, at a latitude of just under 52°. This point lies very near the present village of Temple Guiting. To the author's knowledge, following several visits to the village, no major megalithic site has been recorded there since records began. However, within a few miles or so lie the important long barrows Belas Knap, Notgrove and Salperton. In addition, two diametrically opposite points on the rectangle carry names which are directly related to the Knights Templar movement, suggesting contact with sacred geometry via knowledge of ancient ritual landscapes and their geomancy.

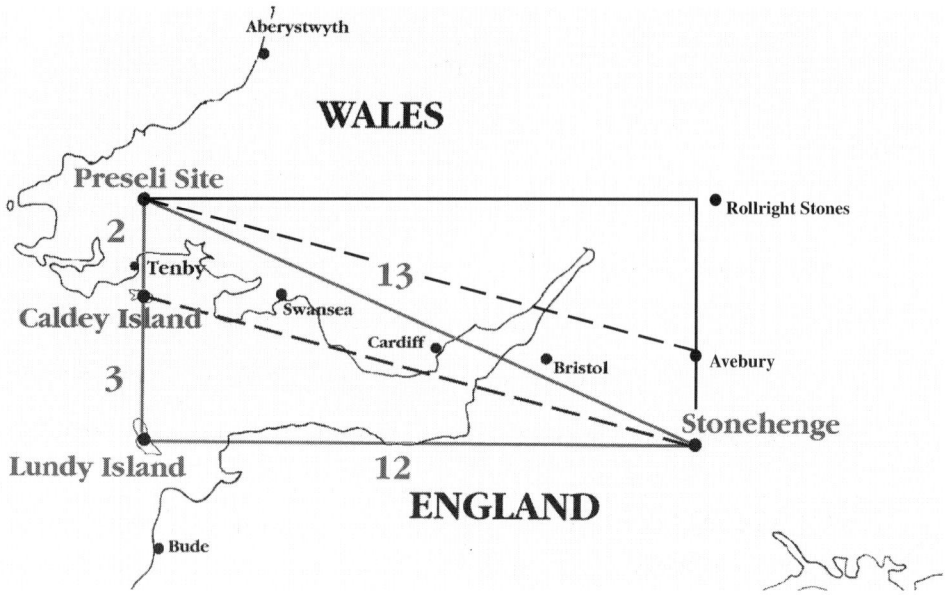

Figure 5.4 The Geomantic Station Stone Rectangle.

However, if we then look for a *second* lunation triangle, produced from the top half of this rectangle, the 3:2 point ought to be located at latitude 51° 27.9' north ; longitude 1° 50' west. The Avebury complex lies within 2 miles, having the correct longitude (1° 51') and a latitude 51° 26'. At this point we might also remember that the Avebury great henge is located at *exactly* one seventh of the Earth's circumference up from the equator - at a latitude of 360/7° north - as the figure (5.4) illustrates. This cannot be coincidental.

The King's Chamber and the Queen's Chamber

The Great Pyramid is probably the most surveyed building in the world. Every dimension and angle has been scrutinised by expert and crank alike in order to elucidate whatever theory the interpreter has wished to pursue. It is, at one and the same time, a King's tomb - although no body has ever been found there; a blueprint for human evolution; an encoded message about the purposes of human life and many other things, some so bizarre as to be tiresome. However, be that as it may, numerical facts arising from the many surveys have at least furnished us with accurate mathematical and geometrical data integral to this remarkable structure, which was built around 2650 BC - five centuries *after* the Aubrey circle of Stonehenge I was built.

The number 153 may be found here, at many places within the building. From the summit platform (masonry course 202), there are 153 masonry courses down to the base of the King's Chamber. One may be forgiven for thinking this to be another coincidence, until one discovers that there are 179 courses to the base of the Queen's

Chamber. 179 happens to be the nearest whole number to the square of the number of lunar orbits in the year - 13.368.[12]

The squares of both annual lunar rates locate a King's Chamber and a Queen's Chamber sharing exactly the symbolism and astronomy we have already discovered from fundamental observations at Stonehenge. The King's Chamber - which surely has something solar about its name - suggests the number relating to the Sun/Moon phenomenon which is caused by the Sun and its light - the lunation process, whilst the Queen's Chamber - which is feminine and hence lunar - suggests the number relating to a purely lunar phenomenon - the annual number of lunar orbits and entirely independent of the solar light.

The Search for the Silver Fraction

When using the Lunation Triangle, the easiest way of extracting the required lunar over-run of 0.368 lunations (10.875 days) is to bring the end of the '13' side rope down to the 3:2 point on the '5' side, whence 12.368 becomes the new internal length of the '13' side and the total number of lunations in a solar year.

> *0.632 of whatever units chosen to represent the triangle's sides fall outside of the triangle's perimeter.*
>
> *The 0.368 length, which is almost an exact seven nineteenths as a fraction[13], becomes what I term the* silver *fraction of the Moon.*
>
> *0.368 of a lunation is 10.875 days, and is the fractional over-run of the Moon in a solar year[14]. All calendrical understanding can proceed once this number is evaluated, geometrically or arithmetically.*

Does any historical evidence exist for knowledge of this fraction within the Neolithic culture? The *Book of Enoch* shows a knowledge of and fascination with this same 'overplus' of the Moon and I shall later be able to show that Enoch may have much more to do with European megalithic cultural aspirations than we currently think. This must wait, for the present there is much useful evidence coming directly from the numbers themselves. They can speak eloquently about just what did go on in the past - cosmic time periods and units of length from various cultural origins will be seen to be completely intertwined.

Professor Alex Thom showed that the Megalithic yard (MY) was the favoured unit of length used by the megalith builders. This unit he defined as 2.720 feet plus or minus 0.003 feet. In other words, a unit of measure which varied between 2.717 and 2.723 feet, a variation of only 72 thousandths of an inch (1.8 mm) in a measure of 32.64 inches or 0.83 metres. This was the astonishing conclusion stated on page 43 of Thom's *Megalithic Sites in Britain*, [OUP 1967].

This writer, hearing Thom lecture in 1968, was drawn to the curious fact that the Megalithic yard, so defined in feet, is remarkably similar to the universal physical constant *e*, whose value of 2.71828+ lies within Thom's own tiny tolerance margin for the unit[15]. At the time I thought this to be a remarkable coincidence, and it was not clear why the foot should be the chosen unit from which the 2.72 length is given birth. However, the foot, as a unit of length, has a pedigree longer than almost any other, and dates right back to the Sumerian cultures of prehistory[16] and their emerging metrology. John Michell has repeatedly stressed to me that the 'British' foot is the starting place for all sacred mensuration. Once one works intensively with the design of calendars and the numbers of the Sun and Moon, this connection between *e*, the foot and the megalithic yard, is seen not to be a coincidence at all.

The reader is about to meet head on with something which is highly disturbing to our present scientific paradigm, *for the reciprocal of e, and hence the reciprocal of the Megalithic yard is none other than our 0.368 fractional component of the lunation triangle.* There is no immediately apparent reason why this should be the case - that the extra fractional part of a lunation period needed to complete a solar year after completion of a lunar year should equal the reciprocal of the Megalithic yard expressed in feet and the universal exponential constant *e* governing growth and decay - and we have therefore discovered something strange, even numinous, which commands our attention. It demonstrates cosmic order - *the Moon's relationship to the Sun is arranged to annually 'overflow' with 0.368 of a lunation, 1/e.*

If one constructs a 5:12:13 Lunation Triangle using the Megalithic yard as representing one unit, the 'lunation hypotenuse' then represents the annual lunation rate and then the Megalithic yard, in time terms, represents one lunation period. What then would the fractional 0.368 MY length represent? 0.368266 times 2.718282 feet, the silver fraction times the value of the constant *e* (and well within Thom's tolerance limits for the megalithic yard), results in 1.00105 feet, *almost exactly one foot*[17] - the oldest known unit of measurement from Sumeria. Over the past four years, using a lunation triangle, I have demonstrated the truth of this calculation on many tours and lectures at megalithic sites, even inside Stonehenge itself.

$$\frac{1}{MY} = One\ Foot = 0.368\ MY = Annual\ Lunar\ Over\text{-}run\ [10.87 days].$$

Here we find a known unit of length, still in widespread use, based on this reciprocation between lunar over-run and the Megalithic yard - the present beleaguered British Foot. Furthermore, the Megalithic yard so divided forms an N:N+1 ratio, 1.71828.. feet + 1 foot = 2.71828.. feet (*e*)[18].

> *One Foot represents the annual over-run fraction only if we are working with a Lunation Triangle whose quanta are measured in whole numbers of Megalithic yards.*

This is precisely as Alex Thom discovered most stone circles and rings to be; only now we can suggest that the Megalithic yard, in time terms, also represents the lunation period of 29.53059 days. This establishes a firm lunar connection between this unit and megalithic sites.

In this search to confirm ancient knowledge of the lunation triangle, many aspects of the megalithic cultural story come together - the missing 'puzzle-box lid' picture. In fact, these aspects were never fragmented other than by our ignorance of the priorities of a culture long since surplanted. We have now found a seamless garment where units of measurement were based on the immutable lengths of time of solar and lunar cycles. The Megalithic yard *defines itself* through the use of the lunation triangle and the foot and this is strong and compelling evidence indeed, connecting both units and the lunation triangle to a coherent origin based on objective evidence. This is perhaps as close as one can get to proof - these three artefacts emerge from the fog of the past and are seen to be physically real and interconnected.

The whole subject of ancient measurement may now be reviewed from this new perspective which the rediscovery of thelunation triangle has facilitated.

THE BRITISH IMPERIAL UNIT SYSTEM SEEN AS LUNAR METROLOGY

The Inch

The twelfth part of the 0.368 MY, which is a twelfth of one foot, is a familiar unit within our present culture. Remarkably, despite edicts from European parliaments, the inch survives in our modern culture and is remarkably alive and well. One twelfth of 0.368 MY is 1.00105 inches, which is *exactly* the so called *primitive* inch - one twenty-fifth of the *Long* or *Sacred Cubit* - used throughout the construction of many important Egyptian religious monuments, including the Great Pyramid itself.[19]

The inch, defined thus, is of paramount importance when using the lunation triangle to date full and new Moons, providing the lunation triangle uses the Megalithic yard or multiples for its unit divisions. *The inch then automatically becomes the correction factor needed to place the lunations within the solar year.*[20]

I conclude that the Megalithic yard, a unit universally used by the megalith builders, appears to have been chosen, according to the fashion of lunation shortfall each month, to correlate with a lunation based calendar system founded on the lunation triangle and using the same units of length used by Britain and the New World. The foot and the inch have thus been related to the Moon, but can the Yard be found here, in order to complete the smaller Imperial measures?

The Imperial Yard

The yard may indeed be readily found here. The '12' side of the lunation triangle is 12 MY long, which is 10.87 Imperial yards. The lunar over-run is also 10.87 days annually[21]. The ratio of the Megalithic yard to the yard is therefore the same as the ratio between the lunar over-run and 12, both expressed in days. The *Silver Fraction*, 0.368 of a lunation, is 10.87 days long, if one MY is taken to represent one lunation. The yard, treated in this way, *represents twelve days of time.*

Thus:

$$\frac{MY}{Y} = \frac{10.87}{12.00}$$

This ratio is almost 11:10, a common scaling ratio found throughout various unit systems in the ancient world.[22] The word *mensuration*, which means the act of measurement, appropriately contains the root *mens*, derivative of the Moon and month. Perhaps we have just discovered why.

The Megalithic yard also links to units of measurement not thought to be connected with the megalithic culture. Firstly, the *primitive inch*, variously called the *pharaonic* or *pyramid* inch, like the Megalithic yard, *defines itself* at many places within another ancient icon, the Great Pyramid, where it is related to the solar year and one inch is made to represent a day or decimal fraction of a day. Secondly, the *Sacred Cubit*, which is 25 primitive inches in length, is found throughout the Pyramid. For both the lunation triangle and the Great Pyramid, these units share dual roles as astronomic constants and lengths. What we had no right to expect was that the inch and Megalithic yard are connected, through the foot one might say, thus apparently linking Egyptian culture with the Stonehenge 'Wessex' culture.

Cultural Connections

The evidence here is powerfully persuasive and, coupled with the other evidence at Stonehenge, to wit, the inner perimeter of the Sarsen circle lintels being ten times the exact length in primitive inches of the solar tropical year in days [23], and the fact that the width of each lintel is one Sacred Rod[24], another Egyptian unit, that we suggest that the megalith builders and the cultures of the Mediterranean and Middle East were either engaged in dialogue and inter-cultural explorations or that *there was an earlier common root culture about which we know almost nothing.*

These cross-cultural measurement systems must have come about through a common shared knowledge of, and reverence for, Sun and Moon cycles. They are further reinforced when we look at the length of the Megalithic yard left over when we have removed the lunar over-run fraction (this is precisely what one does when using the lunation triangle to obtain the 12.368 annual lunation rate). *We are left with 1.720 feet, 20.606 British inches, which is the Royal Cubit, 20.6284 primitive inches in length.* This is the 'other' cubit used by the Egyptian culture in their important monuments.

We can now take this argument along even further, by recognising that the ratio of the Megalithic yard to Royal Cubit, 32.63 : 20.61 inches is none other than the ratio of the lunation period to the period of the Moon's nodes, 29.53059 : 18.62.[25] Thus we find that the Megalithic yard and the Royal Cubit are inextricably connected through

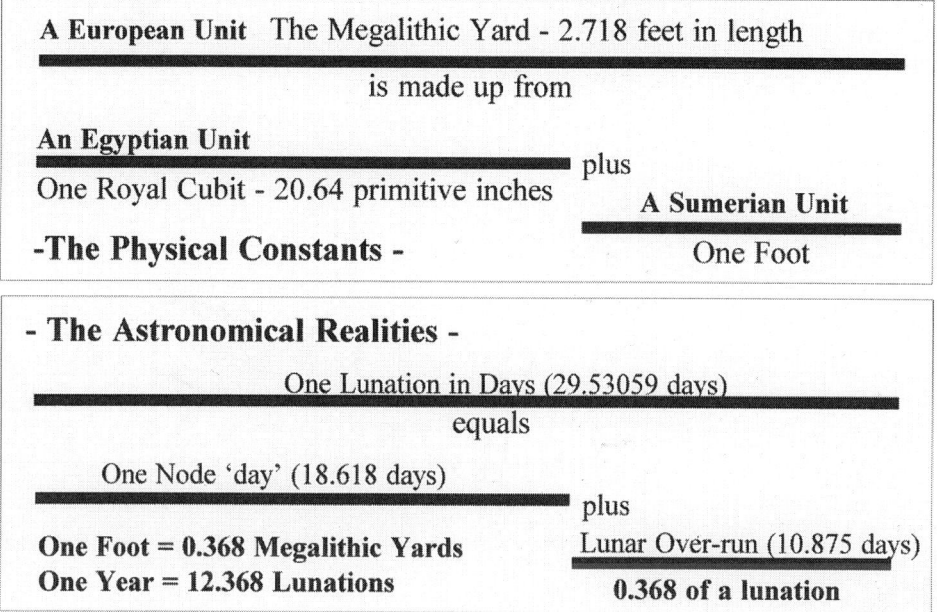

A European Unit The Megalithic Yard - 2.718 feet in length

is made up from

An Egyptian Unit

One Royal Cubit - 20.64 primitive inches   plus

                                    A Sumerian Unit

-The Physical Constants -   One Foot

- The Astronomical Realities -

One Lunation in Days (29.53059 days)

equals

One Node 'day' (18.618 days)

                                         plus

One Foot = 0.368 Megalithic Yards   Lunar Over-run (10.875 days)

One Year = 12.368 Lunations   **0.368 of a lunation**

Table 5.1 Units of length in the ancient world and their connection with soli-lunar constants and the lunation triangle. The universal physical constant e is 2.71828+, whilst its reciprocal is 0.367879+, which is within 0.1% of the lunar over-run in one year [there are 12.36826623 lunations in one solar year]. Here, the Megalithic yard is partitioned into the foot and the Royal Cubit, corresponding to the lunation period in days being equal to the lunar nodal period, 18.618, plus the lunar over-run. The integrated nature of these results suggests that the ancient world well understood these fundamental soli-lunar periods and arranged their metrology around them, using the foot as the most basic measure.

the two lunar periods from which, once known and measured, all calendrical and eclipse knowledge follows. One minus the other leaves a residual length which is none other than the foot.

The Megalithic Yard minus The Royal Cubit = The Foot

One twelfth of this foot, the inch, provides the monthly correction figure enabling the accurate construction of a twelve month calendar, marked with lunations and therefore, if we add knowledge of the 18.62 year lunar node cycle, the times of expected eclipses. This is ancient astronomy as I believe it was practised - apparently in Neolithic Europe as well as the clay tablet and papyrus economies of the Middle East. Table (5.1) above illustrates the simplicity of the whole arrangement.

The Sphinx and the Megaliths

Cultural connection between the Middle Eastern cultures and the Megalith builders has been a continually resurfacing theme within 'alternative' literature on Stonehenge for over a century. To archaeology, it has been like waving a red rag at a bull. However, the demonstrable connections between ancient units of length shown above make it imperative that the evidence for any alleged connection is made clearer, as too are the prime objections.

In his thoughtful book, *The Sphinx and the Megaliths*[26], author John Ivimy does just this, presenting his theory that Stonehenge was an Egyptian outpost or colony. A highly educated man, Ivimy introduced some refreshing new concepts into the cultural connection debate. In particular, he showed a further connection, this time geometric, between the Megalithic yard and the Royal Cubit, shown below (*figure 5.5*).

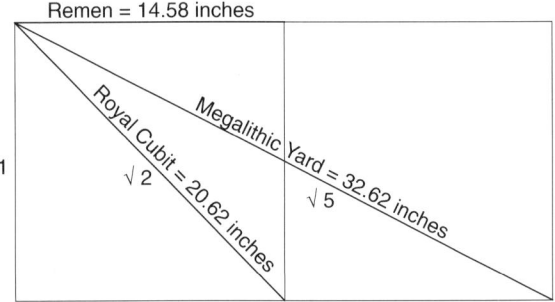

Figure 5.5 A geometric connection between the Megalithic yard and the Royal Cubit.

The Remen is the ancient unit from which the geometrical constructions allow derivation of the Megalithic yard and the Royal Cubit. My own researches demonstrate other connections, i.e. the Megalithic yard equalling the physical constant 'e' in feet, the reciprocal of the Megalithic yard, 1/e, expressed in feet, equalling the annual lunar over-run rate. The Megalithic yard minus a foot equalling the Royal Cubit. These are all *exact* equalities. But now, the Megalithic yard connects with the Royal Cubit through an astronomical relationship[27],

$$\frac{MY}{RC} = \frac{Lunation\ Period}{Lunar\ nodal\ 'day'} = \frac{29.53059\ days}{18.618\ days} = \frac{\sqrt{5}}{\sqrt{2}}$$

Ivimy makes this vital connection between Megalithic yard and Royal Cubit by showing that they relate through irrational factors - √5 and √2. He postulates that such a procedure would have enabled surveyors to avoid having to deal with irrational numbers in land area calculations, the √2 factor between Remen and Royal Cubit allowing easier calculations. This leaves a researcher having to explain why monuments in Egypt appear never to have used the Megalithic yard nor, conversely, why no evidence of the Royal Cubit may be found in British prehistoric building.

But is this true - just who has ever looked for these units within an orthodoxy which denies the possibility? Alex Thom, on his own admission, started with a blank sheet of paper and found the Megalithic yard. Egyptologists have, at least. surviving examples of the Royal Cubit, yet have probably never even heard of the Megalithic yard. Archaeologists would never have dreamt of looking for the Royal Cubit in Neolithic Britain. After reading this, maybe that can change.

The Great Circle Connection

There is further evidence to suggest a connection between Egypt and Stonehenge. In *Sun, Moon, Man, Woman*, I listed a computer program that calculates the unique Great Circle which, figuratively speaking, cuts the Earth into two halves with Egypt and Stonehenge on the dividing line.[28] Although a whole book could be written about this remarkable construct, the importance it holds for this text is that, having passed from the Pyramid to Stonehenge, the line then carries on up to the Preseli site, *forming the '13' side of the giant lunation triangle*. The hypotenuse of the Preseli-Stonehenge lunation triangle thus becomes a section of this Great Circle and this *can only happen at four latitudes on its path over the entire Globe (Figure 5.6)*. The line passes through

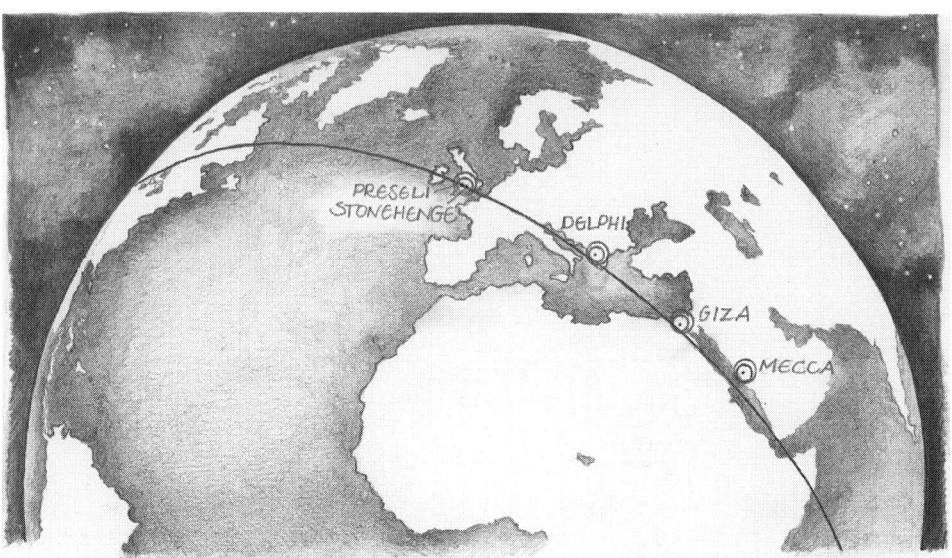

Figure 5.6 The Stonehenge-Pyramid Great Circle

many other special places on the Earth, most notably Mecca, Delphi, Sligo and the Ohio 'serpent' sites.

Whilst it can be shown that the Pyramid is constructed on a meridian which takes in the largest land length possible on this planet, the Great Circle appears to take in the largest possible amount of water length in its serpentine travel around the Earth. This Great Circle presently proves nothing of ancient intent, of course, but it alerts the researcher to something strange, a further numinous connection between ancient sites, and it reinforces the importance of both the Preseli bluestone site and the lunation triangle.

The connections I have demonstrated here, coupled with a rising interest in how the ancient world was defining its fundamental measuring standards, promise a fruitful area for historians and other specialists to explore. At the cutting edge, there are no 'experts'. An inspired layman, like Ivimy, a retired engineer, like Thom, and an informed visionary, like John Michell, have all made real inroads into these uncharted waters. Outside of any orthodox system these pioneers can afford to take risks and speculate in a way which can be extremely difficult when towing a party line, needing a regular salary and trying to build a career.

Within the orthodoxy, researchers like Dr Aubrey Burl forge a different type of progress, nontheless vital for advancement in understanding our megalithic heritage. Dr Burl has forced us to recognise the schism between the archaeological record and the apparent megalithic expertise in geometry and astronomy shown by Thom, Hawkins, Ivimy and other authors, including myself. His books and research are very thorough, showing a complete grasp of this complex subject and a closeness to the 'megalithic mind', whilst remaining within the boundaries of the current orthodoxy. Dr Burl continually draws attention to the dangers of projecting the twentieth century mind back to a culture so remote from our own and has valuably pointed out how different Stonehenge is from any other British megalithic monument. His abilities as a lecturer to lay (ley?) audiences is reknown. Regrettably, Alex and Archie Thom, Richard Atkinson and Stuart Piggott are no longer here to contribute to this new and exciting era of debate.

Other Triangles, other Astronomical Constants

In terms of providing important astronomical constants relating to the Sun, Earth, Moon system, my research went on to discover that the lunation triangle is just one of a family of right-angled triangles. The lunation triangle is therefore neither a fluke nor a coincidence - it may be extended and developed. It forms part of a cosmology based around whole numbers and the right-angled triangle. The reader may reject everything in this book concerning the ancient past, but he will be left with these triangles as a highly practical way of accurately finding the numbers of the Sun and Moon, and predicting eclipses.

The Lunar Orbit Triangle

A right angled triangle may be constructed using the two lunar numbers 13 and 14. Dividing the third side into the ratio 3:2 produces an intermediate hypotenuse whose length is 13.368 - the exact number of lunar orbits in a solar year.

This is a remarkable development, for within the two triangles one may find nearly all the information an astronomer needs to understand fully the way in which the Sun, Moon, Earth system interacts. The lunar orbit triangle is shown below.

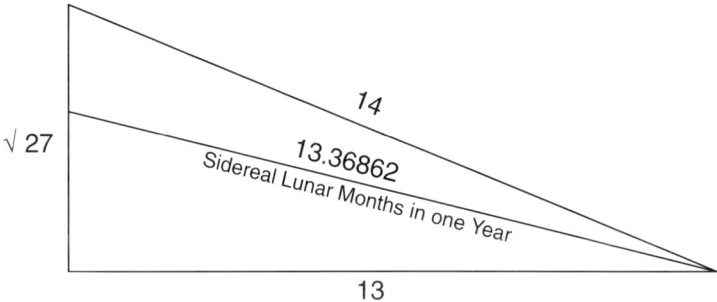

Figure 5.7 The Lunar Orbit Triangle.

This is a similarly simple geometric technique by which the other lunar time period may be extracted. Both these triangles offer a technique which is very precise, mathematically, geometrically, astronomically and symbolically. The lunation triangle is accurate to 0.008%, the lunar orbit triangle to better still. Neolithic techniques marry right and left brain activity, a form of solar/lunar integration in itself, and their designs are at once aesthetic as well as wholly practical, having immediate applications, as the following chapters will amply demonstrate.

Before we develop the practical applications of these two triangles, we must look at the third one in the set, one which carries vital astronomic and calendrical information concerning eclipses.

The Eclipse Year Triangle

Astronomers refer to an 'Eclipse year' of 346.62 days in order to calculate the two 173 day periods which separate the twice yearly time when eclipses are likely to occur. This is 11.38 months, the time taken for the Sun to return to one of the Moon's nodes as it appears to journey around the zodiac. (The reason why it is less than one year is due to the fact that the nodes rotate backwards around the zodiac, thus any particular node 'meets' the Sun more than once a year). The nodes rotate with a period of 18.61 years, which represents 18.4 degrees per year around the perimeter of the year-circle.

This period may be found using a third triangle, shown below (*figure 5.8*). Here, the right angle formed by two longer sides of 11 and 12 is, once again, divided into the ratio 3:2, whence the new hypotenuse holds a length of 11.37. If the '12' side is then taken to represent the solar year, with its twelve months, then the '11.37' side represents 346 days - the Eclipse Year.[29]

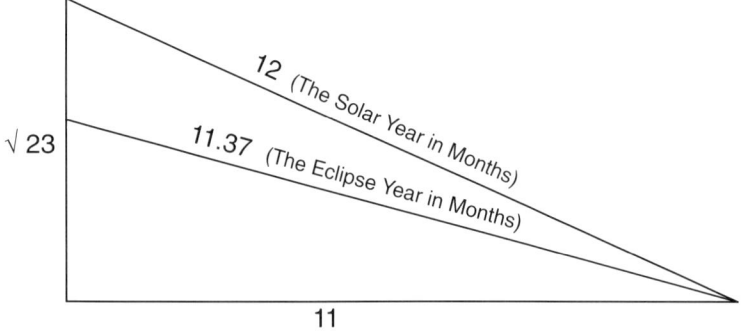

Figure 5.8 The 'Eclipse-year' Triangle. A month is here defined as exactly one twelfth of the solar year of 365.242 days (30.437 days).

A Pythagorean Cosmology

We now have three triangles, which are contiguous and form part of an infinite set of right angled triangles whose design depends on whole number hypotenuses in right angled triangle whose lengths increase by unity. I have called these N:N+1 triangles and their design can be drawn out, whence an interesting and familiar spiral shape is produced (*figure 5.9*). Stonehenge is built on chalk - the remains of countless spiral shells which once housed the bodies of emerging life on this planet. It seems entirely appropriate that this triangle series, which includes the 3:4:5 as well as the 5:12:13 lunation triangle, links the motions of the Sun and Moon to the evolution of life on Earth, and hence to the *Divine Proportion*.

Practical Astronomy using Right-angled Triangles

Using these three triangles one can accurately evaluate the dates for soli-lunar events - lunations and eclipses - to well within the day. I can offer no proof that neolithic astronomers were using the lunar orbit and/or eclipse year triangle although the principle remains essentially the same as for the lunation triangle - i.e. right-angled triangles using mainly whole number sides. The information can be gleaned, less accurately, from other sources at Stonehenge and elsewhere[30]. For instance, the diameter of the Aubrey circle compared to the perimeter of the inner circumference of the sarsen circle makes the identical ratio as the eclipse year does to the solar year - roughly 19:18 - and the dimensions in inches correspond directly to 10" = 1 day.

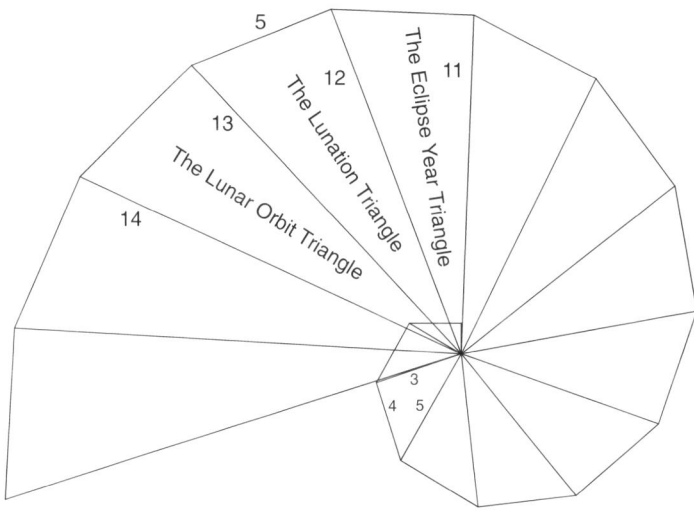

Figure 5.9 The spiral series of lunar triangles. [note that the series begins with a 1:√3:2 triangle. The third triangle in the series is the 3:4:5 Pythagorean triangle.]

Summary

In this chapter, I have shown powerful evidence for ancient knowledge and use of the lunation triangle. This has produced some original material concerning one of the commonest physical constants governing growth and decay, i.e. evolution , well known as '*e*' (2.71828+) to all mathematicians and scientists, here seen to be holding a strong connection to the orbital arrangements of the Sun and Moon and recently outmoded imperial units of length.

This same number is also seen to have been decoded, transcribed and brought down to Earth by the builders of the megaliths - as 'their' unit, the Megalithic yard. This length is seen to hold several connections with the Egyptian Royal Cubit. The lunation triangle, coupled with the Megalithic yard, invokes *the* Royal Cubit *and* the pyramid inch, the foot, the constant *e and* the lunar over-run *and* connects the lunation period with the lunar nodal period, as an N:N+1 relationship. And, of course, it is an excellent and simple lunation predictor!

What better and more appropriate reference standard for a unit of length could one choose than a number based on *e*, which, like the *Golden Section* number, *phi*, is totally connected to processes of evolution on the Earth and their original cause, the evolutionary engine of the Sun and Moon? I stand in complete awe of a culture which appears to have understood all these things before 3000 BC.

The Megalithic yard, re-discovered by Alexander Thom, is a shining landmark in human cultural history, as yet unrecognised. Using the Megalithic yard within the dimensions of the lunation triangle has revealed the underlying reason for its employment in megalithic monuments, monuments used for Sun/Moon astronomy and calendrical predictions. This triangle and its derivatives provide the decoding functions necessary to pull several apparently disparate calendrical and cultural artefacts into a coherent whole. This family of triangles, having two longer sides forming an integral N:N+1 ratio, answers the calendar maker's prayers.

The lunation triangle *was* an icon of the ancient world, a well preserved secret at Stonehenge and across southern Britain, in the Bible and in folk-lore. We shall take this statement much further in chapters nine and ten, when we analyse the dimensions of Stonehenge and study the cultural impact of the monument on British folk-culture.

Whilst we may not yet have seen all of the 'puzzle-box lid', we may have blown the lid off the puzzle! Through the discovery of the lunation triangle we have been able to assemble a major new section of the jigsaw, which is now like the sarsen circle all safely and strongly interlocked together. This will be enough to change the history books our children read.

Footnotes to Chapter Five

[1] This corresponds to a lunation period of 29.528 days, an error of 3.61 minutes in 29.53059 days.

[2] J.E.Wood. *Sun, Mon and Standing Stones*, page 169

[3] Venus = Vendredi = Friday = Freya. The fifth day of the week is connected, straight from the creation story in Genesis, chapter one, with reproduction and procreation, hence the link with Goddesses of Love.

[4] *The Gospel of John* - G.H.C. Macgregor, D.D., D.Lit., ed.Prof James Moffatt, D.D. Hodder & Stoughton (1928).

[5] In English one would say *starboard* - originating from *steer-board*, both words deriving from the old English *steorra* and *steor* respectively.

[6] The radius to side length of a regular octagon is 200:153.

[7] See *The Gospel of St Thomas* amongst many texts where the male/female polarity is directly addressed by Jesus.

[8] Two sources deal with this confusion between St Elen and the word *elen*. Rachel Bromwich's *Triads of Britain* (University of Wales Press 1978, 2nd ed.) and Charles

Kightley's *Folk Heroes of Britain* (1982). I am grateful to Peter Berresford Ellis for assistance in confirming my hypothesis that Lundy, as *Ynys Elen* is appropriately named as *The Island of the right-angle, corner or elbow*. It may be of interest to note that the same root word is found in the Uilleian pipes, so named because one plays them by using the elbow to squeeze the bag!

[9] It is suggested, albeit with no other evidence, that the strangely named *heelstone* at Stonehenge, which marks the summer solstice sunrise, may stem from this same root.

[10] I am grateful for the help given to me by Robert Farrah.

[11] Beacon Hill is the highest point, site of the old light, at 420'. Tibbett's Hill is 400'.

[12] This information derived from survey information published in *The Great Pyramid Decoded* by Peter Lemesurier (Element Books).

[13] The best known superannual cycle of the Sun, Moon, Earth system is the Metonic cycle of 19 years, when 235 lunations have taken place. After nineteen years from an agreed start date, the Sun, Moon and Earth lie in the exact same relative positions to each other. 12.368 is 12 and *seven nineteenths* which becomes 235/19. Fractions are much more useful at allowing the underlying meaning of cycles to be understood.

[14] 10.875 is ten and *seven-eighths* days.

[15] The constant e is found to explain many processes in evolution, growth and decay processes. It is another irrational number - 2.718281828459045235360287471....or very very nearly 19 divided by 7.

[16] John Michell states this within the original *A View over Atlantis*. It is confirmed by many more traditional academic textbooks.

[17] This is less than 0.3mm in error from the present British Foot.

[18] N:N+1 triangles are worth exploring - the lunation triangle is just one of many - see page 88 onwards.

[19] *The Great Pyramid Decoded* by Peter Lemesurier (Element Books), Appendix A.

[20] If we assume the 12.368 MY length to represent the solar year, then division by twelve produces a 'month' length of 30.4368 days. But 12.368 MY is also 403.7 inches, making one inch equal to 0.905328 days. Cumulative subtraction of quanta of inches thus produces the required lunation period, for 30.4368 minus 0.905328 days equals 29.531522 days, a figure within 0.003%, or just over one minute, of the lunation period.

[21] The difference, using 2.71828 ft for the MY, is within 0.02% of exact.

[22] See *The Keys to the Temple*, David Furlong, Piatkus(1997). Figure 104.

[23] Illustrated in *The Great Pyramid Decoded*, Appendix, p 295.

[24] John Michell in *The New View over Atlantis*. The Sacred Rod is 3.4757485 feet (approx two Royal Cubits)

[25] To 0.18% accuracy. The author defines a 'node-day' as 18.618 days (which multiplied by 365.242 equals 18.618 years, the nodal period.)

[26] Abacus, 1976.

[27] Because I have linked the Megalithic yard and the Royal Cubit to the lunation period and lunar nodal period, there appears to be a lawful *astronomic* relationship between these two periods - connected by the irrationals $\sqrt{2}$ and $\sqrt{5}$.

[28] *Sun, Moon, Man, Woman* by the author (1992). Privately published.

[29] Because there are chambers in the Great Pyramid corresponding to each of the two monthly lunar periods, we might expect any future chamber discovery within the monument to be found 129 masonry courses down from the summit platform - the square of the Eclipse Year period, in months.

[30] Found in Chapter six - the sections on flattened circles and compound rings - page 101 to page 115.

Figure 6.1 A Magnificent Temple of the Cosmos. *Pentre Ifan*, near Newport, Pembroke-shire was constructed around 3500 BC. This photograph may be more recently and uniquely dated to February 1997, thanks to the fleeting visit of Comet Hale-Bopp. The capstone weighs over 16 tons. (*Photograph by Mr E. B. Johnson, Haverfordwest*).

Chapter Six

- TEMPLES OF THE COSMOS -

The prime task of this chapter will be to undertake a review of the surviving megalithic architecture still to be found in Britain, enabling the reader to understand better the consistency of design, levels of accuracy and astronomical purpose to be found throughout the megalithic culture. I will show that the design rules for stone rings are much more involved than simply hammering in a peg into the turf and measuring a radius, digging a few holes around the perimeter of the resulting circle into which are thrown a few very large stones for a purpose which yet eludes us. Of course the purpose will elude us if we think that the *process* of building a temple was undertaken so mindlessly! It is also to be greatly regretted that this view is, more or less, the sum total of most people's understanding of stone rings, sustained and supported by many archaeological books.

Because Stonehenge is a rather untypical example of the *genre*, such a review will place the Stonehenge material within a broader framework. Also, and vital to the process of understanding the mind-set and cultural requirements of the Neolithic age, we need to assess the level of technology available to the megalith builders in Europe, technology which produced the elegant and complex architecture of this epoch. Whilst children of nine or ten years old can produce a circle using a rope pegged to an intended centre, they could never construct the geometries shown here. Indeed, it has been my experience that many modern-day adults find great difficulty in emulating the geometrical designs of megalithic man. The assumption that megalithic builders were somehow much less intelligent than ourselves will be seen to evaporate with the fog that lifts when correct analysis is performed on their designs.

The Design Rules

For a first and very basic example, we might consider the Aubrey and sarsen circles, which must have been laid out using a radius rope pegged at the centre of the intended circles. Thus, we must conclude that the builders had access to long and, in view of the accuracy of their work, non-elastic ropes. No traces of such rope are ever likely to be found - they are therefore hypothetical, yet it is completely inconceivable that Stonehenge could have been planned and built without ropes and pegs used for this purpose. The same argument then applies to the many stone ellipses, egg shapes and flattened circles, each of which has a quite specific and consistent geometry wherever these forms were built throughout north-western Europe.

To implement each of the above non-circular shapes requires or involves the construction of right-angled triangles, an interesting point to which we shall shortly be returning. Pegs and ropes were the obvious and appropriate technology available to the builders. Marked sticks or rods must also have been used as measuring standards and here, at least, a couple of well-rotted examples have survived the centuries, although these are not Neolithic.[1] The ubiquitous Megalithic yard, found incorporated into sites from the Orkneys to the *Basque* region of Spain, must have travelled as a rod, a standard length. Alex Thom produced ample evidence backed by his usual thorough statistical analysis to show that only a standard measuring stick or 'first-generation copy' taken from site to site would accord with the accuracy with which this length is reproduced at site after site.[2]

Thom discovered that the builders of stone circles liked to produce perimeters with a length equal to a multiple of $2^{1/2}$ MY[3], which he termed the *Megalithic rod*. He also found that the diameters tended to be in even numbers of MY, based on the *Megalithic fathom* as he termed 2 MY. Thom found evidence that subdivisions of the MY indicated repeated division by two but no evidence of division by three, which does not accord with the 0.368 MY discussed in the last chapter for using the lunation triangle.[4] This is not unexpected, as we will discover a possible function for stone rings which makes different requirements on the design process.

Alex Thom became the first man to begin the process of unravelling the techniques being used by megalithic architects. His data was extremely accurate - he professionally surveyed over 300 sites with a theodolite and his conclusions were these:

> (i). The builders were using the Megalithic yard (2.72 feet ± 0.003ft).
> (ii). They preferred to work with whole numbers of Megalithic yards.
> (iii). Multiples and submultiples of Megalithic yard were evident.
> (iv). There was a "headquarters" from which rods were issued.
> (v). The accuracy of linear measurement was to 1 part in 1000 (0.1%).
> (vi). The Megalithic rod = $2^{1/2}$MY. The Megalithic fathom = 2 MY.

During the megalithic period, an estimated five to ten thousand stone rings were built in Britain and Ireland, over a period of not much more than a thousand years. The cultural importance of this endeavour was enormous and it is hard for us to conceive of a continuity of purpose lasting over a millenium.

Having laid out the designs found throughout the moors and hills of Britain, the builders then had to organize the task of fetching huge monoliths and placing them into their precise locations within the ring or circle. Often local stone was eschewed in favour of stone from many miles away. The extreme example of this remains the famed bluestones, brought 135 miles to Stonehenge, as the crow flies. The largest known stone to have been moved by this culture, *Men Er Hroeg* (the Fairy Stone), was erected near the Carnac *alignements*, in Brittany. Now in four pieces, apparently having fallen in antiquity, it once stood nearly seventy feet high and weighed an awesome 260 tons. Near St Malo, the *Dôl Stone* stands 31 feet high and weighs 125 tons, brought from an outcrop over 2½ miles away. No glacier conveniently ferried these monsters to the site!

Although no one remains in any doubt that early man had the ability to move huge blocks of stone over long distances, very few people take the trouble to consider the implications of such an endeavour. The erection of an Egyptian obelisk in St Peter's Square, Rome, was of comparable size to the Fairy Stone, weighing 240 tons. It took 850 men, seventy horses and forty-six cranes to raise it and eye-witness accounts tell of a near disaster, with ropes jamming in their blocks and other precarious moments, and this was in comparatively recent times. Men and horses (or oxen) must be fed and kept serviced with the basic living requirements; ropes, levers and other equipment must be fabricated and maintained. Wooden spars, levers, pallettes and rollers would have had to have been hewn from timber, often felled remotely.

The Artefact Crisis

Whilst there has been some success this century at finding out *when* stone rings were built, within a few hundred years or so, we are still theorising as to *how* ancient man performed such Herculean tasks. In truth there exists almost no physical evidence to support how these stones were moved or placed into position - the damp climate of these northern latitudes quickly rots wood, fibre rope and even metal. The result is that there is an *artefact crisis*, and readers must decide here and now whether or not monuments like Stonehenge and Avebury were built using the technology of the period, of which there isn't much evidence, or whether they just built themselves.

Perhaps the reader may feel that we are here dealing with *belief*, as though lack of physical evidence for the methods utilised in the construction of countless accurate circles, ellipses, egg-shapes and the like means that we must suspend normal scientific method and indulge ourselves in an act of faith. But we are not dealing here with blind belief nor faith. These monuments exist in hard stone, hundreds of them; ancient Man built these accurate monuments and it is entirely scientific to conclude that they possessed enough technology to achieve their goals, else how were these precision monuments built? The conclusion must be that their inventory included pegs, ropes, rods, plans, methods, resources and facilities for workers, forward planning and the many other necessary facets of such huge civil engineering projects.

Denial of this conclusion is, of course, completely safe and maintains the *status quo* in terms of ancient history, but it effectively smokescreens a sad truth: we still do not know *how* or *why* the stones were moved nor *why* they were laid out as they are. This denial effectively stops much useful research work on megalithic sites and, because nature abhors a vacuum, it positively encourages theories concerning extraterrestrial involvement with the building of ancient monuments.

Acceptance of this inventory of materials and qualities frees researchers to ask much bigger questions about the megalithic culture. This is not cheating nor is it unscientific, for 'proof by induction' begins with a premise and then looks to follow the consequences of this premise being true. The whole development of mathematics is built on such 'proofs' and many of the most important discoveries in the natural sciences have come from people who asked a bigger question and then saw how the consequences fitted - or not. The French physiologist, Claude Barnard, wrote that *'Theories are neither true, nor false; they are fertile or sterile'*. On this basis, I have already shown that Stonehenge is an oasis, because using the monument and the proportions built into it, one can derive all the major astronomical constants of the Sun and Moon, even build an integrated soli-lunar calendar - something that our present calendar fails miserably to achieve.

This book is no attack on archaeology nor its practitioners. It is perhaps a necessary requirement that mainstream archaeology remains so conservative, and one has only to look at the explosion of material within the category 'earth mysteries' to begin to understand how the more bizarre end of the subject of archaeology threatens to render meaningful discussion and debate useless. Much so-called New Age literature reflects a problem with objectivity - described by Atkinson in the immortal phrase, "the loony fringe of dotty archaeology" and, not surprisingly, the archaeological establishment cannot embrace such material. Their stance may be seen as a healthy counterbalance, but only if any genuinely new material which challenges the boundaries of this subject is treated with same objective analysis, respect and fairness that archaeology claims for its own mainstream researchers. Dogmatic views are unpleasant, whether one finds them within archaeology or coming from New Age gurus.

Megalithic architecture is a mysterious curiosity to the majority of folk when it could and ought to be seen as a priceless proof of early man's first attempts at astronomy, geometry, maths and the shaping of ritual landscapes. Heaven was being drawn down to the Earth, and early Man was taking a really good look at the 'gods' that came with this package.

I have endeavoured to make this look at megalithic architecture an exploration for the reader. To this end some diagrams show pegs in order to encourage actual construction of these shapes on lawns and beaches, making the geometry other than a purely theoretical subject. To begin this study, let us look at what megalithic engineers built, and the equipment they undoubtedly employed in the process.

The remainder of this chapter comprises the material presented at various lectures and seminars over the past six years. The majority of the plan diagrams are from the valuable collection of survey plans prepared by Alexander Thom, and are reproduced here by kind permission of his son, the late Archie Thom. This chapter would not have been possible without the thousands of hours work put in by the Thom family.[5]

THE GEOMETRY OF STONE RINGS

Circles

Of the 600-odd sites investigated throughout northern Europe by the Thom family, over two-thirds showed themselves to be true circles. Stonehenge is one obvious example, the Rollright Stones and the Ring of Brodgar are other examples. Their geometry is simple - all one needs to mark out a circle is a peg staked where the centre is to be, and a loop of rope which is pulled taut with the perimeter 'marker' at one end of the loop and the central peg at the other. Such a construction invokes the irrational number constant, π - the relationship between radius or diameter, which can never be expressed as a ratio or fraction of the perimeter or circumference of the circle. Arithmetically, the absolute evaluation of π (pi) is is an insoluble problem whilst geometrically this constant is invoked naturally each and every time a circle is created, and a child (or a raindrop falling into a pool) can produce first-class circles without even being conscious of π.

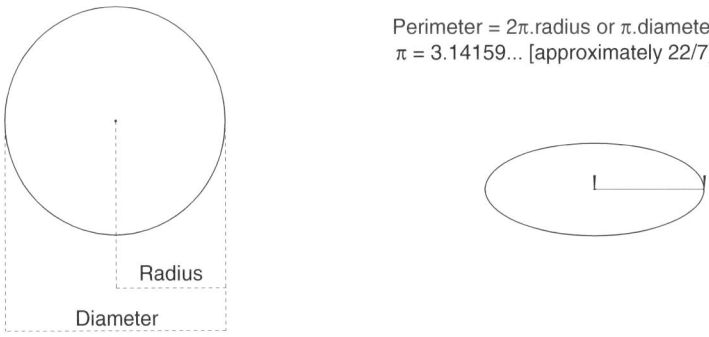

Perimeter = 2π.radius or π.diameter
π = 3.14159... [approximately 22/7]

Radius

Diameter

Figure 6.2 Using pegs and rope to construct an accurate circle.

I suggest that the perimeter of a megalithic circle, in addition to providing a sacred space, represented the sky - more specifically the zodiac or year-circle and thus the solar tropical year of 365.242 days. The present number of degrees within a circle (360) reflects the calendraic origins of angular measure. So too do the many 'medicine wheels' having 28 spokes, and the 28 lunar mansions of vedic astronomy, each suggesting the lunar sidereal month. These two vital time-circles, year and month, combine in a single culture within the Aubrey calendar.

During each year, the Sun appears to make one complete round of the zodiac, inhabitants on Earth experience one cycle of the seasonal round as the Earth revolves 365.242 times with respect to the Sun and 366.242 times with respect to the universe. Similarly, in just under 28 days, the Moon makes its round of the zodiacal stars. This is how our species originally defined *year* and *month*.

Non Circular Stone Rings

These fall into several categories. Thom identified roughly 300 sites left in a condition where their original form remained evident. *Ellipses* represent one ninth of all megalithic 'circles', whilst *flattened circles* form a sixth of all megalithic 'circles' and *egg shapes* represent one eighteenth of the total. Lastly, the magnificent *compound rings* total just four surviving constructions, Avebury being the best known and largest of these. There are reckoned to be 900 surviving stone rings in Britain.

Taking these in turn, we can see their geometry unfold.

Ellipses

To draw an ellipse in the ground, all one needs to do is to drive two pegs into the ground at a pre-determined distance apart. A loop of rope is passed around these pegs and a perimeter marker tool pulls the rope taut. This forms a triangular shape with the loop and the two focal pegs and, as the marker tool is moved, the tool traces the perimeter of an ellipse. John E. Wood, in *Sun, Moon and Standing Stones*, postulates that megalithic man may have discovered the ellipse shape when trying to scribe out a circle.[6] A second peg - not at the intended centre of the monument - may have snagged the rope which may have led to the tracing out of an ellipse. A human leg could, he also supposes, have become entrapped briefly within the loop, but these are explanations based on events happening to a culture of near ape-men, and I believe much more cerebral things were going on as these shapes were being surveyed and marked out - from the sheer weight of evidence now before us.

The geometry of the ellipse depends on it having *two* focal points instead of the single centre of the true circle. The further apart one places these focal points, the 'flatter' will be the resulting ellipse. The degree of flatness is termed the *eccentricity*

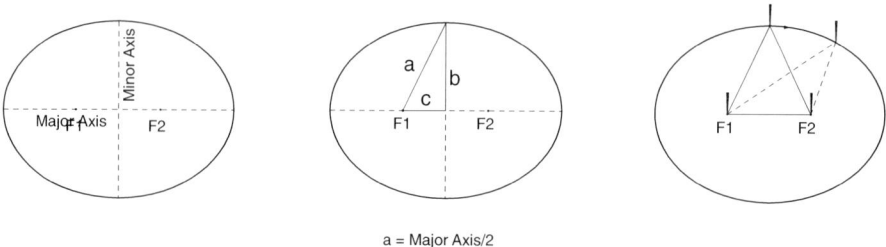

a = Major Axis/2

Figure 6.3 Ellipse construction using peg and rope. The single centre of the circle is replaced with two foci. A loop of rope placed around pegs placed at these foci enables the perimeter of an ellipse to be drawn, as shown in the diagram. The geometry is determined from the forming right-angled triangle, *abc*.

of the ellipse. This is easily defined geometrically. The two axes of symmetry of an ellipse are called the *major axis* and *minor axis* respectively. The ratio between the smaller length (minor axis) and the longer length (major axis) becomes the eccentricity of a the ellipse and can vary from 1 - when the ellipse has its foci together and then produces a circle - to 0, when the ellipse becomes so flat that it effectively becomes a straight line having length equal to the major axis. Megalithic ellipses have eccentricities which lie within the range 0.8 to 1 - they are never wildly oval and thus their elliptical shape *is rarely visible on-site*, an important point.

The megalithic ellipses have been well catalogued by Thom, Burl, Piggott and other archaeologists. Thom published considerable evidence that there was a tendency to produce whole numbers of MY in perimeters as well as radii in stone rings, and the ellipse allows some measure of control of perimeter length within its design rules.

Professor Thom also showed that the builders of these ellipses tended to use whole number ratios for the defining right-angled triangle *abc* - measured in Megalithic Yards. This right-angled triangle completely defines the shape of the finished ellipse and Thom established considerable statistical evidence that the builders understood this fact and deliberately chose whole numbers of MY, perhaps because these were easier to remember. However, the purpose of these ellipses still eludes researchers.

Most ellipses date from 2,000 BC onwards. They are therefore Bronze Age and not Neolithic constructions, if archaeologists have now established the correct dating.

It is very difficult to date stones; carbon dating relies on the discovery of organic material contemporaneous with the placing of the stones. Human remains or fragments off an antler 'pick' or shoulder blade 'shovel' found underneath an excavated stone can enable archaeologists to make an estimate of the date of the stone's placement. This can often mislead - the cremation in Aubrey hole 32 is now[7] dated 700 years after the holes were dug, hardly a synchronous event and John North recommends[8] that we, "get rid of the idea that the cremation is of much significance for the use of the site as a whole." And later, "It is all too easy to become sidetracked by radiocarbon dates when attempting a final periodization."

Flattened Circles

Thom identified two main types, to which he appended the rather stark and inelegant titles, Type A and Type B. There are many survivors, but the best surviving examples are to be found within a small area of the British Lake District. The geometry of both types is shown overleaf.

It was the perimeters of these shapes which interested the author during initial work. An astronomer or calendar maker must know, in addition to the length of the solar year (365.24 days), the length of 12 lunar months (354.37 days) and the length of the eclipse year (346.62 days). The former enables the average lunation time - the time between each full Moon - to be calculated, whilst the latter enables prediction of eclipses to be undertaken.

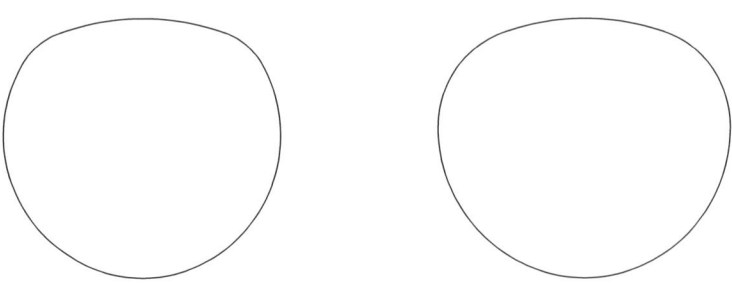

Figure 6.4 The Geometry of Type A and Type B Flattened Circles.

I have assumed that the perimeter of the forming (defining) circle of either type of flattened circle represents the year-circle, a not unreasonable proposition since the concept of the 'year-circle' was well established before 2,000 BC in several other cultures. It then turns out that the Type A flattened circle enjoys a perimeter length which represents the lunar year of twelve lunations whilst the Type B provides the eclipse year of 346 days. I suggest that this may be why the builders should have consistently produced such odd shapes over such a wide territory - the shapes supplied the constants for calendar and eclipse calculations.

No matter how big or small such constructions were made, the astronomical truths about the lunar and eclipse 'years' are delivered from the shape in the form *of a ratio*, independent of the dimensions chosen for the initial circle. This is then directly comparable to the perimeter of the forming circle, which then *always* represents the length of the solar year.

It is very easy to verify this statement by buying some good rope and visiting a beach or flat field. Indeed, it is a remarkable lesson in neolithic thinking to generate these shapes and work with them. Constructing these shapes on a local beach, a group of students were able to predict the total lunar eclipse on December 9th 1992 to within two days, working with ropes, pegs and using the initial 'start' condition of the previous eclipse, on 15th May 1992. Used in such a fashion, the geometric shape thus becomes an *icon*, a ritualistic *function* to extract lunation and eclipse dates - in effect it is a decoder made from stone - a physical constant set in the Earth and mirroring an important astronomic constant referred to the solar year. In comparison, the same students predicted the same eclipse to the day using the 'Aubrey' eclipse predictor and to within four hours using a lunation triangle.

Constructing a Type-B Flattened Circle

The construction of the 'Type B' flattened circle begins with a commonly met sacred geometry construction called the *vesica piscis*, which literally means "fish's bladder".

Throughout the Christian world, this fish shape symbolises Christianity itself, even being found in the design of a Bishop's hat. Today, a streamlined and geometrically incorrect version may be seen on the back of cars owned by Christians. Many religious icons are framed within the shape and, much earlier, it found employment in pagan icons symbolising the female labia. It is ironic that even the pagan and pre-Christian *Sheelagh-na-gig* contains a *vesica* form, and yet it has often been used to symbolise the Virgin Mary. Its vulva-like shape is obvious, although another name for the shape is the *mandorla*, Italian for almond.

Sacred geometers understand the *vesica* as the generator of the irrational number √3, although the *vesica* may readily be invoked in geometrical constructions without knowing about this *numerical* attribute of the shape[9].

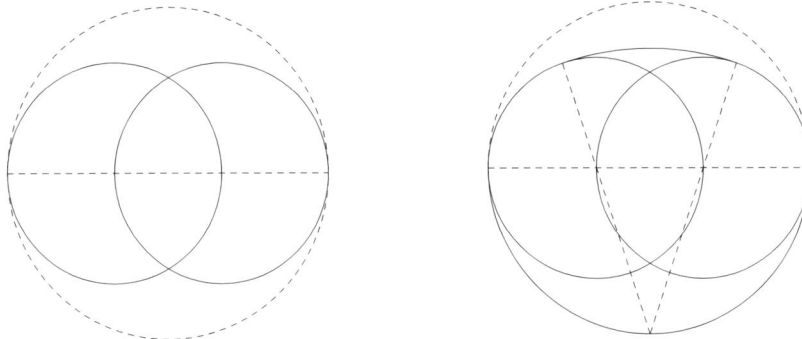

Figure 6.5 Flattened circles and the *Vesica Piscis*.

Construction begins by defining a straight line, a line which will ultimately be perpendicular to the axis of symmetry of the completed flattened ring. Using this line, two circles are constructed, each of which has its centre on the circumference of the other. Bisecting the *vesica* so formed by this construction defines the centre of a circumscribing third circle. Extending the bisecting line to the circumference of this larger circle defines a point from which the flattened arc takes its centre. A peg is staked at this point and the end of a long loop of rope placed over this peg.

The construction now requires two pegs to be driven into the ground where the width of the *vesica* is greatest, i.e. where the *vesica* cuts the original line. The long loop of rope is now taken around either peg and brought to the extreme side of the construction. A knot is then tied and a scribing or sharpened peg is inserted into the loop. To complete the design all one must do is 'walk' this marking peg around the top half of the construction whence it traces out the 'Type B' geometry.

Because the geometry of the 'Type B' circle is the more simple of the two designs, it is here placed first. All over Britain and Ireland may be found examples of both types of ring, each constructed using exactly the techniques illustrated here. 2000 years before Christianity adopted the *vesica piscis*, its geometry was being invoked in neolithic Britain.

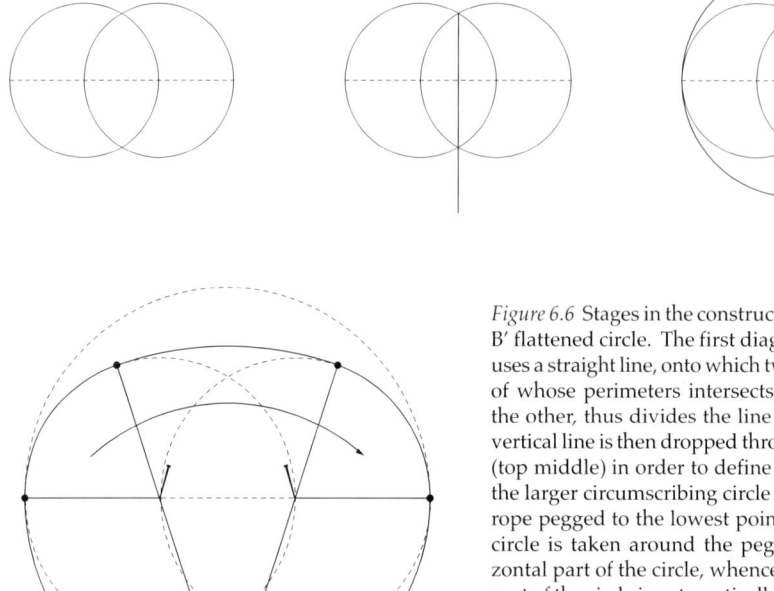

Figure 6.6 Stages in the construction of a 'Type B' flattened circle. The first diagram (top left) uses a straight line, onto which two circles, one of whose perimeters intersects the centre of the other, thus divides the line into three. A vertical line is then dropped through the *vesica* (top middle) in order to define the centre for the larger circumscribing circle (top right). A rope pegged to the lowest point on the large circle is taken around the pegs to the horizontal part of the circle, whence the flattened part of the circle is automatically drawn as the rope is 'walked' around the top half of the circle (lower diagram). The pegs define the three arcs required to produced the flattening, as shown.

Constructing a Type-A Flattened Circle

The 'Type A' flattened circle is somewhat different. The initial procedure is to produce a hexagram within an enclosing circle. The radius of this circle is used to produce 60° sections around the perimeter, beginning from the bottom peg on the circle. This is the standard high school construction shown in figure 6.7. A six-petalled 'flower' is produced. A line is taken from the perimeter peg through the bisector of each 'petal', this too being pegged, from whence the two smaller arcs - the 'corners' - will be drawn. The line joining these two top pegs is extended to cut the circle perimeter, and this defines the limits of the two 'corner' arcs, which connect the flattened arc to the circle. Finally, from the original perimeter peg, the long flattened arc may now be drawn.

From this description we can understand that both Type A and Type B constructions show an impressive knowledge of geometrical techniques and practical skills, but that the Type A is the more complicated of the two forms. In the field, with student groups, the author uses a slightly different technique, nominated a 'Type A1', which is much more akin to the Type B in the constructional techniques needed - this method is described and illustrated in Appendix 2 (*page 232*).

Many examples of these shapes still survive and *ipso facto*, ancient man was clearly working with this level of geometrical skill before 2500 BC, *for there is no other way to construct these shapes.* To attempt to mark out these geometrical constructions yourself provides a salutary lesson, for our modern sophisticated minds find such things extremely difficult. We have forgotten the technique, the reasons and the importance - no wonder we cannot quite believe what our ancestors were doing all over the British Isles four and five millenia ago!

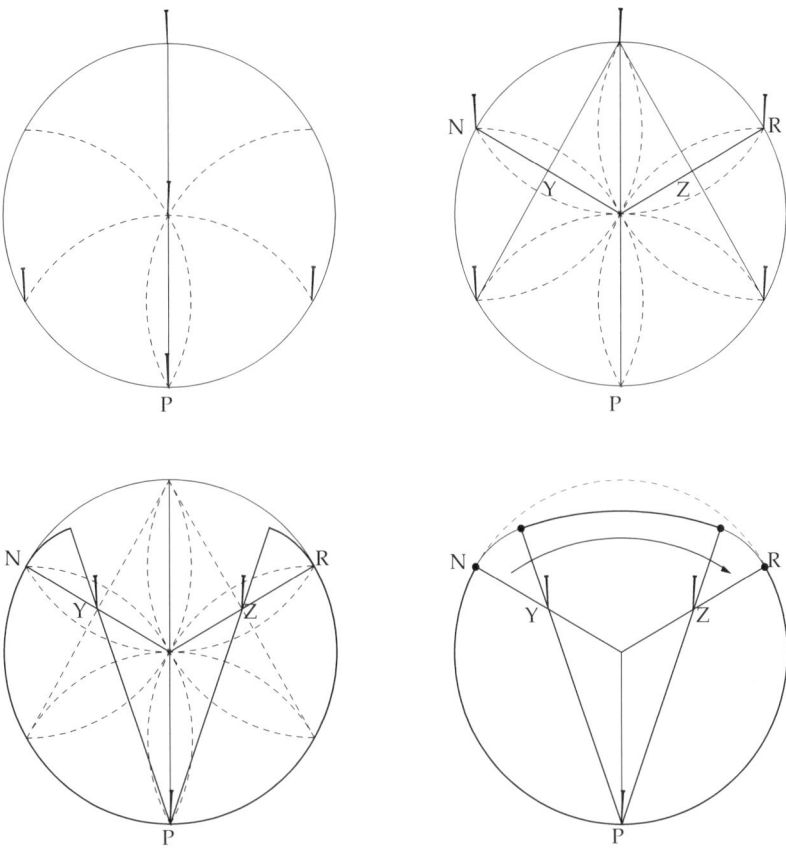

Figure 6.7 Stages in the construction of a Type A flattened circle. *Top left*: The perimeter is divided into six, marking the points of a hexagon around the circle using the radius (centre to the lowest point). *Top right*: The hexagram is completed and pegged ropes are used to define points Y and Z. *Lower left*: Points Y and Z are pegged. Each defines the centre of a smaller circle whose radius is half that of the original circle and which defines the radius of the small arc (*lower right*). *Lower right*: Completing the flattening, just as for the Type-B, by 'walking' a rope, pegged at P, from N to R.

The most convincing way to show just how consistently and accurately these shapes were constructed by megalithic man is demonstrated below, where the outline shapes of four 'Type A' flattened circles are shown superimposed. Considering that each of these 'circles' is over 4000 years old, subjected to wind, frost, rain, the puddling and scratching of herding animals and the attention of humans inimicable to their function, the precision remains astonishing.

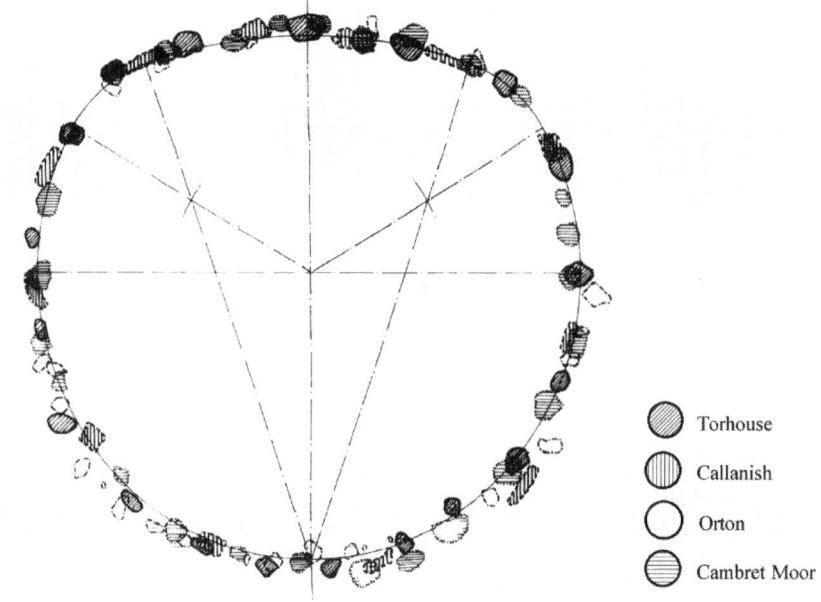

Torhouse

Callanish

Orton

Cambret Moor

Figure 6.8 Four Type A flattened circle constructions superimposed.

Perhaps the best example of a Type B circle is found at the site known as Long Meg and her Daughters, at Little Salkeld, in Cumbria. Despite being constructed on variable sloping terrain, the integrity of design is remarkable (*figure 6.9*). It is a very large ring, some 360 feet across, and the site holds additional interest because there is a large (13 feet high) red sandstone outlier, Long Meg herself, upon which may be found an anticlockwise spiral motif. Through the large flanking stones within the supposed entrance, the outlier stands in line with the midwinter sunset at a distance of 30 MY. Both John Aubrey and William Stukely visited the site, a sign of its importance. It is only surpassed in area by the huge outer circle at Avebury, Stanton Drew in Somerset and the Ring of Brodgar in the Orkneys. Like so many other stone circles, the name stems from a legend that the stones were once people, punished by God for dancing or otherwise revelling at the site on a Sunday. Looking at figure 6.9, we must stand in awe of Long Meg's evident fertility.

Examples of Flattened Circles

There are many more of these 'squashed' circles lying across England, Wales and Scotland. They are flattened according to clear design rules which, to Alex Thom, suggested that the builders were attempting to make the circumference equal to 3 times the radius, rather than the irrational π (3.141592654..). If this was the case, then the builders didn't totally succeed, for their designs spill out two distinct categories of number - 3.059 and 2.957 - for π.

Considering the high accuracy with which the circles were laid out, Thom's explanation seems unlikely - and why two designs? As mentioned earlier, the former number gives flattened circle to full circle perimeter ratios which offer the lunation data - accurate to 0.35% (Type A), whilst the latter offers ratios which directly offer the eclipse year proportioned to the solar year - accurate to 0.8% (Type B)[10]. For reasons mentioned earlier, we have no way of establishing whether or not such designs

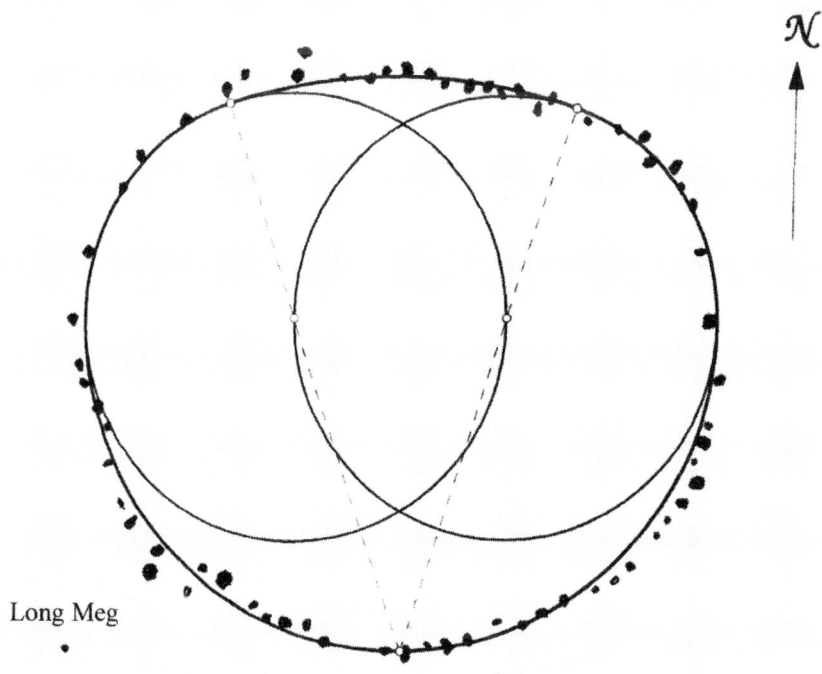

Figure 6.9 Long Meg and her Daughters. This large stone ring in the English Lakes is 360 feet across. Its curious name partakes of a common legend associated with stone circles - that the stones were once singers, dancers, pipers or other revellers who were petrified by God for revelling on a Sunday. Other examples are the Piper's stones in Wicklow, the Hurlers and the Merry Maidens, both in Cornwall.

were deliberate or coincidental. However, there has as yet been no explanation as to why so many megalithic circles were flattened in such a precise way, thus any basis for a better understanding starts a process. Professor Thom recorded just how precise the flattening was, putting to an end any assumption that the circles were circles which went wrong or were laid out on a Friday afternoon. These last few pages should inform the reader that such an assumption is ill-founded.

It is interesting to note that the designs of both types of flattened circle incorporate a right-angled triangle. This time, it is not Pythagorean, but it is filled with astronomical ratios and *phi*. Adventurous readers may like to study this shape in order to access some more revealed cosmology.

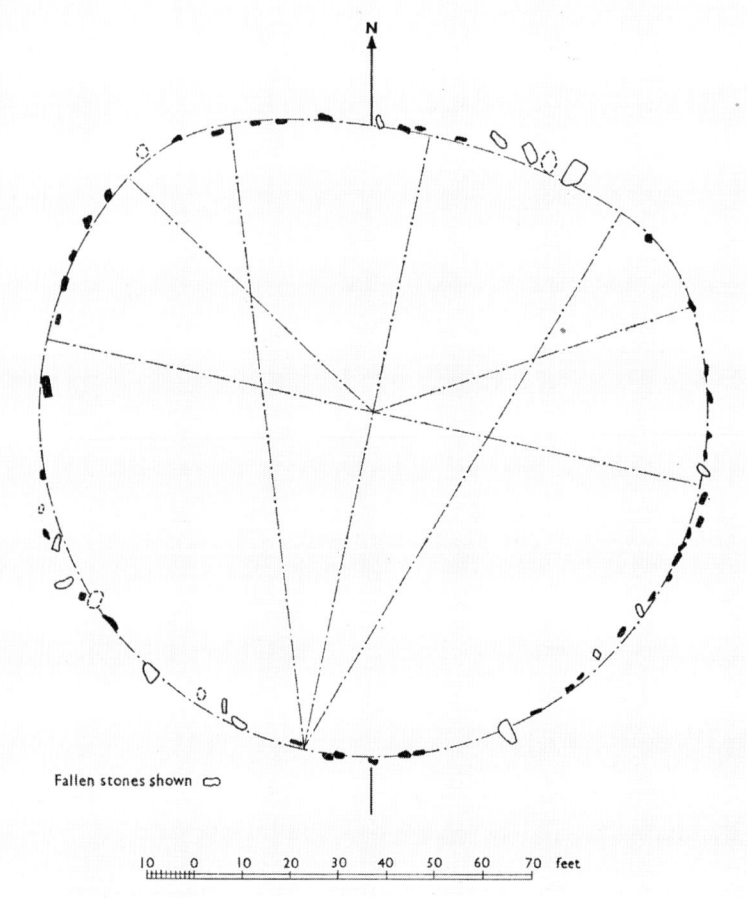

Figure 6.10 Dinnever Hill, Cornwall, a large Type A flattened circle. 130 feet across, comprised of small stones which barely rise above the grass in the summer. This suggests that the stones were not used as astronomical sight lines. The geometry is extremely faithful to the Type A structure (*after Thom*).

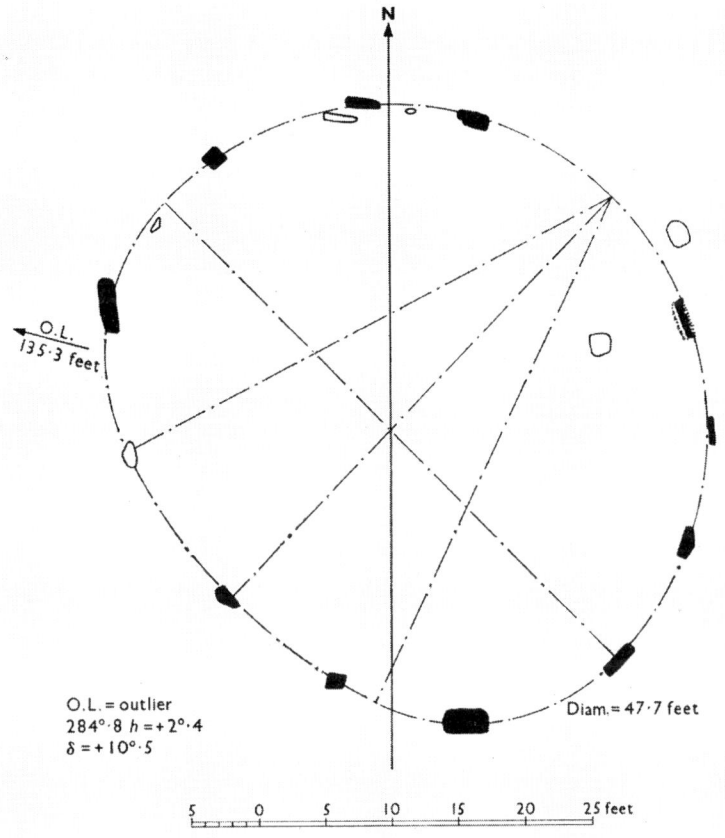

N

O.L.
135·3 feet

O.L. = outlier
284°·8 *h* = + 2°·4
δ = + 10°·5

Diam. = 47·7 feet

5   0   5   10   15   20   25 feet

Figure 6.11 Bar Brook, Derbyshire. A fine Type B flattened circle, using just a dozen stones to define its geometry. It is seven Megalithic rods in diameter (*after Thom*).

Egg-Shaped Rings

Egg shaped stone rings are quite rare. They are again based on right-angle triangles (usually whole number ratios) and, again, cannot be constructed without using them. Thom identified two types of design and we are indebted to him for so doing even if his nomenclature reflects his academic background - Type I and Type II.

The Type I is formed by taking two congruent (identical) triangles and placing the middle-length sides (the side adjacent to the apex angle) together. The Type II has the hypotenuses clamped together. At Carnac, in the Aurac district of the Baie de Morbihan (Brittany), both types may be found together, one at each end of the impressive stone row alignments which form *Le Menec*. Again, we find control of the perimeter length for a given radius.

Surviving examples of both types show us once again that the surveying and constructional techniques of the builders was astonishingly precise. The illustrations show two eggs from Scotland. The reader will note the alignment with whole numbers of Megalithic yards, or halves, in the construction.

This completes a look at the simpler 'stone circles', although the word simple is hardly applicable in terms of the techniques employed nor the questions they raise about our forebear's intentions. Many are not true circles, and there are over 160 survivors remaining in Britain, testimony to their durability. There are perhaps over 1600 identifiable survivors left in northern Europe, an indication that there may have been many thousand such constructions during the period when they were evidently so important to the culture (3000 - 1500 BC).

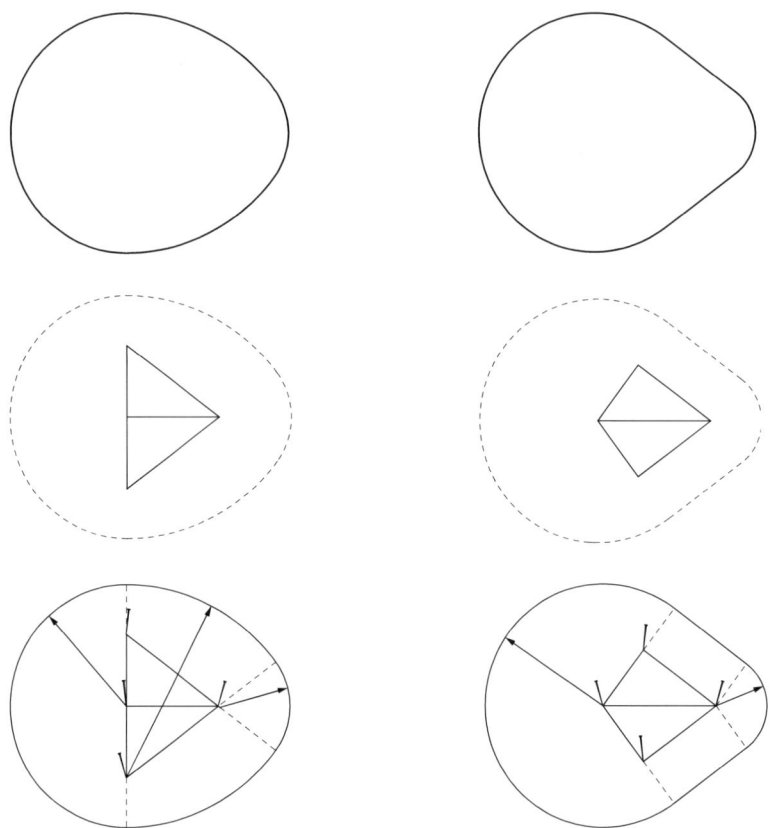

Figure 6.11 The geometry of Type I (*left*) and Type II (*right*) egg-shaped rings.

Examples of Egg-shaped Rings

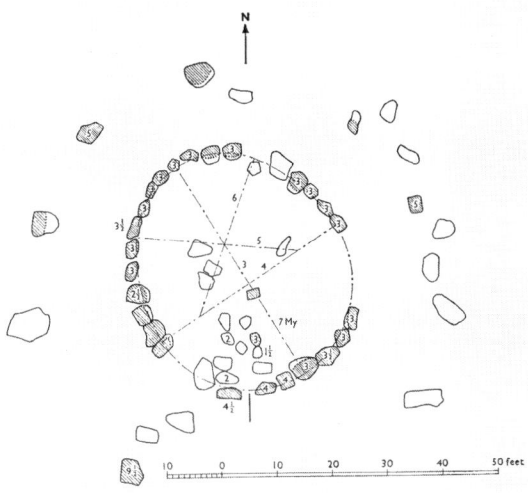

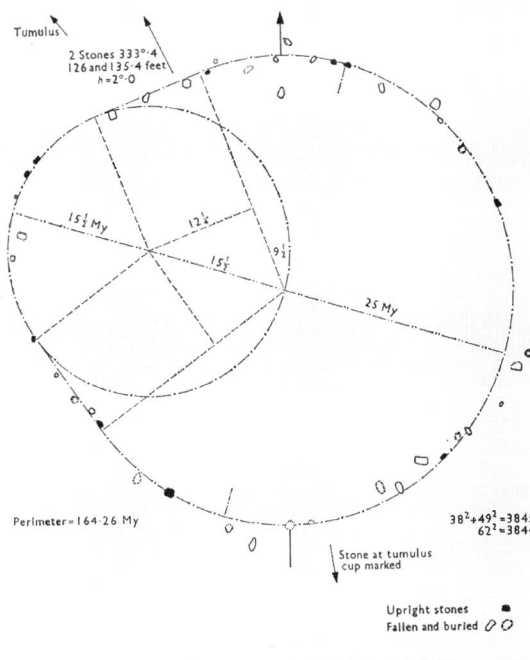

Figure 6.12 Examples of Type I and Type II Egg-shaped rings.

Above left: Druid's Temple, near Inverness, formed from a 3:4:5 triangle and with an interesting outer 'egg-shell'.

Above: Allan Water, near Hawick, is located in and amongst a complex of ancient sites, and is beautifully sited. The 'sharp end' points to the maximum moonrise and the site fills with water during the winter months, producing a 'Type 1 pond' and, at the maximum moonrise, this would reflect the Moon from within the ring. In recent years, cattle have badly damaged the site. *Below left*: Borrowstone Rigg, near Edinburgh, is a very unimpressive site in its present state, although enough erect stones remain to confirm its geometry. At *Le Menec*, in Brittany, an example of both types of stone egg may be found at each end of the long stone alignments, where the triangles used to define the eggs are 30, 40 and 50 Megalithic yards, the corresponding perimeters being 304 and 370 Megalithic yards. The triangle is the ubiquitous 3:4:5 (see also the *Crucuno* rectangle, page 162).

We must now move on and look at the rarest of all the types - the *Compound Rings*. There are only four survivors, two in Wales, one in Scotland and perhaps the most magnificent megalithic ring of them all - Avebury, in Wiltshire, England. They are all highly interesting and show no little mastery of technique in their construction and siting. They represent the showpieces of Neolithic and Bronze Age geometry.

Compound Rings

The best preserved and arguably the most beautiful compound ring may be found near Llandrillo, Bala, the site known as *Moel ty Uchaf*. It is remarkably sited, perched on the only level ground for miles, on the top of the Welsh hills with panoramic views to the south and west (*figure 6.13, below*).

If the siting is breathtaking, the geometry of this ring is equally so, for *Moel ty Uchaf* is based on a *pentagonal* format and, fortunately, is so remarkably well preserved, even after over 4,000 years, that the radius ropes never stray more than an inch from the top of each stone. Easter Delfour, in Scotland, is less fortunate, whilst Kerry Pole, also in Wales, is now a very unimpressive site on the ground, although its geometry is certain and the site utilises a 5:12:13 triangle.[11]

Figure 6.13 Moel Ty Uchaf - A Compound Ring on Top of the World.

Moel ty Uchaf, which may be a kerbed cairn rather than a stone ring, has a functional value which compliments its exquisite geometry. The site commands a panoramic view extending to over 80 miles over much of the compass. The solar and lunar alignments on the horizon are evident to anyone who has visited the site armed with a theodolite and knowledge of the azimuths of sunrise and sunset at this latitude during the year. Major and minor standstill alignments of the Moon are also suggested. However, it is not these alignments which concern me here, rather the geometry of *Moel ty Uchaf.*

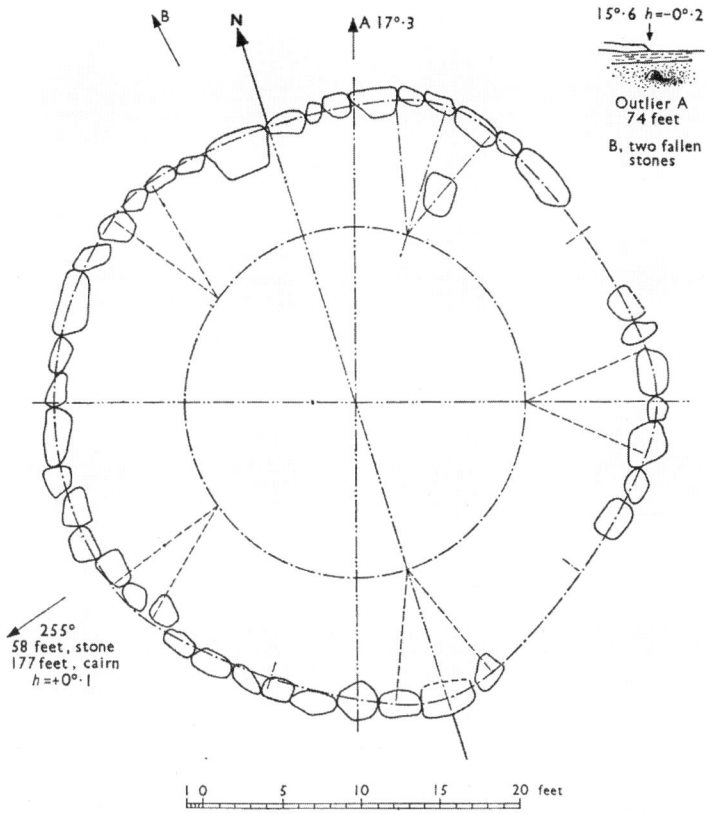

Figure 6.14 A Plan view of *Moel ty Uchaf (after Thom).*

To construct the monument, the builders began with a circle of radius 7 Megalithic yards, inside which they inscribed a concentric circle of radius 4 Megalithic yards. This done, they divided the perimeter of both circles by five - a technique thought not to have pre-dated the Greeks. Presumably they placed pegs at the division points. Interestingly, the axis of symmetry of the monument is aligned at about 18 degrees to the cardinal points of the compass, this being one quarter of 72 degrees, the pentagram angle. Using ropes or measuring poles, the builders then proceeded to produce the flattening effects so visible on the plan diagram yet barely noticeable on site, as the photograph demonstrates. The illustrations below show the necessary stages in laying out the geometry.

The reader may now begin to glimpse the commonality of general procedure involved in laying out megalithic sites. This process can be greatly helped by attempting to mark out the designs illustrated here on beach or flat field, connecting to the culture that originally pioneered these designs in a remarkable way - for one is certainly mimicking *precisely* the identical methods and order of construction originally undertaken over four thousand years ago. You may require outline planning permission if you then wish to consider the placing of fifty ton stones within your designs!

The plan of *Moel ty Uchaf* is very beautiful to the eye but this is hardly evident to someone viewing the site from the ground - so why go to all that trouble? The perimeter of the 7 MY circle was just under 44 MY (43.98MY), whilst the perimeter, as built, is 42.85MY. The ratio between these two numbers is so close (0.4%) to the ratio

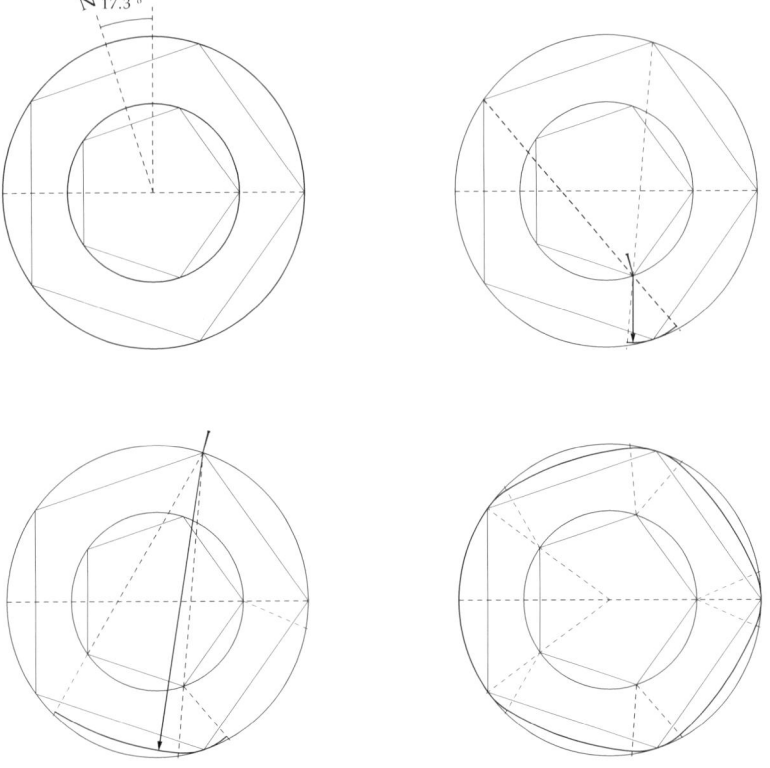

Figure 6.15 The Geometric construction of *Moel ty Uchaf.*

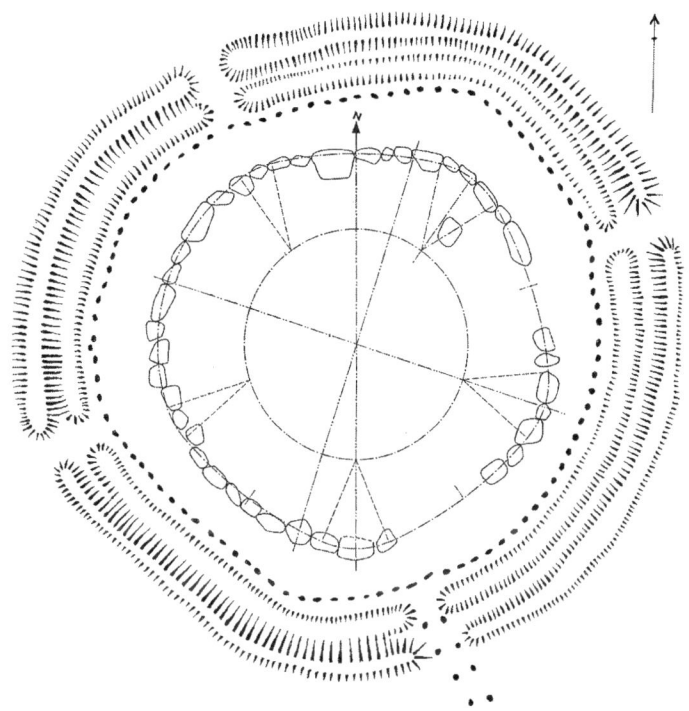

Figure 6.16 Similarity in Form. *Moel ty Uchaf* set inside a plan of Avebury. Both sites are aligned to true north as indicated. (*not to scale*)

of the lunar year to the solar year that the flattening holds a practical component. To discover when full Moons will occur in a given year, then laying two ropes side by side - a 'year' rope (44MY) marked with the days of the year and a 'lunar year' rope (42.85MY) divided into twelve equal lengths will indicate the exact day of full Moon each month. For the past few years I have taken groups of up to thirty people to visit *Moel ty Uchaf* and, time and weather permitting, facilitated such work. Having confirmed the geometry, using ordinary rope marked in Megalithic yards, each lunation has been determined for the current year and never found to be more than 8 hours in error. This is better than 0.6% accuracy. *Moel ty Uchaf* is aesthetically superb *and*, intentionally or not, holds a useful astronomical outcome.

Moel ty Uchaf is constructed using design principles which, even without the suggested astronomic component, demonstrate that it cannot be attributed to the random strugglings of near-savages. It is *a variation on a theme* of neolithic design, as the comparative diagrams 6.16 (*above*) and 6.17 (*overleaf*) will confirm.

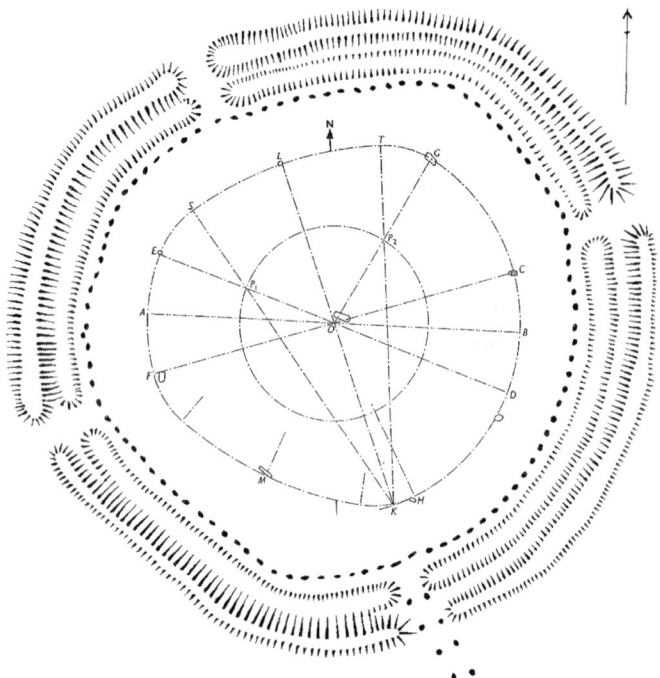

Figure 6.17 Similarity of form between another compound ring (Kerry Pole) and Avebury, both sites aligned with north to the top. (*not to scale*)

Concentric Rings

In addition to the compound rings, there are several stone rings where a smaller circular ring may be found placed concentrically within the larger ring. Miltown of Clava and Loanhead are perhaps the best examples (*see opposite*). At both sites, a pentagram star may be drawn between the two circles. Later in this book, this same shape will be seen as a vital link between the cosmos and mathematical/geometrical realities - an *interface* or *transducer* between the Sky-gods and the Earth.

Both Miltown of Clava and Loanhead of Daviot reveal to us the thinking processes behind their respective designs. The Miltown double ring has its pentagonal geometry not in the placement of five individual stones around its outer perimeter, but by implication, because the inner ring fits very closely with the inner pentagon formed by the outer pentagram 'star arms'. In addition, to confirm the geometry, an outlier, some 140 feet from the site, is exactly aligned to the outer pentagram star. Finally, the site is aligned to the compass such that one of the 'star arms' is within three degrees of being parallel to the north-south line.

In contrast, the Loanhead of Daviot double ring uses ten large stones to define each point of the pentagonal geometry. Here, we are left in no doubt as to the function of the outer ring of ten stones, which divide the outer circle into ten. The illustration below shows how this outer circle relates to the inner circle, again leaving no doubt as to the intended design and confirming the principles of construction expounded throughout this chapter. The division of a circle into whole numbers was a regular part of megalithic culture and in chapter nine we will apply the same technique to Stonehenge. Integrated with the compass and the major astronomic alignments of the year, stone rings were thus geometry *in space and time*.

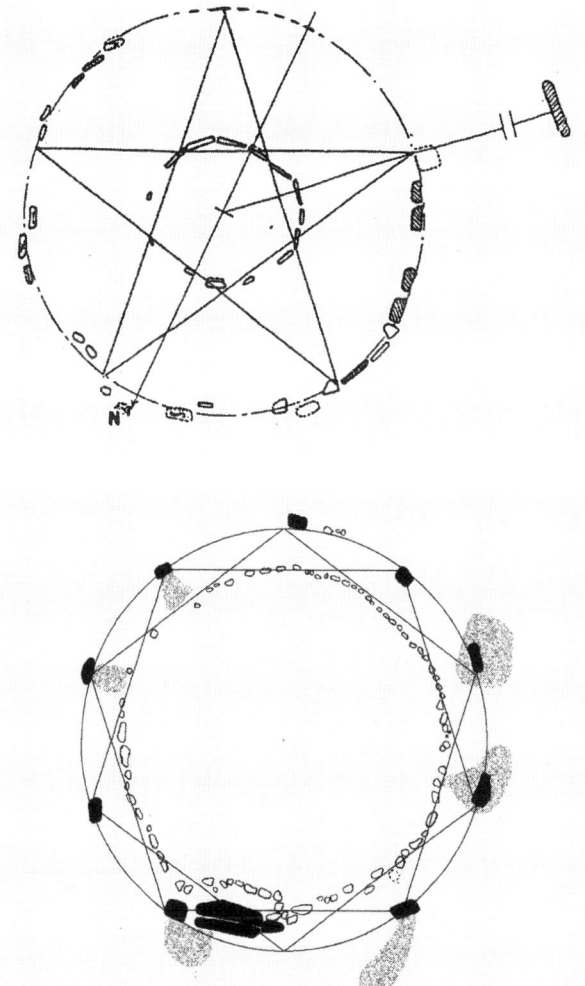

Figure 6.18 Concentric Rings. Miltown of Clava (courtesy Anne Macauley) and Loanhead of Daviot (courtesy John Martineau). Pentagonal geometry is clearly shown in the construction of both rings and, at Miltown, even in the outlier stone.

Summary

The collection of monuments presented here forms our surviving legacy from the megalithic culture. No doubt other examples remain to be discovered, but it is unlikely that they remain in a well preserved state, although their geometry may be recoverable. Every year, for over a millenium, an average of between three and five of these remarkable constructions was being built in Britain. When Richard Atkinson mused on how megalithic astronomy attained continuity through many generations without written texts[12], we can now suggest an answer - that the very astronomical constants so conveniently listed in modern ephemerides are merely refinements of a process of discovery which began five millenia ago in Europe, using the geometric forms illustrated here. Continuity of knowledge became a matter of remembering simple geometric procedures, rituals which preserved the coded information.

Whether or not an elite astronomer-priesthood held close the astronomic secrets of what was being built into these monuments, or whether the general principles were known by many, at least enough stone rings remain for us to make a clear assessment of their astronomical and geometric principles. These 'signatures in stone' can tell the modern anthropologist much about the intellectual abilities and aspirations of our forebears.

Figure 6.19 Building a Type B flattened circle on a beach. The shape of the *vesica* can be clearly seen in the central area, as can the stakes used to define the geometry. White quartz pebbles are used to provide an authentic neolithic appearance. The perimeter can determine the length of the eclipse year, as described in the text.

Footnotes to Chapter Six

[1] Measuring rods have been found at Dutch sites.

[2] *Megalithic Sites in Britain*, page 34.

[3] 6.8 feet. Thom's histogram on page 46 shows distinct peaks at 12.5, 25, 37.5, 50, 62.5, 75, 87.5 and 125 MY. Diameters show strong peaking at 4, 6, 8, 10, 12, 16, 18, 20, 22, 30, 38, 40 and 42 MY

[4] A third of a MY is 10.873 inches long , 0.368 of a lunation is 10.875 days long. The error is less than two parts in ten thousand.

[5] This section of the text is based on a seminar hosted by the *Centre for Living Art and Science,* Tremadoc in 1993.

[6] *Sun, Moon and Standing Stones*, John Edwin Wood, Oxford (1978). Page 40-41.

[7] Following M. W. Pitts work in 1982.

[8] *Stonehenge*, p. 498 and p. 500.

[9] Probably the best simple introduction to Sacred Geometry, and its fundamental shapes and qualities, is Robert Lawlor's Thames and Hudson classic *Sacred Geometry.*

[10] Divided by π, 3.059 and 2.957 yield 0.9737 and 0.9412. If π is now taken to represent the solar year, these fractions become 355 and 344 days respectively. 12 lunations take 354 days and the eclipse year is 346 days long.

[11] Kerry Pole is part of the Kerry Hill circle complex, Grid ref: SO157861. See *Britain, A Study in Patterns*, published by RILKO 1971. Professor Keith Critchlow's excellent book *Time Stands Still* discusses the remarkable geometry of Moel ty Uchaf in depth.

[12] "...supposing that the *Astronomical ephemeris* is not published, but is transmitted by word of mouth from its compilers to its users in the form of epic verse which must be strictly memorized and reproduced". Quoted in *Earth Magic* by Francis Hitching, Cassell and Co. Ltd (1976), Page 86.

Above: : The Inner Sanctum of the Temple. This English Heritage photograph enables many of the design features referred to in this book to be seen. Tenon joints are clearly visible on many of the sarsen stones, the curvature of the lintels is evident as is the curve followed by the trilithon ellipse. At the top of the picture, in front of the ditch and bank, station stone 91 can be seen and, to its right, the outline of the mound that once surrounded the now missing station stone 92. The half width sarsen (top right) may be seen and, inside the sarsen ring, the remains of the bluestone ring and horseshoe are also clearly visible.

Chapter Seven

- STONEHENGE AND -
THE RITUAL LANDSCAPE

To a casual observer, the siting of megalithic monuments is not likely to be the main reason for making a visit to see them. Whilst the stones may be very impressive, perhaps placed in a beautiful location, and the apparent remoteness of the culture which built them highly mysterious, it is not at all obvious on a single Sunday afternoon's fleeting contact that the siting of a monument is often quite exquisitely chosen. In this chapter we look at the factors which influenced the megalithic architects in their choice of a site for a monument.

If one pays frequent visits to a particular megalithic site, preferably over many years, it is almost certain that the site will begin to offer a whole spectrum of meaning linking the local sky patterns to the landscape. It is these which have pre-occupied the astro-archaeologists. However, the manner by which the site also resonates with the local environment - patterns of hilltop, valley and major landscape features - is often so astonishingly well thought out that regular visits to selected sites can also greatly assist in the understanding of, and admiration for, the underlying motives behind the megalithic process.

It is far too easy to become obsessed with the astronomical end of this subject, perhaps because it comforts our overheated left-brains to show a continuity of thought process between our forefathers and our modern Space Age. Astronomical alignments can be just as accurately and much less arduously constructed from wooden posts than from megaliths weighing many tons - clearly the choice to build in stone lies partly with reasons other than just astronomy.

It is also very easy to become over-engrossed in the macabre contents of neolithic burials, the injuries and diseases, the apparent nastiness and occasional violence of ancient mundane life. The catalogue of diseases is truly depressing and the average life-expectancy of Neolithic souls, at least those whose remains have been discovered, was a little over thirty years of age.[1] A large number of discovered child burials suggest horrendous infant mortality or, even worse to our culture, human sacrifice. But we do not dig in the churchyard to discover the higher aspirations of a culture, we instead pay a visit to the church. Even in modern times, great scientific achievement goes on alongside acts of brutality, deprivation and unnecessary hardship - why should things have changed that much?

In our modern world, we have moved our culture way over onto the solar side of the soli-lunar continuum. We value thinking far more than feeling and, in our buildings, functionality far more than aesthetics. We abuse our environment in a way which shocked and astounded the doomed American Indian tribes, who some anthropologists relate as the closest social typology to our megalith builders. It should not therefore seem so surprising that we often fail to notice or appreciate the care which went into the siting of a stone ring, long barrow or a burial chamber. *Mother-Earth*, until the last few decades, had become a quaint concept until James Lovelock resuscitated her under her original Greek name *Gaia*.[2] Indeed, until a few years ago, visiting a megalithic site, except as an excuse for a picnic, was also thought quaint. Only professional archaeologists visited with intent - and what an intent that was!

The Legacy of Archaeology

The traditional archaeologist was armed with spade and pick-axe. After millenia of resting in comparative peace, an onslaught of up-market pirates hacked out the few ancient treasures they could find, often to leave these badly catalogued, re-entombed in museums, private homes or collections, and the site irreparably ruined. Old School archaeology, as practised by Sir Richard Colt Hoare and his side-kick William Cunningham (late eighteenth century), Lieutenant-General Pitt-Rivers (late nineteenth century) and the notorious Colonel Hawley (early twentieth century) possessed all the subtlety of a demolition squad. As John Michell informs us in his delightful *Megalithomania*,

> *"And the most damning criticism of excavations at ancient sites, whether by simple treasure-hunters or highly trained archaeologists, is that the sum total of all their labours has contributed scarcely at all to resolving the problem obviously presented by the substantial presence of megalithic monuments, the problem of why they were built".[3]*

This is the very essence of the megalithic problem, and it raises the prime question to which this text is devoted - *why*?

Whilst the legacy of archaeology is not admirable it merely reflected the empire-building colonisation of a rapacious military-orientated culture. Its practitioners were very slow to connect astronomy with the subject, despite the strongest intimations, even from way back in William Stukeley's time, that megalithic monuments incorporated key astronomical alignments in their design. The publication of Sir Norman Lockyer's *The Dawn of Civilisation*, in 1894, indicated that a theodolite and knowledge of astronomy were now to be considered an essential part of any professional archaeological investigation at major sites.

Then as now, the majority of the public wanted gold and silver trinkets, torques, spears and shields. The romance of the period demanded Druids buried in high honour. More often than not, they received their thirty pieces of silver in the form of bone buttons, quartz chippings, shards of pottery and sea-shells; their pound of flesh was exhumed in the form of mutilated skeletons, arthritic bones, rotten teeth and cremated bone-flakes. Apparently, there were very few Druids and even less gold. And astronomy was far too technical for savages.

The Enclosure of the Dead

There is no doubt that many megalithic sites served a function relating to the reverence and treatment of the dead. Whilst it is fashionable today to talk about spirit-paths and not ley-lines; *totenwegs* ('pathways of the dead') instead of processional walkways, we are still not at all clear concerning the treatment of the dead ancestors of the tribe. It is postulated by several eminent authors that the centres of stone rings, including Stonehenge, were sanctified places - charnel-houses where the corpses were left to make the transition to the afterlife. There is evidence that some cadavers were left to be picked clean by buzzards or other birds of prey prior to the bones being brought back, sanctified and placed to rest within a site, or a nearby long-barrow. The bones of the ancestors were apparently used in ceremonial rituals.

The placement of burials in cists and barrows, with the cadaver aligned to the cardinal points, *is an act which must involve astronomical observation* (of pole star or the culmination of Sun, Moon, stars or a planet). Even in so simple an example the sky and death are seen to be linked - and suddenly astronomy is seen not to be too technical for savages.

It is, however, in this arena that archaeologists deliver their most powerful arguments against the astronomical and geometrical theorists. Their probing of the contents of bell-barrow, cist and tumulus has produced a powerful corpus of objective fact concerning the social conditions and life expectancy of Neolithic and Bronze Age Man.[4] The remains of these people do not appear to square at all with a culture which understood the motions of the Sun and Moon better than any fifteenth century astronomer, placed fifty ton dressed stones within a few millimetres of a location predetermined by quite complex geometry and surveying and perhaps having dragged these many miles, and was using a standard unit of length throughout Britain. Yet all these things are also facts, well substantiated by equally valid scientific evidence.

The result of this dichotomy is very evident - an enormous impasse where researchers usually find themselves aligned on one side or the other, with a highly charged chasm between each faction, across which one side periodically throws abuse or new evidence at the other. However, at an enlightened inter-disciplinary conference in Glasgow in September 1975, Dr Euan MacKie centred a discussion on this 'Thomist paradox', i.e. the evident gap between the social culture of the megalith builders and the advanced level of astronomical and mathematical knowledge shown in their megaliths. He also admitted in a review of Ivimy's book, *The Sphinx and the Megaliths*, within *The New Scientist*, that the metrological evidence suggested "links of some kind with the Near East" and added,

> *"If prehistorians are not satisfied (with Ivimy's theory) we must provide a better one".*

Whilst the worst excesses of the archaeo-astronomical and 'earth mysteries' camp are obsessive and tedious, finding alignments in everything and everywhere, so too has been the obdurate resistance to new ideas from the traditionalists. Over quarter of a century after MacKie's conference, the 'Thomist paradox' remains unsolved and not only has no better model been found, but no model at all has been forthcoming from the establishment archaeologists which answers the simple question - *why*?

The Sky and the Dead

The mythologist Joseph Campbell suggested that, in order to ascertain accurately what a particular culture worships, one looks for the most important or impressive building erected by that culture, and its function. Taking his advice, we find Canary Wharf, Millbank Towers and other huge financial 'monuments' dominating the skylines of modern London, verifying his statement within our own culture. Six centuries ago we would have found the newly built cathedrals also confirming his statement. Projecting this practical advice back five millenia we then find Stonehenge, Avebury, Kermanio and Newgrange. Each of these constructions has a proven astronomical component as each also has a connection with the treatment of the dead.[5] These two facets run side by side at monument after monument so that we might reasonably assume that to ancient Man they were inseparable. In this regard, ancient Britons appear not dissimilar to the ancient Egyptians, who also mixed death (and rebirth) with their astronomically-based mythology, and many other cultures around the globe have also linked Sky and Earth in this way.

In the early decades of this century, before the discovery of carbon dating, the stone circles of Europe were thought to be of much *later* origin than the wonderful Egyptian artefacts that Carter was then pulling out of Egyptian *sarcophagi*. These really *were* treasures. The whole world culture was, at this time, dancing to *Ballet Egyptien*, looking East for proof of ancient culture, apparently so much older than our own dull megaliths. So it came to pass that a "collection of battered old rocks" became seen in the national consciousness as having nothing of any importance to say to us - in fact, they were an indictment of Europe's dismal level of primitiveness. Except, that is, for one notable exception - Stonehenge.

It should therefore be seen as no surprise that this century has seen more damage inflicted on these sites than the preceding forty. Industrialisation and the demands of increased population on farmland has caused incalculable damage to site after site. Yet, to quote Thom, "The clues which eventually led the author to the unravelling of the geometry of Avebury did not come from Stonehenge or Stanton Drew but from small unimpressive circles on the Scottish moors and the hills of Wales."

These "small unimpressive circles" are our oldest heritage which, despite being the property of a nation which is well nigh obsessed with 'heritage', have remained almost totally neglected and until recently have defied all explanations as to why or how they were built. Some of the reasons for this state of affairs have been addressed earlier on in this book, but it is now high time to account for our collective failure to solve the megalith problem.

A History of Imported Beliefs

Britain's recorded history is a Judao-Christian history whilst our administrative structure is still organised along essentially Roman lines. This floods the waking consciousness of every modern westerner, whilst lingering in the unconscious one can sometimes glimpse a vast reservoir of pre-Roman cultural material. Some of this can and does surface into the light of consciousness from time to time, and then we discover our love of anything 'Celtic', folk-lore, delight in ancient customs, hunting, gathering and fascination with prehistory.

The history of the Church's attacks on Paganism - 'The Old Religion', certainly included megalithic monuments within its *fiat*, and what we cannot imagine is how strong remain the effects of countless generation's worth of injunctions against becoming involved in the 'devilish' stones, evil circles, tumuli etc, etc. When the Christianity of Rome arrived in force into Britain, circa 600 AD, its proponents found a country where the megalithic sites were still important to the ceremonies and spiritual beliefs of the majority of Celts (many Christianised) and their conquerors, the Anglo-Saxons. To convert the population to Christianity - at least the Roman Church's version of it - required certain time-honoured tactics, those of brainwashing, fear and persecution of miscreants.

One has only to glance at the names of many of our most well known megalithic sites to recognise the link being forged between ancient sites and their connection with evil and disobedience to God's law. The *Devil's Quoit* and the *Devil Stones* are two rather obvious examples, as too is the vast folk-lore concerning revellers whose antics, often sexual, at these sites caused the good Lord to turn them into stones. Examples of this genre include the Merry Maidens, the Piper's Stones and the Hurlers. Other names conjure up giants, witches, dragons and monsters, such as the Welsh *Bedd yr Afanc*, Grave of the Monster. The majority of the population stayed well clear of such places, building up over many generations a fear of any relic of the megalithic culture, a fear which still lingers in twentieth century minds.

Pope Gregory the Great (590-604 AD) described the British as a nation, "placed in an obscure corner of the world,..hitherto..wholly taken up with the adoration of wood and stones". As a result of this, the Pope dispatched St Augustine from Rome to England in 596 AD to complete a process of Christianization begun by St Patrick around AD 440. By 681 AD, at least on paper, the process appeared complete and successful, although repeated edicts by the Church were issued until at least 1100 AD, telling the historian a somewhat different story. Augustine's instructions, direct from Rome, were to destroy the pagan idols by building Christian churches on the same sites, and these were adopted wholesale. In all parts of the British Isles today, the casual observer can find churches built on mounds, tumps, ancient crossroads and holy wells. This probably had the effect of preserving the very sites Pope Gregory wished to see destroyed. His instructions were, in some cases, wholly impractical, as in Brittany, many churches were built incorporating huge and immoveable megaliths entombed *in perpetuo* within their superstructure. In the *Laws of Knut* it is revealed that, even after 1000 AD, the main objects of worship in England were, "The Sun and Moon, fire and water, springs, stones and trees". In 1035 AD King Knut banned all of this, but enforcement was clearly another matter, rather like attempting to stop a incoming tide, another of King Knut's famous failures.

By the fourteenth century, Avebury was being systematically attacked and, in the fervour that followed the *renaissance*, many of its finest stones were steam-split and carted away. People actually died in this 'battle of the stones'; those pitiful barber's scissors in the splendid Alexander Keiller Museum[6] giving us an incisive picture of the perils involved in the demolition of megalithic sites and, four millenia previously, in erecting the self-same huge monoliths. In the eighteenth century, 'Stonekiller' Robinson became a local hero, rebuked in the village church by Stukeley himself, in 1724, for supplying Avebury villagers with 'building stone'. Whilst Stonehenge appears to have escaped the worst attentions of the anti-pagans, the same isolation which protected it for so long throughout its history has more recently made it a tempting target for a variety of military weapon systems. Incredibly, and mentioned by Atkinson in *Stonehenge*, in 1917 a demand was made by the military to demolish Stonehenge as "..its stones constituted a dangerous hazard to low flying aircraft."

Mercifully, Stonehenge and an adequate number of other sites have survived all that the human race and the British weather has thrown at them over the past few millenia and it is from these relics that we must piece together the reasons why such things once occupied our ancestors for over a thousand years. What were the criteria for building a megalith?

Megaliths and Ritual Landscapes

To attempt an answer as to why a megalithic site is placed at a particular location, we need to address several key issues:

(i). *Site-blindness*. Many otherwise excellent books covering or cataloguing megalithic sites fail to give a plan of the monument itself. Even those that do may encourage site-blindness, my own term for over-focussed attention onto a site without any consideration of its placement within the larger landscape. As an obvious example of site-blindness we could do worse than cite Avebury, whose *ambience* is incomplete without an attempt to integrate this huge stone ring within the local landscape of Windmill Hill, the Kennett river, the Marlborough Downs and a whole host of other natural features which define the natural landscape. Then, in addition, the ritual landscape includes the sites of the Sanctuary, West Kennett long barrow, Silbury Hill, the West Kennett and Beckhampton avenues and miscellaneous standing stones, dolmens and tumuli dotted across the natural landscape. The siting of each of these

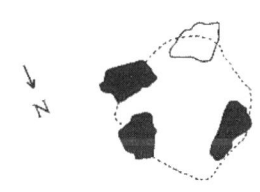

Figure 7.1 (a) *Pentre Ifan*, (b) *Llech y Drybedd*.
Author's photographs, with included site plans by
kind permission of Logaston Press.

features was chosen with some consideration and Avebury will not be fully understood unless these other sites are integrated into the whole picture.

Here we find the key strength of researchers like Michael Dames, who wrests his audiences spellbound out of the twentieth century into the ancient landscape around Avebury - enthusiastically reminding us that humans like ourselves once populated the site. Whilst we have many archaeologists, we have very few Michael Dames', and his published works[7] and guided tours act as a valuable counterbalance against the tendency to overdo the rational scientific aspects of megalithic research.

Site-blindness is also incurred whenever an archaeo-astronomer wishes to understand Sun and Moon patterns from a site plan. Unless the features of the whole 360° horizon with appropriate azimuths and horizon altitudes are included, then little useful work can be done unless actually on-site. Many researchers, including the writer, have made profound errors due to a failure to account for a high horizon altitude. It is therefore true that great errors of conclusion can be made by reference to site plans and that lugging a theodolite to the site still remains the most fruitful and accurate way by which to fully integrate how the site resonates with the sky and the earth. Modern computer techniques now make it perfectly feasible to film around each site and compile the information on an interactive CD-ROM for indoor researchers. This technique can also make possible the correction for the change in the Earth's tilt since Neolithic times, enabling a researcher to view the interactions with the sky as seen by the site's builders, a valuable step forwards, but this too is no substitute for an actual site visit. In this chapter, I have used my local sites to build up a picture of the factors which may have determined the location of megalithic sites.

(ii). Intervisibility. In just a few seasons of visiting sites, one becomes aware that the sighting of one monument relates to another, each clearly involved in the choice of location. Territorial, political or social reasons are assumed to be the main factors involved in this choice, whilst geomantic researchers look for patterns in the landscape. In and around Newport, Pembrokeshire, lie several separate yet quite similar burial chambers all invisible each from the other yet each visible from Wales' most famous chamber - *Pentre Ifan (see figure 7.1).*

Figure 7.2 (a) *Coetan Arthur* and (b) *Trellyfant.* Author's photographs, with included site plans by kind permission of Logaston Press.

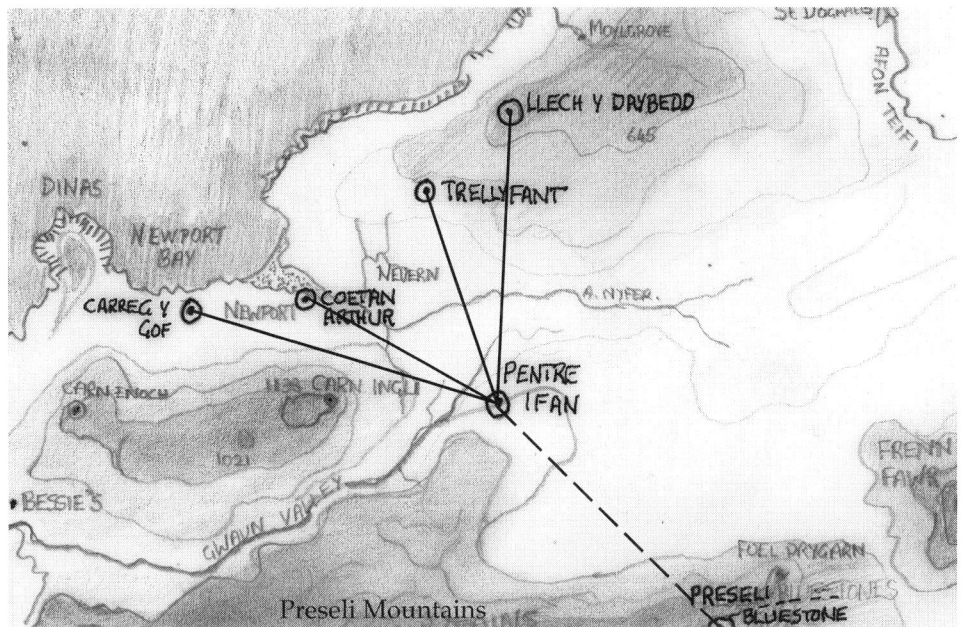

Figure 7.3 Location map, with sites connected. See text for details.

The site plans for each of these monuments are useful in that one can clearly see design and structural similarities. Each monument was originally built having a large and 'chunky' capstone supported by four upright stones. The capstone of *Coetan Arthur* is now somewhat precariously supported by just two uprights, whilst *Llech y Drybedd* still enjoys three. Study of these site plans (*figure 7.2*) tells us nothing about the nature of this 'intervisibility', whilst a map begins to unravel an important picture of a coastal escarpement running down from *Llech y Drybedd* along a sweep of countryside ending on the beach at Newport, *Coetan Arthur* is less than 400 metres from the Nyfer estuary in Newport. The ley-hunter joins these sites up with straight lines and makes calculations (*figure 7.3*). Although these sites - and *Carreg y Gof* - very roughly align, they are not related in the rational manner a ley-hunter seeks to find and he or she must conclude that there were other factors involved in their placement.

(*iii*). *Astronomical factors.* Unless the whole ordnance survey map is studied, one fails to see the larger picture - the impressive range of the Preseli mountains to the south and east of each of these sites. The midwinter sunset at *Llech y Drybedd* takes place into the saddle shaped top of one of them - *Mynydd Melyn* [*figure 7.4 (a)*]. We have already seen how the midsummer sunset aligns to this monument [*figure 2.2.(a)*, *page 20*]. In addition, this remarkable monument has its most northerly stone placed such that the flat edge inside the chamber only receives the glancing rays of the setting sun on the days around the winter solstice [*figure 7.4 (b)*]. The capstone is symmetrically aligned to the midsummer sunset. The axis of the monument is aligned to the same sunset and two triangular gaps made by the supporting stones allow the

Figure 7.4 (right) Midwinter sunset through *Llech y Drybedd*.

Figure 7.5 [below] The rays of the setting Sun glance the flat side of the front supporting stone only at the solstice.

setting Sun's rays to illuminate the inside of the chamber just as the Sun sits on the horizon and descends into *Lugnaquilla* peak in Wicklow, Ireland. From the northwestern side of the axis, the Sun and Moon rise up parallel to the angle of the left-hand side of the capstone. None of these things will one find noted in any archaeological book; only by regular visits over many years has the writer been able to begin to piece together the possible deeper processes involved in this particular monument's construction. A casual visitor just sees an unfeasibly large stone held on several upright stones and wonders what was going on a long, long time ago.

All of this information can, of course, be dismissed as coincidence, although we are then unlikely to learn anything more in the future from the culture that built sites such as these.

(*iv*). *Landscape mirroring.* At many sites, it is not possible to ignore repeated imitation of natural features within the landscape produced in the shapes of stones chosen for the monument. Within the examples I have used here, the undersurface of *Pentre Ifan*'s magnificant sloping capstone mimics the local horizon to a remarkable degree (*figure 7.6*). *Llech y Drybedd*'s sloping capstone emulates the peak of *Carn Ingli*, the dominant landscape feature at the site (*figure 7.7*). *Coetan Arthur* and *Pentre Ifan* both have their capstone oriented in the same direction and the similarity in shape is obvious (*figure 7.8*)

(*v*). *Visual Cues.* At some sites, a nearby cairn or singleton stone may draw the eye on to a distant peak or notch on the horizon. These are not always astronomical alignments but can indicate the direction of ancient trackways or other monuments. Looking almost due south from *Llech y Drybedd* one can see *Pentre Ifan*, if one knows

130

where to look, behind which lies the massive backdrop of the Preseli mountains. Directly above the monument, on the horizon, are the summits of *Foel Feddau* and *Foel Cwmcerwyn* - Preseli 'Top' as it is known locally.

The astronomer might suggest that, from *Llech y Drybedd*, the clearly visible tumuli on top of the Preselis above *Pentre Ifan* indicated the direction where the Sun, Moon, planets and stars culminated in the sky. The historian might recognise that an ancient trackway - 'The Golden Way' - runs along the spine of the Preselis and perhaps suggest that *Llech y Drybedd*, which is later than *Pentre Ifan*, was built as a further outpost or spur to this grand-daddy of all burial chambers. An archaeologist could reasonably suggest that the tumuli were important territorial outposts and that *Llech y Drybedd* was built to acknowledge this via an alignment.

Finally, a ley-hunter would suggest that three places on a straight line is suggestive of a ley, and would search for other sites on or adjacent to the same alignment in accord with Alfred Watkins' original definition of what did and did not comprise a true ley-line.[8] If we avoid the question of just exactly what is a ley-line, then our ley-hunter would no doubt be delighted to see that this extended line passes through a further three clearly acceptable points before passing off the map sheet near Narberth. A standing stone, various bridges and crossroads, churches (perhaps, *Augustine-fashion*, built on an ancient site) and an prehistoric earthwork do, curiously, crop up along this 'alignment'.

Figure 7.6 Landscape mirroring at *Pentre Ifan*. The slope of the capstone runs parallel to the local horizon, where pyramidal outcrops indicate extreme midsummer moonsets.

Combinations of some or all of the above factors may have been involved in the total process of deciding where to site this "small and unimpressive" megalith. To fully note and incorporate these factors it is important to embrace the environmentalist maxim: *think globally, act locally*. It is vital to visit sites frequently and therefore, like the builders, it is best to live locally.

(*vi*). *Use of non-local stone*. At some sites, petrologists have ascertained that, despite ample provision of local stone suitable for the task in hand, the builders instead sought to transport stones from a distant location. Three types of stone which found important use at Stonehenge circles are non-local (*see page 13*). This curious and not uncommon practice suggests that the path of least resistance was not a primary concern of the builders and may hint at an important function held by the *original* site of the stone or its visual or tactile quality.

Here, we might usefully cite Preseli bluestone, which was painstakingly transported to Stonehenge. This stone may have been an important part of an earlier henge structure originally located in the Preseli mountains of West Wales. There is some solid evidence to support this. Atkinson informs us, describing the bluestone horseshoe that, "The tooling of the surfaces of the stones has been carried out with great care, the standard of workmanship and finish being far higher than that exhibited by the sarsens, and matched only by the two former lintels in the bluestone circle" (*Stonehenge*, page 42). It is notable that the harder bluestone was far more skillfully dressed than the softer sarsen stones.

Figure 7.7 Landscape mirroring between *Llech y Drybedd* and *Carn Ingli* peak.

Fig. 7.8. Mirroring of capstones. *Pentre Ifan (right)* and *Coetan Arthur*, in addition to sharing the same angle of slope, both have their capstones orientated in the same direction and their axis of symmetry is within three degrees of the north-south line.

Visually, bluestone - a form of spotted dolerite - is a blue-green igneous rock with variegated nodules of white crystalline quartz spattered throughout its structure. Particularly when wet, it quite resembles a starry night sky, although this may be a fanciful explanation for its evident popularity down the hypotenuse at Stonehenge.

Strangely, bluestone possesses a wholly unexpected quality which is *audible*. A visit to the bluestone outcrop at *Carn Menyn* will allow the visitor to demonstrate that, by striking one bluestone against another, a curious metallic or bell-like tone is produced, just as if the stone was hollow. The local town, Maenclochog, apparently takes its name from this effect, for the name means, "Ringing stones" in Welsh.[9] Such an experiment at Stonehenge is, for obvious reasons, to be discouraged, although English Heritage could usefully provide two large bluestones off the site to allow visitors to witness this curious effect.

(*vii*). *Subsumption or deference*. A law of subsumption or deference appears to be the case at several important sites where the site must respond to other over-riding factors. Some of the other factors listed here contribute to this phenomenon, but sometimes the monument is sequestered into a much larger regional scheme. The Stonehenge-Preseli lunation triangle is one suggested example. For a long time, many different specialists have commented that the site of Stonehenge is not a particularly well chosen one in comparison to other, less splendid monuments - a curious fact for such an imposing and important building. The ground slopes, the horizon skyline is not very remarkable and its altitude is variable. Subsumed into the lunation triangle, Stonehenge, as the only man-made point, was required to lie exactly east of Lundy Island and at a distance which would align the other three sites into a lunation triangle. It is apparent that Stonehenge, under these strict criteria, had to be built within a mile wide strip between Shrewton and Bulford - just three square miles tolerance if the builders were looking to make a creditable lunation triangle.

Having now delineated some of the factors in the selection of a site for a megalithic monument, perhaps we might finish this chapter with two delightful pieces of confirmation that our forebears were involved in a consideration of some or all of these factors.

Castle Rigg

Castle Rigg is a large Type-A flattened circle, with a diameter of about 40 Megalithic yards (1293 inches or 32.83 metres). It is found on the only piece of level ground for miles around within the most mountainous of landscapes near Keswick, in the English Lake District. (54° 36′ N; 3° 05′ W).

One of the first things a casual visitor will see at this site is the remarkable mirroring between the tops of the stones and the local mountain terrain. A stone placed facing a steep mountain side will, from the centre of the ring, have a shaped matching slope. This is simultaneously a visual cue, landscape mirroring and an aesthetic factor, and was clearly an important aspect of the design.

An archaeo-astronomer would, in the course of a single year and blessed with good weather, recognise four cardinal solar risings and setting alignments originally built into the ring. An alignment to the rising of the fixed star *Altair* may be found, involving the largest stone in the ring. After a period of many years, the extreme

Figure 7.9 Castle Rigg, Cumbria, perhaps the best Type A flattened circle. Geometry, astronomy and the local landscape coincide in a single space. (*courtesy John Martineau*).

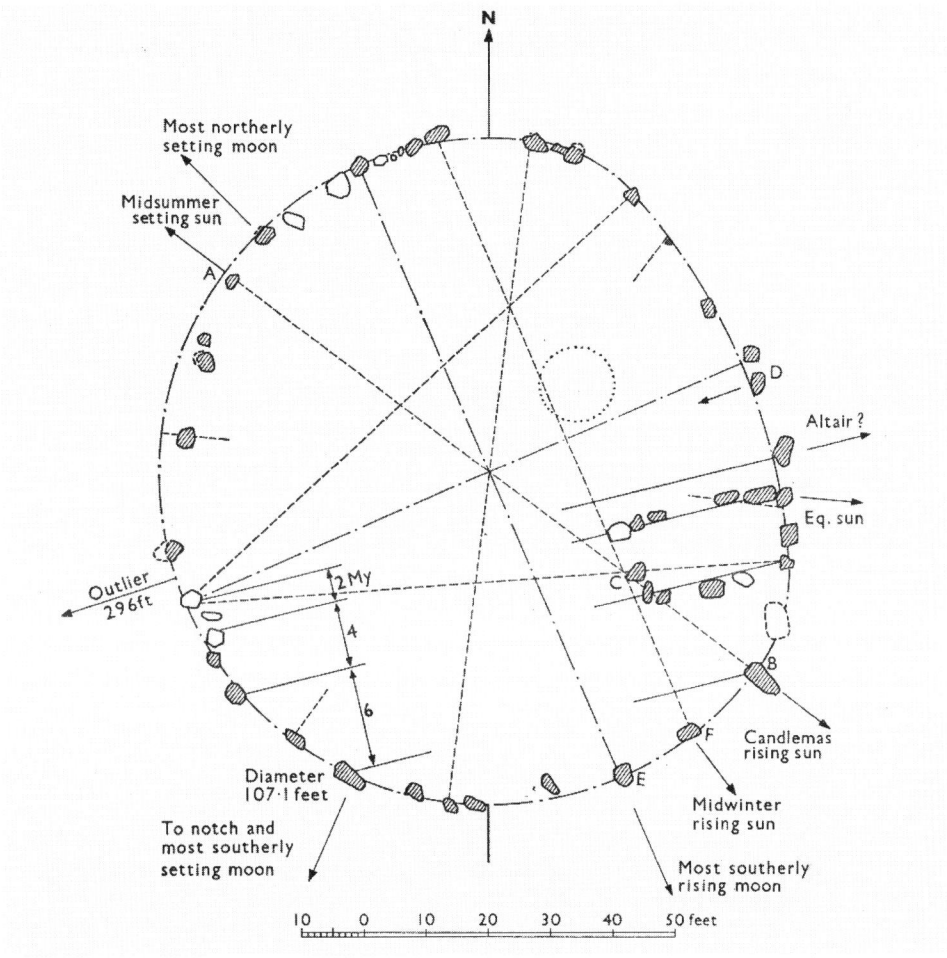

Figure 7.10 Castle Rigg, site plan, showing the unique relationship this site holds between local astronomical alignments and the Type A geometry (*after Thom*).

positions of the rising and setting Moon would be found, these completing the known astronomical factors built into this astonishing piece of engineering.

However, four of these seven alignments are arranged to fit the inherent structure of the Type-A geometry. A casual visitor would never be aware of this nor the defining astronomical factors. Only a surveyor could ascertain the geometry; any consideration that the circle was merely a deformed attempt to create a true circle would hinder any attempt to understand the culture that built Castle Rigg. A site plan would be of little help, unless the astronomical and horizon factors were overlaid onto it to illustrate the crucial point - *at Castle Rigg, the Type-A geometry and the astronomy of local space coincide.*

Although the English Lake District sports many wonderful examples of the art of flattened circle building, Castle Rigg is sited perfectly and this invites us to take off our hats and applaud the designer and builders - it is a true masterpiece of megalithic art. We must conclude that the architect was a geometer, an astronomer, a surveyor of high calibre and completely familiar with the total local environment - sky and earth.

Alex Thom wrote,

> *"Ask any engineer with experience of field-work to locate a site with similar properties (to Castle Rigg) and he will want a large group of surveyors working for an indefinite time fully equipped with modern instruments and calculating facilities. Add that the ring must occupy a level piece of ground and he will ask for equipment to level the ground when he has located the exact spot. It will be realized that it is only the mountainous nature of the country which makes it possible to find a site with the necessary properties, and yet Castle Rigg, as tens of thousands of visitors know, is beautifully situated on a flat level part of the field."[10]*

Stonehenge

Stonehenge also has its unique placement defined by a variety of factors. The Station Stone rectangle can only be a rectangle having side ratios 5:12 at the latitude of Stonehenge if it is to resonate to the right-angle difference between extreme solar and lunar risings and settings and to 'quarter-day' sunrises or sunsets. This allows about a fifty mile allowance in the latitude before the rectangle becomes a parallelogram, whence it cannot be fitted into the Aubrey circle and the quarter-day alignments are lost. Stonehenge is built within the middle third of this allowable variation. The placement of Stonehenge appears, like Castle Rigg, to reflect the astronomical alignments of the location.

We suggested earlier that the final choice of site was subsumed into the requirements of the larger Preseli lunation triangle, which define a three square mile area, fortunately well within the boundaries of the soli-lunar alignment above.

We might also consider that the azimuth of the midsummer sunrise was chosen to coincide with the latitude of Stonehenge, which it did to a remarkable degree when the monument was being built. Various factors must be taken into account when calculating this angle, and the casual reader may become bewildered by values quoted in books which vary from 49° 34' to 51° 36'. This variation depends on (a) which part of the Sun is used to define sunrise, (b) the change in azimuth over 5,000 years and (c) just exactly where the axis of Stonehenge is to be taken. However, the azimuth from the Sarsen Centre to the top of the Heelstone is 51° 51', the same as the Great Pyramid's angle of slope. If this is deliberate then it presents us with some new questions and invites us to remove our hats once again and applaud the designer.

The questions raised by the fact that Stonehenge's stones were brought from two main locations each many miles from the site are actually simple: (i) Why? (ii) How? and (iii) When? If we are to consider the original location of the stone to be of

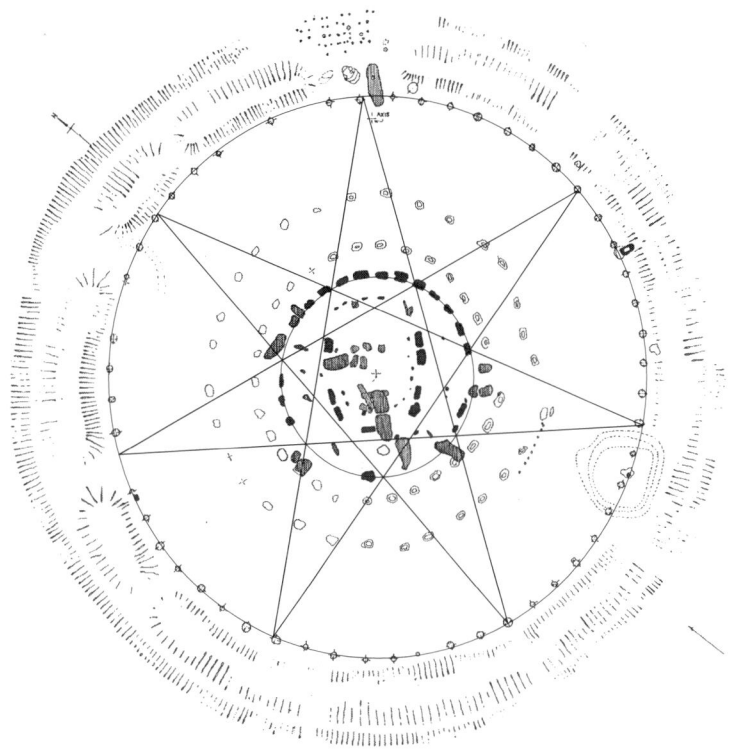

Figure 7.11 The seven-fold connection between the Sarsen Circle and the Aubrey Circle. The inner star 'arms' cross at the mean diameter of the ring of lintels.

significance, then we may answer the first of these questions, discovering that the sarsens came from Fyfield Down latitude 51° 26' north, longitude 1° 48' west, whilst the bluestones originate from latitude 51° 57.3' north and longitude 4° 42' west. *The former site is at latitude 360/7°; the latter 364/7°.*

Multiplying the latitudes by seven, perhaps not an immediately obvious calculation to want to undertake[11], we then discover that the sarsen site latitude = 360° and the bluestone site latitude = 364°. Thus, expressed as a ratio:

$$\frac{\textit{Sarsen site latitude}}{\textit{Bluestone site latitude}} = \frac{360}{364}$$

The equality is as exact as the areas of the two sites allows and is doubly remarkable because the two types of calendar structure defined by the respective phases of Stonehenge connected with each stone type are the 360 and the 364 day calendar.

137

The original sites of the two major types of stone at Stonehenge reflect perfectly the astronomical, numerical, calendraic and geometrical structure in which they were eventually utilised.

Here, at last, we appear to have a reason for the choice of stone type used in the two major design stages of Stonehenge, offering us an explanation as to why it was necessary to drag all those huge stones all that way. It is also pleasing to discover that the sarsen stone site lies at one seventh of the Earth's polar circumference up from the equator, as does Avebury. Hats off again, gentlemen!

Summary

This chapter has categorised many of the design criteria with which the architects of megalithic sites were juggling. I have attempted to set clear categories for their final choice and attempted to show, using my local sites, how these factors balance out. It has taken fourteen years to begin to understand some of the finer components of this design process.

The reader now has a clearer grasp on why the ritual landscape must include the sky, in particular the astronomy of the two luminaries, within any analysis of a site. Geometry and number theory needs to be considered. The importance of a holistic approach to the site has been stressed in order that, in the future, site plans will include as a matter of course a *thorough* survey, details on local landscape, horizon profiles and possible identification of regional factors which may involve subsumption. In so doing, it is hoped that increased clarity can be brought into this subject, so that specialists in various fields can unite to discover a more accurate account of this culture.

It is also now very clear why Alex Thom was so successful at understanding this culture. A skilled and highly qualified engineer, with a life long love of astronomy, an expert in astro-navigation and a first-rate surveyor - these are precisely the qualities and talents demonstrated by the architects of megalithic sites.

It is no longer professional to snigger behind one's specialist qualifications at alternative approaches to understanding aspects of the megalithic culture. Until we have solved the 'Thomist paradox' and come to understand the megalithic culture more completely, then dowsers, ley hunters, sacred geometers, psychics and shamans all have an equal validity with archaeologists. As Professor John North reminds us[12] in *Stonehenge*,

> *"A rigorous search for alternatives is often far more important than a blinkered analysis of only one."*

Footnotes to Chapter Seven

[1] The exhumed bodies may not be a random cross-section through the community - indeed, burial may have been reserved for warriors whence the picture we would get of Neolithic or Bronze Age life would *ipso facto* be martial. If death from natural causes did not involve 'heroic' burial, we should not then be surprised to find so many lodged arrowheads, crushed skulls and amputations.

[2] *Gaia - a new look at life on Earth*. J.E.Lovelock. Oxford 1979.

[3] *Megalithomania*. John Michell. Thames and Hudson (1982).

[4] *The Stonehenge People* by Aubrey Burl (J.Dent, 1986) is an excellent text on this material.

[5] Burials and cremations at megalithic sites continued long after archaeologists think that the sites were 'active'. Certainly, the *astronomical* alignments of some monuments gradually deteriorated through precessional effects, limiting their life to a few hundred years. It is possible that the burials were later additions to an already venerated site.

[6] The author recommends this as the finest museum on matters Neolithic in Britain. Set right in the middle of the largest stone circle in the world - Avebury. Thanks to the custodians, Dave Davidge and Mike Powell for much of the information about the history of the site found on this page.

[7] *The Avebury Cycle* and *Silbury Treasure*. Both published by Thames and Hudson.

[8] *The Old Straight Track*. Alfred Watkins (1925). The pioneer of ley-hunting, Watkins defined a good ley alignment as having five or more historically prominent sites aligned within fifteen miles.

[9] *Maen* is the same word as *meini*, hence *Caer meini*, another name for the bluestone outcrop means stone fortress. *Clochog* shares the same root as the French word for bell - *cloche*.

[10] *Megalithic Sites in Britain*, OUP, 1967. Page 148.

[11] Until one sees the diagram (*figure 7.11*), that is.

[12] *Stonehenge - Neolithic Man and the Cosmos*. J.D.North. (1996). Pref, xxxvii.

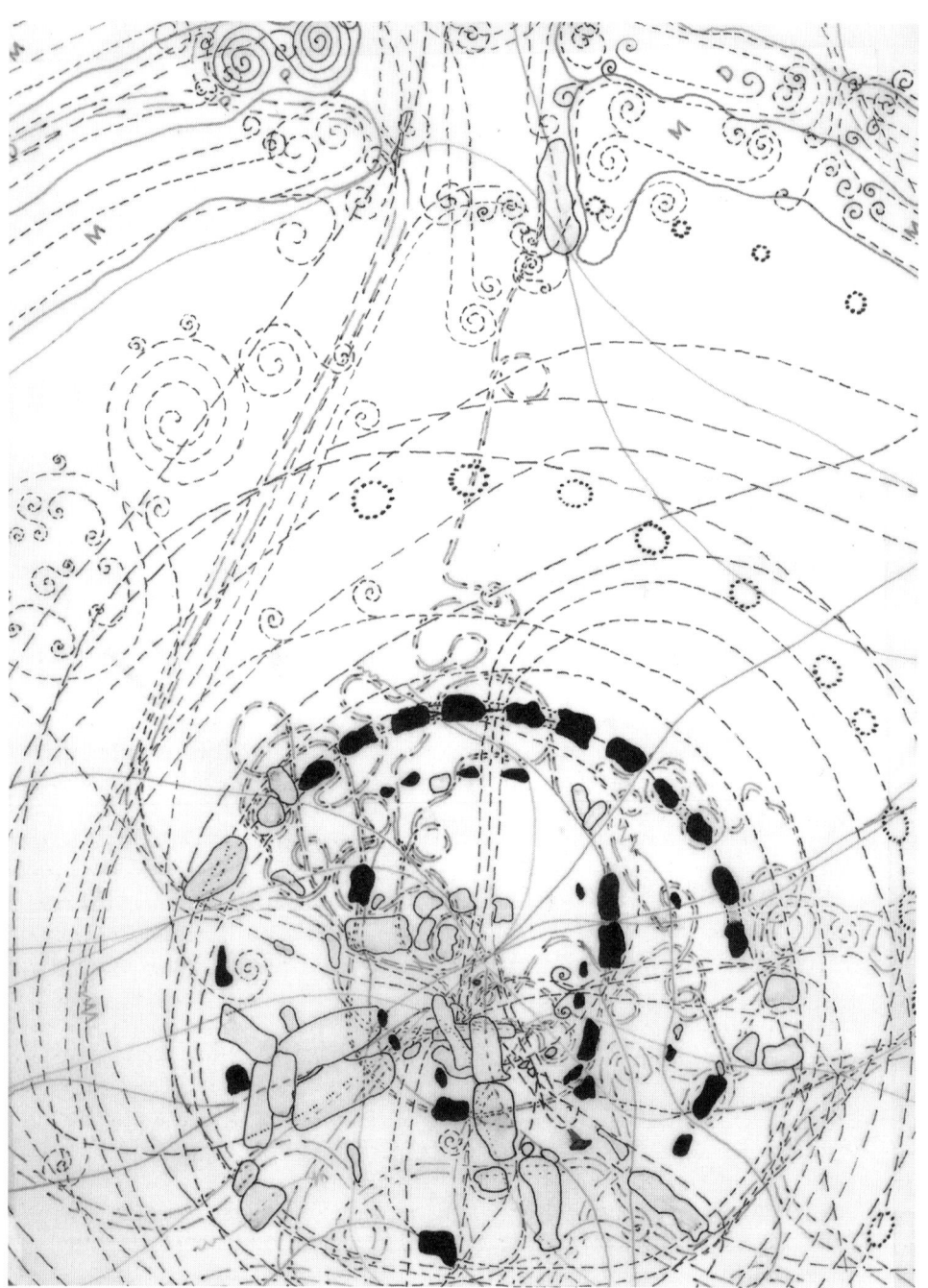

Above: A Dowser's view of Stonehenge. A superimposition of twelve maps made by the late Guy Underwood from 1946 to 1948. Dowsers can still trace the same lines today, and were the first to suggest the current dating for the site. *(Courtesy John Martineau).*

Chapter Eight

A RIGOROUS SEARCH
- FOR ALTERNATIVES -

In chapter three I described the inevitable design and form of a soli-lunar calendar which would accurately plot the rhythms of the Sun and Moon. The Aubrey circle at Stonehenge contains this same design and form. The immutable numbers of orbital periods lead to difficult but clearly identifiable choices in the nature of an earthly calendar which reflects both solar and lunar rhythms. Again, Stonehenge reflects these same numbers in the design of both the earlier Aubrey circle and later sarsen circle. The latitude of the original sources of the bluestones and sarsens, plus the chronology of Stonehenge, also confirms an earlier lunar emphasis of the site becoming, during the evolution of the monument, a solar emphasis. Stonehenge began as a lunar temple and became Apollo's temple, reflecting perfectly the changes in the social fabric of the societies which evolved the monument.

In chapter five, the lunation triangle was brought into the arena to show both a level of integration and increased accuracy within these same rhythms, this simple geometric technique offering an immediate practical application - the accurate forecasting of lunations and, through integrating the solar and lunar cycles, solving outright the calendar problem. Other right-angled triangles were shown to facilitate accurate forecasting of lunar position and eclipses. The hardware and every technological aid for implementing these highly accurate techniques was also to be found at Stonehenge, for it is plainly evident that the monument was built using similar hardware. I suggested that accurately marked ropes and rods formed the storage medium enabling these techniques to provide a continuity throughout at least fifteen centuries of megalithic endeavour.

In this chapter we investigate further reasons why we remain so ignorant concerning Stonehenge and the megalithic culture. Our current perspective concerning the growth of civilisation and scientific endeavour has been quite wrongly slanted towards the Middle East, primarily because of two reasons already discussed in chapter seven. These are the simple fact that rope and measuring rods, as vehicles to convey and store information, decay quite quickly in the damp northern climate whilst clay tablets, heiroglyphics and papyrus, in the dry climate of the Middle East, do not. Secondly, the remarkable artefacts discovered in Egyptian tombs make the contents of European barrows and tumuli seem very dull to an uninformed public which is not, by and large, educated to appreciate mathematical and geometrical refinement, particularly of megalithic buildings, nor their subtlety of siting.

All of these things build up a clear picture of thet obstacles that have to be overcome before the megalithic culture can begin to become better appreciated. However, there is a third reason why such an appreciation is so long in coming - the time needed to assimulate and integrate the revision of the new datings of megalithic sites within the global historical context.

During the last fifty years, many of the key megalithic sites in Britain and Ireland have been re-dated to push their construction horizon back way beyond the building of the Pyramids, whilst Babylonian astronomy is not thought to have amounted to very much before 2000 BC. Yet, in schoolbooks and museums in England, Stonehenge remains dated at around 1500 BC. Modern books are slowly changing this - the sarsen circle is recently dated by North[1], to 2600 BC - over a millenium earlier, and thereby contemporary with the building of the Giza pyramid complex.

Ages in Chaos

Any reader of books on the subject of Stonehenge, or any other megalithic site, will quickly understand the effect of the progress made in the dating of these monuments over the last half century. Depending on when a book or journal article was written will determine the dating of the site, with about a thousand year sliding scale!

The introduction of radiocarbon dating theoretically enabled accurate dating of any organic matter found on ancient sites. Unfortunately, the technique was originally inaccurate, and the later calibration curves provided by the known dates of Bristlecone Pine tree rings have demanded a complete revision of this early data. As a direct consequence the Stonehenge ditch and bank is now dated at around 3100 BC, whereas Atkinson, from early radiocarbon samples taken in 1950, centres the same feature at 1700 BC. Unfortunately, as both these dates come from impeccable authorities on the monument it is hardly necessary to labour the point that this variation, of nearly 1500 years, lingers throughout all the derivative literature on Stonehenge as a source of confusion to students of matters megalithic.

This same sliding scale applies to the whole of ancient prehistory - the arrival of the Beaker people, quoted in books of the 1950's at 1750 BC, has now been pushed back to 2500 BC. A lot of professional reputations hung in the balance when this revised dating became available - hence the dating scale was slid silently and almost imperceptibly backwards, so quietly that most people have not recognised the implications of such a revision. Which are? Well, with Newgrange now dated at 3500 BC, Stonehenge at 3100 BC, Avebury pre-3000 BC and many other sites dated pre-2500 BC, it must now be accepted that the culture which built these monuments possessed all the necessary surveying skills, astronomy, mathematics and geometry prior to the known Middle Eastern cultures to which we presently attribute their first discovery and application.

Meanwhile, the excavations at Catal Huyak and other sites are simultaneously pushing back the time boundaries of the Near Eastern civilisations. Truly, the traditional dating of the great civilising cultures of the world is being challenged beyond its structural limits, models of prehistory are crumbling and the wheel is still in spin as the re-appraisal of Man's development in time is being researched and recorded. History may not exactly be bunk, but its chronology rests on shifting sand now being swept by the strong tidal currents of new evidence.

An Unavoidable Choice

A prime question to be addressed in this chapter is whether or not the European megalithic culture received cultural assistance from other lands.[2] If it did not, then the current model of this period of British history must now be redefined, away from the 'woad covered savages' theme still prevalent in some quarters. However, if the megalith builders can be shown to have received assistance from any other culture, in order to plan and build monuments like Stonehenge, then the current history of the world has many missing pieces. Both you cannot have, but there could be a third option, explored later in this chapter. First, however, we need to be clear about what exactly might be involved in making this choice.

The 'Isolated Culture' Model

If we adopt the 'cultural isolation' model, then questions such as the following have to be addressed:

> *(a). Why do units of measurement from other cultures appear at Stonehenge and other sites, notably the foot (originally alleged as Sumerian)?*
>
> *An answer to this question has already been attempted, on pages 80-86.*
>
> *(b). Why is the area of the sarsen circle identical with the ancient Egyptian unit of area, the aroura?*

The *aroura*, from which the British *acre* and the ancient French unit, the *are*, were derived is simply the area of a square of side length 100 Royal Cubits, this definition coming directly from Herodotus. This area is, of course, 10,000 square Royal Cubits. In primitive inches, the side length is 2060.659 P", the corresponding area becoming 4,246,315.514 sq. P".

It is possible to obtain the same area within a rectangle, and the Egyptians favoured one with a side length of 3652.4235..P", which left the other side as 1162.6025 P". In other words, *one side of the rectangle was made to represent ten times the solar year in inches.*[3] The reasoning behind this particular choice of rectangle is very neat indeed - *the rectangle's two side lengths are also the diameter and circumference of a circle whose area becomes exactly one quarter aroura.* This is illustratedoverleaf and an application of this application may be found in figure 9.11, on page 177.

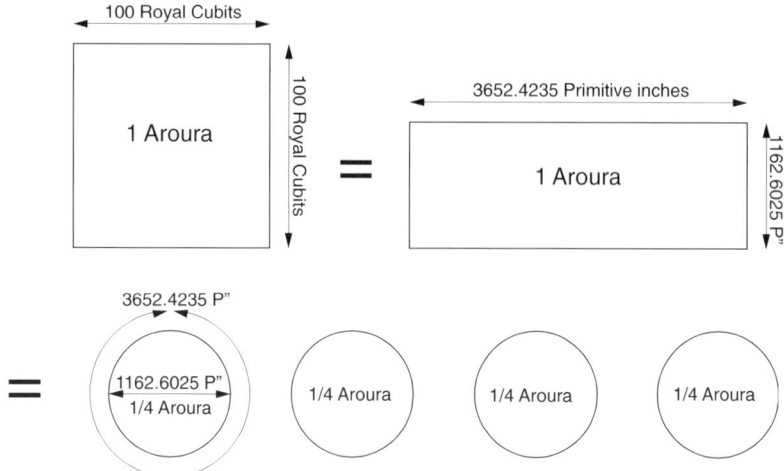

Figure 8.1 The Aroura Rectangle. The Egyptian unit of area derives from the geometry of the circle through two units of measurement, the 'Primitive inch' and the Royal Cubit (20.62 P"). The interplay of circular and linear geometry using the numbers of the solar year is, to say the least, impressive.

Figure 8.2 The quarter aroura is seen to be identical to the inner area contained by the sarsen circle. This cannot be coincidental and shows cultural as well as geometric congruency.

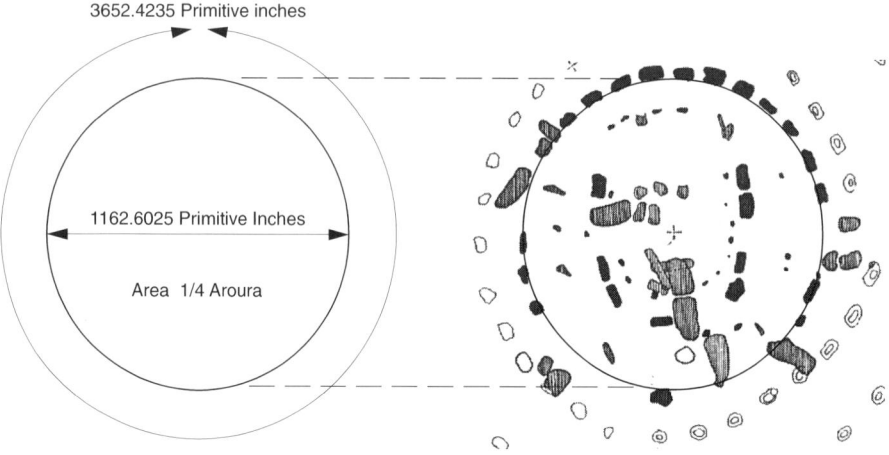

The ancient Egyptians were evidently aware of this geometry, Horapollon informing us that,

> *'To depict the current year they draw the fourth part of an aroura'.*

And if one draws this circle and places it next to a plan of the Sarsen Circle, drawn to the same scale, the result makes us sit up and face something important about our cultural heritage (*figure 8.2*).

Here we discover that the Egyptian year-circle is none other than the year-circle 'henge' platform, the remains of which still tower defiantly above Stonehenge. The two are *identical*, based on the same units of length and same astronomical purpose. They are linked through their congruency, a word which means 'of equal size and shape', but also 'to come together, to agree'. Here we have a physical artefact representing historically validated measurement techniques which are taken to be Egyptian in origin. The two cultures, Megalithic and Egyptian, appear to have 'come together' and to have 'agreed' to build the sarsen circle - culturally signed as 'A Wessex-Egypt artefact'.

These answers to the two fundamental questions suggest that it is no longer tenable to assume that the European megalithic culture was isolated from other civilisations. In making this statement one does not have to include visits from armies of Egyptians coming to build Stonehenge, nor droves of free-roaming surveyors, stonemasons, astronomer-priests and geometers bamboozling the local population with flattened stone circles, eggs and rings. All one needs to accept is that *information* - a system of measures and techniques - had spread just as the axe-heads did, finding widespread acceptance alongside the trading routes of the ancient world. The mercurial quality of merchants has always included the qualities of the ancient god, Hermes or Thoth, one as the god of the crossroads and byeways and the other the god of weights and measures, astronomy and seasons, to whom our Wednesday, Mercredi, Woden's-day still remains dedicated, in Genesis, chapter one, verse 14. Where trade goes, so always goes cultural development.

The 'Cultural Interchange' Model

If someone is to suggest that the Egyptians or any other foreign influence came over to Britain, circa 2500 BC, tramped up to Salisbury Plain and built the later phases of Stonehenge, most notably the sarsen circle, then they must address the following questions:

> *(a) Why have no traces of any other notable Egyptian artefacts been discovered in or around this region of Britain?*

Apart from a few *fiance* beads of uncertain origin, there are no signs of the required army of Egyptian megalith builders within the archaeological records. As John Wood points out in *Sun, Moon and Standing Stones*,

> *"..since no Egyptian artefact has ever been discovered in southern Britain in a sealed layer dating from the Neolithic or Early Bronze Age, we can only suppose that they were unfailingly meticulous in keeping all their possessions together and over hundreds of years never lost any, and that they finally took everything with Egyptian connotations back to Egypt. The human race is not normally so careful."[4]*

This is a powerful point, yet the Egyptian quarter-aroura equates to the sarsen circle[5]. Is the sarsen circle then merely 'Egyptian litter'? Looking at any modern building site, one sees the *detritus* and mundane rubbish of the current period, some of which becomes buried into a 'time-capsule', rather a layer, with which the archaeologists of the future can have a field day. At Stonehenge, this *detritus* is the normal material of megalithic sites. It is certainly true that not a single pin nor button has heralded a foreign presence - yet the sarsen circle emulates an Egyptian surveying practise and this is certainly a *cultural* if not a physical artefact left behind.

If we adopt the view that maybe an elite few Egyptians came across, with the knowledge to build Stonehenge, then maybe no trace would be left of their presence save the end product of their visit - the monument itself. However, we are then forced to ask how these Egyptian astronomer-priests coerced the labour force needed to transport, dress, erect and construct the monument - was it historically too early for whisky and rifles? At present any answer to these questions is speculation, but demand for objective 'proof' must not prevent useful speculative models from being aired and tested within this whole domain of prehistory. We must become better at asking the right questions - and here's a prime example:

> *(b) If megalithic astronomy, which (on the revised dating) was apparently at its heyday long before the Babylonians reached their peak and began at least four centuries before the Great Pyramid was built, why have no accounts of it been found in the Middle East cultural record?*

Who says or writes that there are no accounts of the European megalithic culture and its astronomy in the Middle Eastern cultural record? Perhaps more importantly, who has been looking for it?

Enoch's Portals

The *Book of Enoch* used to be found within the Old Testament of every Bible. It was removed during one of the revisionist periods which led to the King James' version yet may still be found in some of the many translations of the Old Testament and is freely available as a separate book from SPCK, London.[6] Most interestingly, present day Druidry draws on the work.

There are two quite distinct versions of Enoch, the first is a pre-Christian text called *1 Enoch* or *Ethiopian Enoch* to distinguish it from the later *2 Enoch* or *Slavonic Enoch*, discovered in Yugoslavia in 1886 and which is thought to be contemporary with the Christian era. The former text contains a calendar which is 364 day based, the latter a 365 day calendar. *1 Enoch*, originally an aramaic text is filled with references to factors 2, 4, 7, 14, 28, 91 and 364, whilst *2 Enoch* dishes up the familiar *soup de jour* of the Roman Calendar.

Both versions drop the 13 month factor and adopt a 12 month format, although the authors or later revisionists of *1 Enoch* appear to be struggling hard at times to comply with this within factors which so suit a 13 month year. The calendar of *1 Enoch* is the 360 day calendar with an extra day (the *neter* days) added every three months, to total 364 days, thus hiding the 13 factor. By the time *2 Enoch* was written, after the revision of the calendar 45 AD, its Greek editor presumably knew which side his bread was buttered on, and realigned the text to the new Roman calendrical dictates.

The whole structure and subsequent history of the Western Christian era is based on foundations which are rooted in the New Testament of the Bible. Whether you believe the Christian story or not is irrelevant here, what is important is to recognise that religious historians attribute much of the material in the New Testament directly to Enoch, i.e. to a text written *before* the alleged time of Jesus.

Within the Jewish heirarchy, Enoch is listed in Genesis as being seventh in line from Adam, a lineage which includes Moses, Abraham and Jacob. The assumption is then made that Enoch belongs to the Middle Eastern cultural tradition, yet it is stated within *1 Enoch* that, "from thence I went towards the north to the ends of the Earth, and there I saw a great and glorious device." Furthermore, we can read, "And I saw in those days how long cords were given to those angels, and they took themselves wings and flew, and they went towards the north. And I asked the angel, saying unto him: "Why have those angels taken these cords and gone off?" And he said to me: "They have gone off to measure".

This is reasonably specific information about a northern "glorious device" where measurements were being taken using long cords. I am sure the reader can understand my interest in Enoch just on this basis alone, but there is much more specific information in *1 Enoch* to link, if not Stonehenge itself, then the latitude at which Stonehenge is found to his account.

In Chapter LXXII, *The Book of the Courses of the Heavenly Luminaries*, the angel Uriel helpfully and accurately assists Enoch in describing a complete annual cycle of solar and lunar observations within a portal based structure which is implied as being circular in shape. Astronomically, the text is specific, and the Sun and Moon are described as rising within six portals in the east and setting within six portals in the west. (There are also many 'windows' to the right and left of these portals.) For each month following the spring equinox, Enoch tells the reader in which portal the Sun rises and sets and, more importantly, he tells us the specific ratio of day to night lengths during the first day of that month. Because the cycle of the Sun's risings and settings is sinusoidal, each number sequence is repeated four times, so we can be fairly well assured of no errors of translation. Using a simple computer program available nowadays in every secondary school, it is possible to work a little astrophysics on *1 Enoch*. Because day/night ratios vary according to latitude, we can determine the precise latitude where Enoch took his observations.

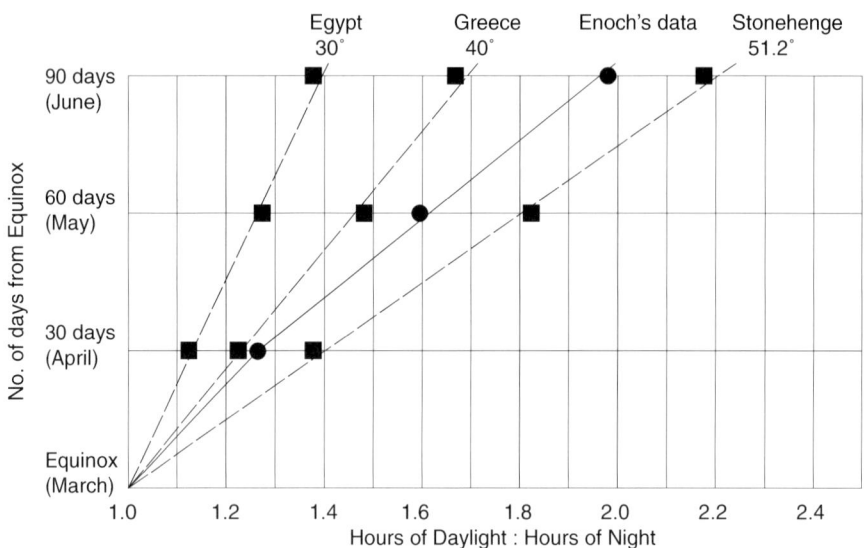

Figure 8.3 (a) Graphical representation of Enoch's astronomical data compared to the latitude of (i) Egypt, (ii) Greece) and (iii) Stonehenge.

It appears from this that *Enoch's observations were taken at or very near the latitude of Stonehenge*, as the graph (*figure 8.3*) ably demonstrates. The day/night ratio gradient is the same as for Stonehenge, and if the definition of 'night' was taken to be half an hour different from sunrise/set, such as the time the first stars became visible, then the graph for Enoch's observations and for Stonehenge would exactly coincide. Enoch's writings, long assumed to contain only Jewish and/or Middle-Eastern wisdom, suggest an influence from 'a great and glorious device' found at a latitude near to that of Stonehenge and from which very accurate and specific astronomical information was observed and recorded using a 364 day calendar structure. Such coincidences begin to look rather like evidence for cultural interchange, don't they, and Stonehenge is in Britain, not Syria or Lebanon?

For the Sun to rise and set within six portals on each side of an observer at Stonehenge, one can deduce that Enoch must have taken his observations within the sarsen circle at the location now referred to as *The Grave* - which is the 'entrance' to the elliptical or horse-shoe shaped set of five trilithons within the sarsen circle (figure 8.4). A line drawn from the final trilithons on either side of the axis locates the site, which is on the axis. This would be a most auspicious and appropriate place at Stonehenge from which to observe. John North suggests that we play down the traditional view that all observations were to be taken from the centre of the monument.[7] The description of the observations in *1 Enoch* are well satisfied by the annual sunrises viewed from the entrance to the trilithon ellipse. If this is thought fanciful, then the reader is left to explain why Enoch took his readings from such a northerly latitude, the text actually informing us that angels, one of whom accompanied Enoch, "went towards the north", with "long cords".. "to measure". The precise data give a latitude which is anything but fanciful.

No-one knows who the authors of this fascinating collection of ancient material were. Astonishingly, in our Celtic heritage, we find in *The Tales of Taliesin*, "I was instructor to Eli and Enoch". Robert Graves[8] was quick to point out the obvious absurdity of Gwion, the Celtic writer, understanding Ethiopian, the language of the only known extant text of *1 Enoch*. Whoever or whatever Enoch represented, we can be sure that his mention within some of the oldest surviving Celtic literature - *The Mabinogion* - links Celtic folklore with the prophet. Even within a few miles of the Preseli bluestone site one can find *Carn Enoch*; the root word *cnoc* is thought to mean *carved or ceremonial stone*. Might the *Book of Enoch* be a written remnant of the megalithic culture?

There are further clues within the text. The oral tradition is seen as avoiding the 'sin' of writing (Chapter LXIX, vs.9), which aligns perfectly with what is known of the Druidic and Pythagorean schools, whilst not at all with the production of a text

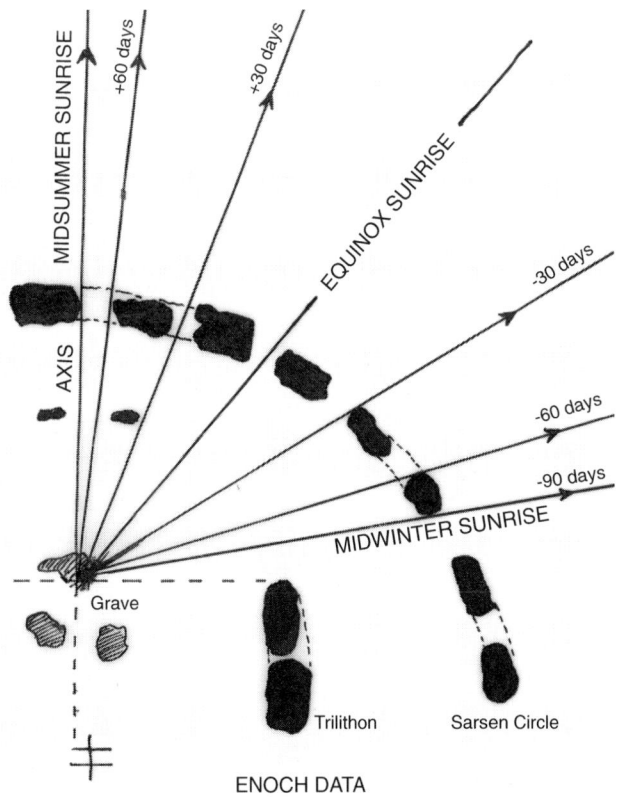

Figure 8.3 (b) Astronomical observations from the entrance of the trilithon ellipse offer the 'six portal' sequence described in *The Book of Enoch*, where the prophet describes the manner by which the Sun changes its rise and set positions through six portals during the solar year. [From the author's book *Sun, Moon, Man, Woman*, 1992 (*privately published*)].

for the Jewish Old Testament. Enoch also informs his readers "And the course of the path of the Moon is light to the righteous"[9] - a most odd remark for an alleged paid-up member of the Patriarchy to make, and quite bizarre within our present Judao-Christian 'solar' context. Anyone who has studied megalithic lunar observatories in northern Europe will recognise their builder's total pre-occupation with understanding just that - *the course of the path of the Moon*. Enoch's phrase has no place within traditional Jewish or Christian philosophic roots. This package of material needs to be urgently considered within any revision of history, quite apart from its implications to Stonehenge.

This brief excursion into the cross-cultural implications of a single text from antiquity shows the need to dismantle traditional boundaries within the study of the ancient world.

Cultural Interchange - A Third Option

Many of the difficult questions posed in the debate over possible cultural interchange can be solved, theoretically, by making the assumption that the specialist knowledge held in each separate culture was, at some time in the distant past, derived from a single root culture which has disappeared, apparently without any physical trace. This theme invariably invokes the dreaded 'A word' - *Atlantis*.

The Atlantis theme runs through the alternative literature like lettering through sea-side rock. Although the location of Atlantis has never been one hundred per cent established, and various parts of the globe having been nominated to take on the role, the *Lost City* offers a Golden Age vision of a utopian past civilisation that somehow went terribly awry in a cataclysm, and was utterly destroyed, bar a few survivors who then became the repositories of ancient wisdom.

The tale then usually pans out to include details such as the survivors finding their separate ways to various parts of the globe whence they attempted to salvage all that remained of their knowledge of a once magnificent culture. This has included space travel, flight, full knowledge of the sciences and, in some versions of the story, free energy from quartz crystals, contact with extra-terrestrials and how drinking *Kombucha* will assist us all to live longer. It is at this point that the archaeologists, plain or astro-flavoured, down tools and leave the site, for, despite all this *brouhaha*, no trace of, nor artefact from the Lost City has ever been discovered yet alone substantiated. There is an artefact crisis and Atlantis remains a fiction as an actual location, although it is not recommended to shout such things along Glastonbury High Street.

Whilst Atlantis remains unsubstantiated, we might profitably look at the term *Golden Age*, which originated in classical Greece. The term describes an original paradise in some cuneiform literature from Mesopotamia, where the Age is allocated a period - pre-3000 BC. However, a Sumerian tablet from about 2400 BC includes within its blissful format the following stanzas:

"Uri, the land having all that is *needful*
The land Martu resting in security
The whole universe, the people *in unison*
To Enlil in one tongue (*gave praise*)."

From Kramer, *Man's Golden Ages*
(italics represent uncertain translation)

Following the Flood, the Babylonian author of the *Epic of Gilgamesh* bemoans the dismal state of the post-diluvian world, complaining that 'Since the days of yore there has been no (*permanence*), The resting and the dead, how alike they are.' Fate is then blamed for having destroyed the once serene world, and things ain't at all what they used to be - a commonly recurring theme in Golden Age literature and poetry.

Thus far, we have two approximate dates for a Golden Age, pre-3000 BC and pre-2400 BC, and we have a description of life after a Flood. But no Atlantis. The Mesopotamian authors, like the later Jewish plagiarists who later hi-jacked these epic tales for their own purposes[10], are thought by some historians to have taken the Flood not as a cataclysmic event but as the chaotic and watery state before God created the world, order and form. Whilst this spiritual allegory may be true, an *actual* real-life account of a flood or a flood myth appears in the folk-lore of over forty cultures[11], where it is clearly a physical event that is being described. Many of these cultures associate the flood with cataclysm, pestilence, famine, plague or a combination of these unpleasant factors.

It is becoming increasingly reasonable to suggest that cataclysmic events have befallen the human race in antiquity. If one such event took place sometime around 3300 BC, from which survivors eventually regrouped, taking what was left of their previous culture, then there are certain anomalies to face. It is certainly true that within a few centuries of this date, Stonehenge was well under way, the massive cultural flowering of Egypt was underway, Avebury was in use, Silbury Hill and Newgrange were built and other important cultures around the world sprang up like mushrooms.

Also true is the strange but notable fact that the Egyptian and European megalithic cultural phenomena never developed - it seems to have arrived already fully fledged and to thereafter degenerate. Somehow, the original knowledge appears to have faded and was lost, inexorably and inexplicably. This does not fit at all with our normal conception of what happens following a cataclysm. During the rebuilding of a destroyed culture we would surely expect the threads of the ancient knowledge to gradually coalesce into a progressive regeneration and not a positive 'blip' followed by a degeneration. This question demands attention, the more so because we live today in a culture which sees 'progress' as always an upward gradient or exponential growth and which cannot 'allow' a negative gradient or step function 'blip'. If such occured in the past then we need to discover why, if only to attempt to prevent a recurrence in the future.

151

The pioneering work of Immanual Velikovsky and other catastrophy theorists provided our species' first serious modern attempts to come to terms with the possibility of a steep negative gradient - the collapse of culture. Since Velikovsky's first work, *Worlds in Collision*, the human race has had to stare face to face with self-imposed annihilation through nuclear war and environmental catastrophy. Predictably, in his hey-day Velikovsky was rubbished by the establishment despite, in the early 1970s, large advertisements appearing in the world's press as supporters of Velikovsky, many with impeccable academic credentials, sought to promote his radical ideas about history and catastrophe theory. They failed then, but sowed their seeds deep within academia.

Within just forty years, scientists in the new subject of *earth-science* have begun to look seriously at the probabilities of meteor-strikes and cometary impacts, weather changes due to volcanic activity and the effects of solar flares on climate. New archaeological and astronomical evidence indicates[12] that, around 2350 BC, a huge number of meteorites raining from the sky caused famine, flooding and bushfires thousands of miles wide, leading to the collapse of the world's first sophisticated civilisations, including Mesopotamia, Egypt and Greece. This information comes, not from a New Age guru, but from a highly respected anthropologist and an Oxford astrophysicist, the latter academic identifying a meteor cluster whose orbital path collides with that of the Earth about once every 3000 years. Come back, Velikovsky, all is forgiven!

It is also now widely accepted, from hard archaeological evidence, that volcanoes drastically affected the climate of Britain and elsewhere around 1640 BC. This coincided with the demise of the megalithic culture, perhaps because astronomical observations were no longer possible, or perhaps because the struggle for survival stole back the man-hours needed for construction and maintenance of sites.

If, at some time, the Earth was indeed affected by the close approach of a minor asteroid, causing widespread tidal and climatic effects, then the historical record should be full of the account and there need be no preceding Golden Age. The archaeological and even the geological record should show dramatic decline in species count, collapse of buildings, anomalous changes to the deposition of silts and dead vegetation, tree rings and ice-sheet movements. At the time of writing, no such evidence is apparent. However, In the *Book of Joshua*, the following account is given:

> *"And it came to pass, as they fled from before Israel, and were in the going down to Beth-horon, that the Lord cast down great stones from heaven upon them unto Azekah, and they died: they were more which died with hailstones than they whom the children of Israel slew with the sword.*
> *"And the sun stood still, and the moon stayed, until the people had avenged themselves on their enemies. Is not this written in the Book of Jasher? So the sun stood still in the midst of heaven, and hasted not to go down about a whole day."*
>
> Joshua, Chapter 10, vs 11 and 13

This is as specific an account of a turbulent episode in the history of the Earth's angular momentum as one could ever hope to read from someone unfamiliar with celestial mechanics. And if 'the Sun stood still, and the Moon stayed' for 'about a whole day', the effects would indeed be catastrophic and global. And what might cause such effects - 'great stones from heaven'? Like *1 Enoch*, this account is a physically accurate description of the effect we would expect from a close encounter with an asteroid. It cannot be dismissed as merely the reminiscences of an heroic Old Testament Jewish battle. Do we wait another forty years to begin to research such a specific account of a catastrophy event?

Large stones falling from the sky normally produce large craters - where are these to be found? Where are the fragments of these meteorites? Human life would have had to seek shelter, only caves (or long barrows), would provide protection against a storm of small meteorites[13]. Is there any evidence for human panic and subsequent relocation to shelters? At present, no, but just who is researching these things?

For the Earth's angular momentum to change so quickly and for 'about a whole day' would also have produced large-scale faulting and earthquakes in the Earth's crust. Where is this evidence? Following the description given by Joshua, the tidal irregularities alone would cause enormous flooding and widespread destruction in its wake. One feels there must be plenty of evidence for such a cataclysm - where is it to be found?

It is certain that the astronomical constants of the day, the lunar month and perhaps even the solar year would change as a consequence of a near approach by a large asteroid, yet we have seen that our oldest megalithic constructions, such as Newgrange, remain faithful to their original alignments to solstices and equinoxes. But if we were to suppose that the described event took place *much earlier* than Joshua's life-time, would not the need to re-evaluate these constants become one of the prime considerations of the survivors? Might not we then discover a reason for such a concerted and prolific effort to measure and record the key astronomical constants of the Sun and Moon? Prior to about 3000 BC, the long barrows suggest that any astronomical emphasis was on *stellar* alignments.

In the context of the megalithic culture one might suggest that the catastrophy described by Joshua caused the astronomical constants of the Sun, Moon, Earth system to become changed, producing dangerous events, mass destruction and strange cosmic phenomena. To determine whether the Sun and Moon had returned to a stable state it would therefore be paramount to observe their motion with more thoroughness and accuracy than ever before and this could explain the total commitment to the building of the megaliths - survival depended on monitoring changes in the solar and lunar cycles and being able to rapidly predict any future turbulence in these cycles.

But this argument may be specious too. The megalithic culture was building alignments to stable equinox and solstice positions of the Sun and Moon for well over a millenium and a half. Whilst the frantic activity alongside the changing axis of Stonehenge during the early days of the monument might suggest a corresponding change of axis for the Earth, and the Station Stone rectangle is several degrees 'out' to the left of the present axis of Stonehenge, megalithic monuments were confirming to their builders a long-term stability within the Sun, Moon, Earth system.

Summary

It is not possible in a text of this nature to pursue this particular 'rigorous alternative' in more depth. However, I may have been able to show the reader that the standard academic dismissal of the catastrophy theory is largely based on pigeon-holing of discipline areas, mismatch of dating chronologies across cultural boundaries, failure to ask the correct questions and/or protection of the *status quo*. Sufficient evidence has been shown for a historical connection between the megalithic culture in Europe and allegedly later Biblical texts and the time is, I believe, ripe for fruitful future research projects.

I have already shown that the 'allegorical' story in St John's Gospel is overlaid with vitally relevant astronomical and historical knowledge, and that Enoch's observations contain an astonishingly literal and numerical account of solar observations which fit the location and design of Stonehenge. Other religious texts have supplied vital corroborative evidence.

The technique which emerges to unlock the secrets of Stonehenge and the megalithic culture suggests that we widen the axioms and subject disciplines under which we analyse the data. For example, conventional scientific thinking cannot embrace the use of the Sun and Moon in their *symbolic* roles. The rules of the game haven't traditionally allowed mythology, folklore and calendar history, nor can they entertain the existence of long-rotted ropes or rods without physical evidence - which will never be found in a month of lunar eclipses. Thus, in the remaining two chapters we will undertake two quite different analyses of Stonehenge based on the two identified available sources of information. In chapter nine we will look at the dimensions, design and geometry of Stonehenge, whilst in the final chapter we will investigate the folk-culture which derives from Stonehenge. Subject boundaries will be suitably widened, not at the expense of thoroughness but in order to demonstrate what it is that Stonehenge is trying to tell us. This approach will prove to be spectacularly successful in shedding new light on the mysteries of Stonehenge.

Footnotes to Chapter Eight

[1] *Stonehenge*, op.cit.,p 500.

[2] Several other books deal with this theme, most notably John Ivimy's *The Sphinx and the Megaliths* presenting the cultural interchange theme most coherently, even if one disagrees with his conclusions (Turnstone Books 1974). Later republished by Abacus (1976). In a letter to the author, Mr Ivimy cites "the founders of the world's first civilisation (c. 4300 BC)". This dating is based on his research into the origins of weights and measures, the subject of which he sees as defining civilisation yet "utterly boring to most people".

[3] This longer side then has the curious property that, expressed in Royal Cubits, it represents the number of days in six lunations, 177.245 RC - half the lunar year of 354.3671 days.

[4] *Sun, Moon and Standing Stones*, page 190.

[5] Within Wood's question, we must assume that the sarsen circle may be included as an Egyptian 'possession'.

[6] *The Book of Enoch*. Translation by Canon R.H.Charles (1912). SPCK, London.

[7] *Stonehenge*, p468.

[8] *The White Goddess*. Faber 1946. First edition, page 193. Graves suggests that Gwion may have seen another copy of the Enoch material in an Irish college.

[9] *1 Enoch*, chapter XLI, verses 3-9; *Astronomic Secrets*. In the Sumerian King list, the *seventh* King is assocaited with Sippar, a city central to the cult of Shemash, the Sun-god Enmeduranki.

[10] Much Babylonian creation material was imported lock, stock and barrel into Genesis and the emerging religious structures of the Patriarchs.

[11] Information from *The Divine Plot* by A.T.('Tad') Mann. G.Allen and Unwin (1986) by kind permission. The author gratefully acknowledges the assistance given by Mr Mann over this and related issues at a conference at Exeter University in 1996.

[12] Information taken from *The Times*, 14th December 1997.

[13] In the nineteenth century, Clara Schumann describes in her diary a violent hailstorm which broke many of the windows in the Schumann's house and killed many people locally. She and her husband thought it "to be the end of the world".

STONEHENGE

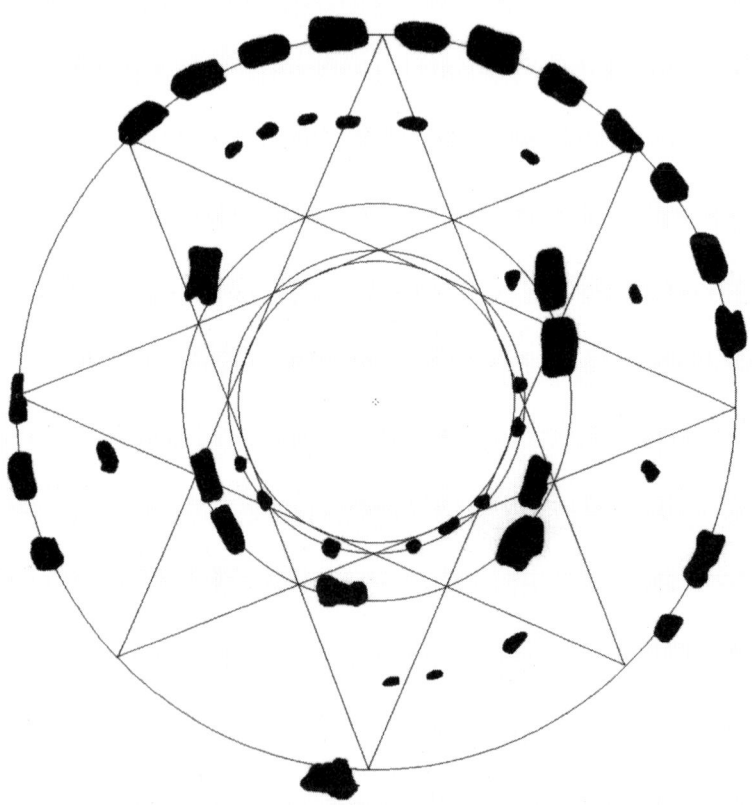

Above: An octagonal construction from the mean sarsen circle diameter places the mean trilithon horseshoe diameter and both the diameter and stone thickness of the inner bluestone horseshoe. The octagon is aligned to the axis, like the station stone rectangle and its associated octagon, as illustrated on page sixty-two and sixty-three.

Chapter Nine

- THE PATTERN OF THE PAST -

The Geometry and Astronomy of Stonehenge

Having established that Stonehenge is a highly practical monument reflecting the eternal rounds of the Sun and Moon, we might begin this chapter by asking why these practical aspects are not better known. Ignorance and indifference to the importance of the rhythms of Sun and Moon are certainly important factors; whilst archaeologists and historians, with notable exceptions, continue to deny any deeper cultural messages emanating from the megalithic designs which litter northern Europe.

During the past few decades it is notable that the leading works on Stonehenge, concerning its possible function, have come not from archaeologists nor historians but from scientists and engineers (Sir Fred Hoyle, Prof. Alex Thom and Dr Gerald Hawkins). Perhaps this reflects the preoccupations of our technological post-war culture, confirming Jaquetta Hawkes[1] famous remark, "Every generation gets the Stonehenge it deserves". However, it is also true that those who designed and built the monument were professionally closer to science and engineering than they ever were to archaeology.

So what view of Stonehenge do we find within conventional archaeology? Professors Richard Atkinson and Stuart Piggott are now, very sadly, no longer part of the debate. However, Dr Aubrey Burl, one of the most knowledgeable experts on stone circles, sees Stonehenge as an impressive charnel house and has also alerted us to the unique qualities of Stonehenge which separate this monument from any other on the UK mainland. In addition, he has written the only guide to the stone circles of the British Isles, Ireland and Brittany, a desperately needed task which places us greatly in debt to the good doctor. Perhaps he "protesteth too much" concerning the lack of mathematical and logical reasoning evidenced by Neolithic and Bronze Age folk yet, with his criteria and working axioms, this is an expected outcome from a highly skilled archaeologist.

Although not taking on board the full conclusions of Thom and Hawkins, Dr. Burl notes astronomical alignments of Sun and Moon indicated by a site. He brings a most valuable and realistic contribution to our knowledge of these distant times, and his book *The Stonehenge People* is essential reading for anyone wishing to understand the social structure and conditions in and around Wessex in Neolithic times, obtained from archaeological evidence.

Professor John North embraces the Megalithic yard and much of the stellar and soli-lunar astronomy that Thom and Hawkins found at Stonehenge and elsewhere. His huge book on Stonehenge - really much more an exposition on Neolithic culture in general - marks a gingerly step in the integration of the material explored by Thom, Hoyle and Hawkins. It is very interesting to note what North has omitted, or played down, rather than what he has included. There is a certain reticence, even coyness in places which is typical of a fermentation of thought, and this fermentation fizzes and bubbles throughout archaeology and anthropology at the moment, promising a fine vintage once the new wine has thrown its sediment.

As this chapter progresses it will become clear that at least some members of the human race, with or without assistance from other cultures, were demonstrating a rather more advanced knowledge of astronomy, geometry and mathematics than either Dr Burl or Professor North have been able to embrace within the axioms of present-day archaeology. Philosophically, Burl writes, concerning a conversation with Chris Chippindale, the former editor of *Antiquity*,

> *"I remarked that he could be right, another colleague could be right, even I could be right. The only absolute I knew in archaeology, I observed, was that all archaeologists die."*[2]

One might add another absolute, *"..and the monuments remain."*

A Catalogue of Errors

One would think that the dimensions and geometry of Stonehenge would be above opinion, but quite the reverse is the case. Recent treatments of the geometry of Stonehenge are legion, often wildly in error, and some just bizarre, making Stonehenge 'fit' whatever preconception was being expounded. Nothing has changed in this department over five centuries; the earliest known sketch of Stonehenge depicts the monument as having a square format and, in the sketch of the 'front portals' the five trilithons become miraculously hexagonal - a most impressive feat of imagination (*see figure 9.1*). In Christopher Chippindale's *Complete Stonehenge*, the artistic license taken through the centuries in the name of our national temple may be seen displayed in plate after plate of inaccurate paintings, *kitsch* sketches and, more recently, photographs, these latter often robust fakes with superimposed aeroplanes, balloons or stormclouds.

Stonehenge can very easily act as a mirror to those who study its form and function. As a monument of collective projection, it too readily becomes something to hang our fantasies on, our hopes, our dreams and our wishes. Then books and articles become published which present a *chimera*, with no reference to Stonehenge's *actual* measurements, geometry and siting nor other archaeological evidence. This is

Figure 9.1 Early Images of Stonehenge. *Left*: The monument has sprouted an extra trilithon. The four neat axis entrance stones suggest that, even in 1794, the slaughterstone still stood(*courtesy Dr Aubrey Burl*). *Above*: Byronic Stonehenge, an 1820s example of the romantic image conjured up by the monument.

relatively harmless fun until it becomes set in the concrete of dogma; New Age or educational curriculum. Then, the confusion spreads like a November mist on Salisbury Plain and swirls around Stonehenge until the reality of the monument virtually disappears from view.

Any attempt to disperse this fog which currently surrounds Stonehenge must begin with an accurate plan of the monument. Unfortunately we find here bad inaccuracies within the one plan which most researchers use as their reference, the old Ministry of Works plan of Stonehenge published within the HMSO booklet on the monument. Atkinson's plan, published in *Stonehenge* and on page 60 here, is much better, and appears with regularity within other books on megalithic matters.

All the dimensions referred to within this chapter have been referred to or checked against the Thom survey plan of Stonehenge, acknowledged as the most accurate ever undertaken. Until now, this has not been freely available to researchers. In a letter to the author[3], Dr Archie Thom wrote,

> " *About our survey, the Ministry plan was a botch. It had two scales on itself which did not fit. It had obviously been made up from several sources. This finally persuaded A.T. (Alex Thom) to do the survey. He never trusted the work of strangers. We carefully left records of where our survey pegs had been; nobody ever asked us about it all. Our survey is the best record of things on the surface. I still keep the tracings for reproduction. We measured the stone positions to half an inch, and then repeated these measurements at original ground level, about three feet up according to what Dick (Richard Atkinson) told us.*"

It is a sad fact that most of the written and graphical material appearing in the myriad number of books on Stonehenge have based their astronomy, geometry and numerology on the Ministry plan, a plan which Alex Thom found so laughably inaccurate that he devoted several months of his life to producing a better one - a reproduction of which may be found facing chapter one.[4]   It is unlikely that any future survey will improve on the ground level accuracy of Thom's work - it is therefore the standard for all future work on the geometry of the monument.

In the analysis that follows, I have endeavoured to obtain fundamental sources for the numerical and geometrical data employed. Primary sources of data are listed in addition to having been carefully checked. The reader may be assured that careful measurements taken from the Thom survey plan, coupled with reliable and checked sources of data from other sources, guarantee the best chance of avoiding perpetuating the errors of conclusion, often numerical in origin, which have been passed down through the literature on Stonehenge, often in good faith, for generations. It is high time this dead wood was pruned out and consigned to the fire.

The Geometry of the Ancient World

John Michell alerted everyone to the geometry of Stonehenge in his classic text, *The View over Atlantis* (1969). In a unique synthesis of scholarship and New Age vision, Michell provided the world with a blue-print for further study, revealing something of the philosophy of the ancient world's metrology and relating this to ancient monuments, including Stonehenge. It became a hugely popular book and it is not far from the truth to state that John Michell, almost single-handedly, re-awoke everyone to the numerical and geometric wonders to be found at ancient sites. *The New View over Atlantis* (1986) showed the continuing value of Michell's approach and a refinement of his technique. Other useful books in the same *genre* include Keith Critchlow's wonderful *Time Stands Still* (1980), Francis Hitching's comprehensive *Earth Magic* (1976), and the rare but indispensible *A Book of Coincidence*, a more recent gift to the human race from John Martineau.

 If one wishes to understand the mind of megalithic man, then Stonehenge is the perfect place to begin. If one wishes to discover the cosmology lying behind Stonehenge, then the ancient world has always informed the would be initiate that "God is a geometer" and that "as above, so below". To begin with simple geometry and then look as to how the rhythms of the sky appear on the Earth would appear eminently sensible as a research programme.

In addition we need to recognise that cultural messages can be just as plainly understood from the geometry, siting and metrology of Stonehenge as they can from jewellery, pottery shards, bones and flint arrowheads. Certainly, all the main astronomical constants of the Sun, Moon and Earth may be read from the monument. And if "God is a geometer" then studying the geometry of the natural universe, including early man's attempts to understand it through geometrical analogues of the motions of the two 'lights' or luminaries, suggests a route to understanding God and hence the evolution of life on Earth, in addition to providing a very direct way of linking 'as above' to 'as below'.

This link between astronomy and geometry, permanently twinned in ancient philosophies, was re-established in our times by that greatest astronomer of the renaissance of modern science, Johannes Kepler (1571-1630), who even went as far as to state,

> *"Geometry has two treasures; one is the theorem of Pythagoras; the other, the division of a line into extreme and mean ratio (the golden section). The first we may compare to a measure of gold; the second we may name a precious jewel."*

It is strange that neither "treasure" may be discovered within Kepler's three planetary laws, yet both pour out from the stones of megalithic monuments and the cultures of the ancient world. The Pythagorean lunation triangle leads us into a better model of the Sun, Moon, Earth system; the geometric design of Stonehenge leads to a better calendar structure, and to simple practical solutions to lunation, eclipse, tidal and other lunar related problems. The Golden Section number, *phi*, we may immediately find at Stonehenge by looking at the monument from above the Earth's axis in space, whence the concentric circles of the monument become ellipses whose major and minor axes take the ratio *phi*:1. *Phi* also infuses the cosmology of the Sun, Moon, Earth system[5].

We will now undertake a study of the geometry and dimensions of Stonehenge where some other "treasures", unmentioned by Kepler, may be found.

The word geometry means "to measure the Earth", yet the subject has become, for most schoolchildren, an abstracted set of tedious theorems offering few obvious practical applications. The ancient world saw geometry as quite something else - a sacred art which was capable of uniting number, form, harmony and the cosmos into a single monument - *The Temple*. It is fairly easy to equate this definition with the obvious geometric skills shown by the architects of Stonehenge, and extremely difficult to reconcile this to the other social and cultural artefacts of the Wessex culture - the 'Thomist paradox'.

How do we begin to address this paradox ? We might do worse than by quoting Richard Atkinson,

> *"The positions at least of the Heel Stone and the Station Stones, and indeed the latitude of Stonehenge itself, were astronomically determined."*

In his admission that the site for Stonehenge was chosen for its latitude, Atkinson was just one step away from informing us that the designers knew that the world was round. For the architects to be aware of the latitude of the site there can be no other conclusion. And if the architects knew that the world was spherical, then the whole nature of our understanding of Stonehenge can and must change.

If we pursue this aspect further, the strange coincidences surrounding the numerous occurences of angles approximating to one-seventh of a circle must also be commented on. The latitude of Stonehenge is just over 51° north. Here, the midsummer sunrise occured, in 3000 BC, at an azimuth of just over 51°. This angle is also within a degree of the base angle of the Great Pyramid, and is the angle which the Great Circle shown on page 87 takes as it leaves the Giza complex and heads northwards towards Stonehenge.[6]

This does not prove that the architects were familiar with the uniqueness of the location of Stonehenge, but it tips upside down our present understanding of the rules involved in siting prehistoric monumental buildings if they did. Placing all the separate fragments of evidence together, we get:

---

1. At a latitude 51° 40' north, in 3000 BC the midsummer sunrise azimuth and the latitude coincided. If intentionally part of the design, the monument was built within 30 miles of the correct spot. However, the azimuth of the Heel Stone is placed at 51° 51' azimuth from the centre of the Aubrey circle - the pyramid angle. This, unlike the Earth's axis tilt, will never change.

2. The Preseli bluestones originate from a latitude which is 364°/7 or 51° 57.5' north, the sarsens from 360°/7 or 51° 25' north. They fit the numerical and calendraic aspirations of the phase of Stonehenge into which they were incorporated.

3. The astronomic alignments within the Station Stones, and the equinoctial alignment from stone 91 to the Heel Stone - those referred to in the above quote from Atkinson - are unique to a very narrow band of latitudes (no more than half a degree) either side of 51° north.

4. Avebury is built with the latitude line 360 /7 (51° 25' 42" north) running right through the centre of the henge circle.

5. Silbury Hill, sited at 51° 24' 56" north, has a slope angle of 30°; the Great Pyramid reciprocates this with a slope of 51° 51' and a latitude of exactly 30°.

Table 9.1 The connections between Stonehenge and angles of one seventh of a circle.

If we wish to widen the evidence beyond Wessex we may cite the *Crucuno Rectangle*, a neglected and overgrown megalithic site in Morbihan, Brittany, sited with its sides aligned to the cardinal points at latitude 47° 6' north, near the town of Plouharnel (*figure 9.2*). Its sides measure 30 MY and 40 MY, thus its diagonals are 50 MY and the rectangle is none other than a generator of the Pythagorean 3:4:5 triangle. The apex angle of such a triangle is tan^{-1}(3/4), which is 36° 52', the exact angle of the midsummer solstice sunrise at the location, seen across the diagonals of this rectangular stone circle by the author in 1992. This monument, like the Station Stone rectangle and Castle Rigg, represents a celebration of the mastered skill of determining the correct latitudes to align astronomical events with geometric designs. The Crucuno rectangle surely could not have been sited by a process of trial and error.

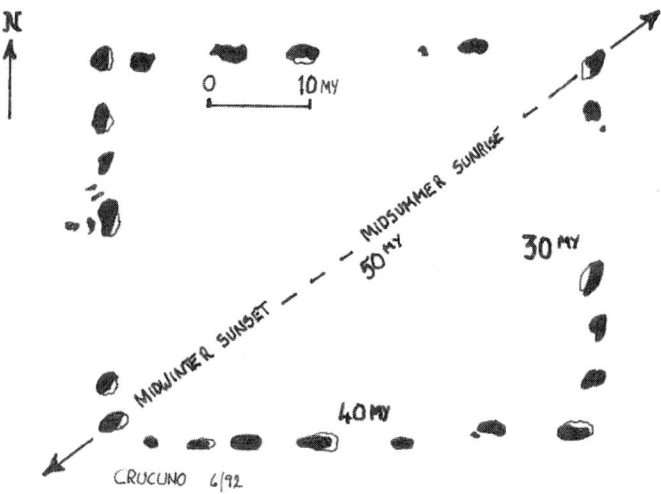

Figure 9.2 The Crucuno Rectangle (after Thom). This 'square stone circle' is a perfect example of Pythagorean geometry fully integrated with a siting based on knowledge of the exact latitude of the site and its solar astronomy.

The Measurement of Latitude

The apocryphal story goes that Erastothenes discovered that the Earth was spherical by peering down wells and noticing that, between Alexandria and Syene, an angle of seven degrees could be measured between shadow-sticks or *gnomons*. Hiring a man to pace out the distance, an unfeasible distance of 800 Km, the fable then runs that Erastothenes, wondering if the Earth was round because a shadow stick in Syene did not cast a shadow whilst one in Alexandria did, multiplied 800 Km by 50 (seven degrees is about one fiftieth of a circle) and discovered that the Earth was round with a circumference of 40,000 Km. Then, according to Carl Sagan in his otherwise excellent book *Cosmos*, "*After Erastothenes' discovery, many great voyages were attempted by brave and venturesome sailors.*" Nobody travelled very much before Erastothenes, then?

This is a nice story, so convincing that one wonders why the western world, which derived so much of its culture and approach to science from these Greek philosophers, promptly forgot that the Earth was a sphere until the *Renaissance* (via the Arabs) re-established the fact to an astonished flat-earth society, then centering its 2-D world, predictably, on Jerusalem. Not only had we forgotten, we even burned people at the stake for then reminding us of what we had forgotten. A cynic might also suspect that Erastothenes, as director of the Library at Alexandria, may have had access to details on the roundness of the world from codices far, far older than classical Greece. Apparently, we do keep on forgetting that the world is spherical.

So important is this issue of geometry and the surveying of the planet to an understanding of the ancient world and therefore the megalith builders that we must pursue it further. The simple demonstration that a shadow stick outside one's own home can readily reveal latitude to a few minutes of a degree is often enough to convince even the hardest sceptic that the latitude problem was easily solved in antiquity. Babylonian clay tablets dating back well into the Neolithic timeframe in Europe carry the tangent 'look-up' tables required to derive latitude from gnomons. The angle of the Pole Star, in our times at least, offers latitude directly, though not quite as accurately. I have used the former method quite often with ten year old children and established the latitude of their school to within 2 minutes of arc. One degree of latitude is just under 70 miles, so this experiment placed the school within three miles of the correct latitude using just shadow sticks.[7]

Figure 9.3 Measuring latitude from a shadow-stick or *gnomon*. Surprisingly accurate, the technique can be used to evaluate the latitude of a site to within a few minutes of arc. Note that a right-angled triangle with one shadowy side and one imagined hypotenuse is invoked in the process. The technique can also enable a surveyor to establish a true north-south line.

Astronomy and map making had long been complimentary arts - Phoenician and Greek mariners had long known that latitude could be obtained from the transits of stars and that the Earth was round. Presumably, they were familiar with ships sinking into the horizon as they left port, and had seen the obvious curvature of the Earth's shadow falling across the Moon at a lunar eclipse. The Moon's position was also used to provide an estimate of *longitude* - that crock of gold at the end of the navigation rainbow.[8]

This is about as much evidence as can be furnished from ancient written accounts. However, there is another source of evidence. If the ancient world understood that the Earth is spherical, then their measuring systems should reflect that understanding. Might we not expect that ancient units of length would reflect angles of arc across the surface of the planet? Navigation and map-making would depend on such, and, just as for the rhythms of the Sun and Moon, there are only going to be a limited number of choices for these units - *based on either the Earth's radius or its circumference.*

164

There are many books on metrology and a large number of different units of length used by the ancient world. The subject is often totally bewildering to a casual student. Therefore, we will start from scratch with the present available figures for the Earth's dimensions and a clean sheet of paper.

Polar Derivations

Presently, the mean polar radius of the Earth is taken (IGY, 1957-8) as 3949.9 miles, offering a circumference of 24,818 miles. To derive units from this standard which are 'human scale' requires that we find divisors which produce two lengths between 10 and 50 inches. All ancient unit systems produce their equivalents of the foot (12") and the yard (36") - only the metric system does not. The middle of this range is 30 inches, very nearly a Megalithic yard and the required divisor is 8.33 million[9]. Either side of this mean we find not one but two standard units from the ancient world - *one ten millionth* of the polar radius is 25 'primitive' inches - the Egyptian *Sacred Cubit* - which is 25.0265 British Imperial inches. (One primitive inch equals 1.001064 British inches), whilst *one six-millionth* of the polar radius delivers the so-called 'Jewish Sacred Cubit' or *Sacred Rod* of 3.4757 feet. The two divisors interestingly link decimal with sexagesimal (and hence duodecimal) counting structures, as we might have expected.

> *The Sacred Cubit is found to be one ten-millionth of the Earth's polar radius.(and divides into 25 'primitive' inches or 25.0265 British inches)*

> *The Sacred Rod is found to be one six-millionth of the Earth's polar radius (3.4757485 feet or 41.709 inches)*

It is now suggested that these units were originally defined with reference to the known polar radius - showing a working knowledge of the Earth's spherical dimensions preserved within the known number bases of antiquity.

The polar radius produces a theoretical polar circumference of 24,817.95 miles. A single arc degree of latitude or longitude (1/360°) thus covers 68.9393 miles   This figure translates into a most interesting 364 x 1000 *feet*, which cannot be ignored, and will shortly be compared with equatorially derived measures.

Equatorial Derivations

The equatorial radius is slightly greater than the polar radius, because the Earth bulges out at the equator, like many of its human inhabitants. Presently, the figure given, by a variety of sources, is always 3963 miles, plus a fractional component which varies from source to source from 0.220 to 0.428 mile - a variation of just over one fifth of a mile - a tolerance spread of +0.0053%.

We can now confidently repeat the calculations above to determine the length of one degree of arc (1/360°) along the equator. The equatorial circumference now becomes 24,902.952 miles, whence one degree of arc becomes 69.1748 miles, which *in feet* becomes a most interesting 365.242 x 1000!

It must be clear that this figure is also no coincidence, demonstrating that the foot is also a fundamental unit, defined such that:

> *The foot is found to be one thousandth part of a degree of arc along the Earth's equatorial circumference divided by 365.242 - the solar year.*
> *or,*
> *The foot is found to be one thousandth part of a degree of arc along the polar circumference divided by 364.*

The conversion factors and the clear philosophy underpinning this choice of length for the foot are no accident. The sexigesimal (60-based) arithmetic involved in "one thousandth of a degree" (1/60000) invokes the original source for the foot - the culture variously known as Sumerian and, later, Babylonian[10]. Of course, the solar year and the number of degrees in the circle may now be reciprocated so that, if the equatorial circumference is divided by 365.242, *just as the year-circle is divided by days in the year*, then there are exactly 360,000 feet around one such 'day-degree' of the Earth.

I am sure that the reader can understand the importance of these figures; *only by invoking the foot can we glimpse this entry into the world of ancient measurement and hence ancient thought*. Metrication obfuscates this entry, as it redefines the way the circumference of the Earth is measured - one metre becoming defined as ten millionth of a quarter of the polar circumference. It is ironic that the highly non-decimal *quarter* lurks at the roots of this ill-founded system!

In the definition of the foot we have found 360, 364 and 365.242 representing logical divisions of the Earth's dimensions. This new data is supported lock, stock and barrel by the findings in earlier chapters. The astronomy of the calendar derives the same three numbers whilst the foot is central to the whole construction of the lunation triangle, re-discovered by the author through study of the Station Stone rectangle.

Thus, we may write:

> *The Megalithic yard may be defined as the reciprocal of the difference between the lunar and solar year [10.875 days] expressed as lunations - 0.368266285. Taking the foot to represent this difference, its reciprocal becomes 2.715426 feet - almost exactly a Megalithic yard - which, in time terms, must represent the lunation period of 29.53059 days.*

> *The inch may now be defined as the twelfth part of a foot, a division which naturally comes about from using the lunation triangle within a twelve month calendar. During each solar year, a twelve month calendar must 'lose' 0.368 lunations - a foot - and therefore, each month, an inch must be subtracted from the twelve monthly divisions.*

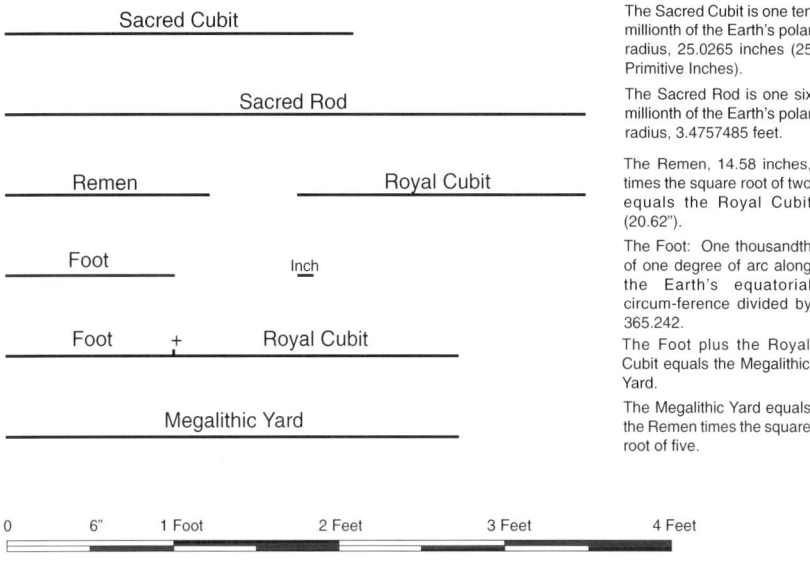

The Sacred Cubit is one ten millionth of the Earth's polar radius, 25.0265 inches (25 Primitive Inches).

The Sacred Rod is one six millionth of the Earth's polar radius, 3.4757485 feet.

The Remen, 14.58 inches, times the square root of two equals the Royal Cubit (20.62").

The Foot: One thousandth of one degree of arc along the Earth's equatorial circum-ference divided by 365.242.

The Foot plus the Royal Cubit equals the Megalithic Yard.

The Megalithic Yard equals the Remen times the square root of five.

Figure 9.4 Derivations of known ancient units of length from the Earth's dimensions.

The Megalithic yard and the foot are therefore intertwined, through the dynamics of Sun and Moon cycles. Because the material here is so representative of the thinking behind the calendrical and other functional aspects of Stonehenge which we have uncovered in earlier chapters, using the same unit and numbers, I suggest that study of the monument's key dimensions might anticipate the sacred rod, foot, inch and Megalithic yard as the key units. If the architects were as adept at siting the monument as well as indicated here, it is highly probable that observable multiples of the above units are to be found at megalithic sites.

The Dimensions of Stonehenge

We need not look in obscure places at Stonehenge. We can begin with the single feature that we all associate with Stonehenge and from which it takes its name - the *hanging stones*. Once there were thirty lintels, jointed and morticed to lock together into a strong and perfectly level platform aloft the mighty sarsen circle. It is "truly circular".[11] Here, John Michell has already postulated that each lintel is precisely one sacred rod in width, and one rod multiplied by π in length. This agrees very closely with Richard Atkinson's measurements quoted in *Stonehenge*, "The lintels measure, on the average, 10 feet in length, 3½ feet in width and 2½ feet deep". Using the

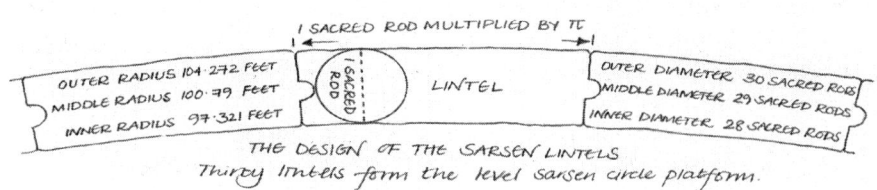

I SACRED ROD MULTIPLIED BY π

OUTER RADIUS 104·272 FEET
MIDDLE RADIUS 100·79 FEET
INNER RADIUS 97·321 FEET

I SACRED ROD

LINTEL

OUTER DIAMETER 30 SACRED RODS
MIDDLE DIAMETER 29 SACRED RODS
INNER DIAMETER 28 SACRED RODS

THE DESIGN OF THE SARSEN LINTELS
Thirty lintels form the level sarsen circle platform.

Figure 9.5 The geometry and metrology of the sarsen circle lintels (*after Michell*).

sacred rod, the outer circumference of the sarsen circle becomes 327.58 feet, radius 104.272 feet, which fits remarkably well to the dimensions measured off from the Thom plan.

The Thom family, during their surveys of Stonehenge, suggested another very simple design plan for the sarsen circle geometry. *The average width of each sarsen upright is made one Megalithic rod (1 MR = 2.5 MY), whilst the average gap between them is made half a MR.*[12] This makes the circumference 45 MR (112.5 MY)[13] whence the inner diameter becomes 97.45 feet. This, within two inches, may be read off the survey plan. Using Thom's plan and figures, 97.45 feet translates to 28.03 sacred rods, almost an integral 28 rods for the inner diameter. The outer diameter of the sarsen circle, in sacred rods, now becomes an integral and most satisfying 30 rods, (the widths of two lintels, each one sacred rod in width, are added to the diameter). Michell's figures agree perfectly with those from the Thom design plan; each fully vindicates the other.

97.45 feet makes the circumference of the sarsen ring 306.148 feet, which is 3673.778 inches, making the area enclosed by the sarsen circle almost identical with the Egyptian 'year-circle'. Therefore, we can state: -

> *The inner face of the sarsen circle has a circumference (within a third of a percent) of ten times the solar year, expressed in primitive inches - one twenty-fifth of the Egyptian Sacred Cubit. This is so close to the Egyptian unit of area measure and their 'year-circle' - the quarter-aroura - that we can assume that this is a deliberate design feature of the sarsen circle (see figure 8.2, page 144).*

> *Each lintel has a width of exactly one rod, and a length along its curved outer face of one rod times π. The outer diameter of the sarsen circle is therefore 30 rods in diameter, whilst the inner face is 28 rods. I have also assumed that this is a deliberate design feature of the monument, eloquently reinforcing the numerical choices faced in calendar design and which are here reflected in the choice of 30 sarsen lintels and 56 (twice-28) Aubrey holes.*

The outer face of the sarsen ring is a much rougher affair than the precise and polished inner face. The uprights are very roughly dressed whilst the lintels are curved well but less polished on their outer surface. Fortunately, the lintels around the axis of Stonehenge remain in place, and therefore it is possible to establish the outer diameter here, at ground level, from the Thom survey plan. Measurements taken on-site at Stonehenge by the author show the outer curve of the lintel above sarsen upright 30 to be vertically above the sarsen's ground level, measured to better than half an inch by Alex and Archie Thom. We can therefore state:

> *The average diameter of the outer face of the Sarsen lintels is 104 feet, which is numerically self-similar to that of the Aubrey Circle in Megalithic yards,*
>
> *Sarsen lintel outer diameter = 104.27 feet*[14]
>
> *Aubrey circle diameter (hole centres) = 104.04 Megalithic Yards*[14]

Here is the *silver fraction* right under our noses, on-site and built into the main fabric of Stonehenge! An accurate 0.368 ratio may be found between the outer sarsen radius and Aubrey radius, providing the vital 'overplus' of the Moon for calendraic calculation. The monument lends itself to measurement of lunations by utilising the *Avenue* to lay out rods or rope equivalent to 12.368 lunar months, whence the 'overplus' 0.368 lunations measures from under the axis of the sarsen ring to the centre of Stonehenge. The length of this rope must total 643 MY or 1748 feet, almost exactly a third of a mile - and the straight part of the Avenue is 1860 feet in length - hardly 'a path that has the unfortunate property of leading from anywhere to anywhere', as John North comments about attempts to derive calendrical information from Stonehenge (*Stonehenge*, p.399). The *Avenue*, into the centre of Stonehenge, is thirteen Aubrey radii in length, perfectly suited for laying out a 12.368 Aubrey radius 'solar year' rope to determine the calendar constants.

This correspondence between sarsen outer radius and the Aubrey radius is exact, and I believe it proves that,

> *(a) Stonehenge was wholly conceived as a symbol of soli-lunar integration.*
>
> *(b) The earlier Aubrey circle was/is integrated with the later sarsen circle.*

The reader will see just how well the pieces of the Stonehenge jigsaw now fit together to provide us with a new and better understanding of the *function* of the monument. We can recognise that calendraic measurements would naturally be best suited to laying out ropes or rods down a parallel and level trackway - and such is provided by the axis *Avenue,* which is the correct length to facilitate such a procedure. A 'lunation' rope, laid along the axis and whose end reaches the centre of the monument, is then divided into the soli-lunar *silver fraction* ratio 1: 0.368 by marking where it passes under the sarsen lintel and where it meets the Aubrey circle diameter. Along the axis, this latter location might have once have been provided by the now-recumbent and ill-named Slaughter stone.

The author has demonstrated this procedure with a group of astronomers and astrologers at Stonehenge. This may have been the first time this ritual had been reenacted for over four thousand years, appropriately at dawn. Using the marked rope, the following year's lunations were then calculated, each to within a few hours.

This is a new *astronomical* correspondence between Aubrey and sarsen circles. We have already seen a geometric and metrical (geodetic) connection and all three are show linked by this analysis.

The Seven-sided Star

Figure 7.11, on page 137, shows the close correspondence between Aubrey and sarsen circles obtained through the geometry of a seven-sided star. Placing on one side for a moment the link found with the *silver fraction* and hence the lunation triangle, this construction has been the only evidence available to date for linking these two most vital constructions at Stonehenge, and it has failed to satisfy archaeologists and other members of the scientific community for one very good reason - *the Aubrey circle and the sarsen circle do not share the same centre*.

The fact that the Aubrey circle and the Sarsen circle are not concentric is an interesting diversion which we must now pursue in order to get to the design rules underpinning the monument.

The arrival of the Preseli bluestones, to furnish the original double bluestone circle discussed in chapter one, began the new 'phase II' stage of Stonehenge. Although the project was apparently never completed, the intention appears to have been to build 38 pairs of bluestones in two circles with mean radii 37 and 43 feet. Note that the mean of these two figures is exactly 40 feet. Along and just to the sides of the axis of the monument three pairs of extra bluestones were placed, inboard of the circles, probably to emphasise the entrance.

These bluestone circles, and all subsequent building work at Stonehenge, were laid out to a new centre, placed 1.73 feet north of the Aubrey centre. The later constructions included the sarsen circle, trilithon ellipse and the later and recycled bluestone circle and ellipse. It is not obvious why a new centre should have been chosen and it has been assumed that the builders were unable to ascertain the original Aubrey centre after four hundred years had elapsed - the holes had, after all, apparently been filled in, and the ditch and bank of the original henge would have been expected to have "worn down", preventing the determination of the original centre.[15] I can smell a rat here: nothing else at Stonehenge, we have discovered, is inaccurate or badly executed, so why should this re-centering be other than a design feature we have yet to understand?

If we are to accept the belief that the builders failed to find the Aubrey centre, yet would have preferred to have built all the subsequent circular constructions at Stonehenge truly concentric, then it is logical that the geometry of Stonehenge should be appraised *assuming that they succeeded*, for that will lead us to the secret of the 'failed' original design.

In his seminal text, *A Book of Coincidence*, author John Martineau lists the ratios of concentric circles for over 200 geometric formations. The constructions either side of

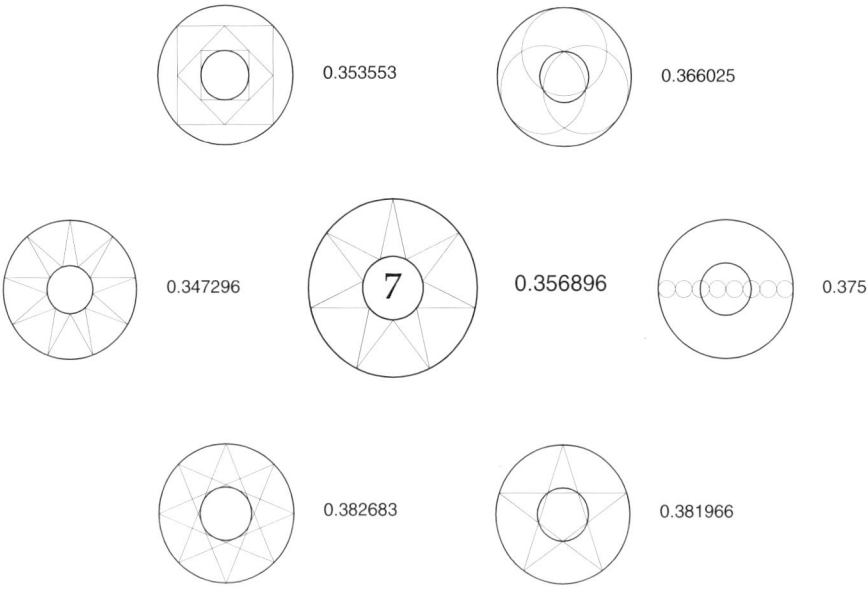

Figure 9.6 The geometry of the seven-sided star with part of the catalogue of geometric constructions which produce similar ratios of inner to outer circle (*see figure 7.11, page 137*).

the seven sided star, where the ratio of the inner to outer circle is given as 0.356896:1, are reproduced here. If we now apply this to the measured Aubrey diameter, taken from the Thom plan as 104.04 MY (282.81 feet), then the star arms cross to define an inner circle of diameter 100.89 feet.

This is remarkably integrated to the earlier analysis of the sarsen inner and outer dimensions, for 100.89 feet, obtained from the heptagram construction and otherwise unrelated to the astronomical and geodetic derivations we have obtained for the sarsen circle so far, lies within just 1 inch of the middle radius of the sarsen lintel curvature (104.272 - 97.320 = 6.95 feet. The midpoint is half this figure plus 97.320 feet, which is 100.79 feet). (*see figure 9.5, page 168*).

Stonehenge holds a seven-fold relationship to the Earth - the monument is actually located at a latitude which is one seventh of the circumference of the Earth referred to the equator.[16] Stonehenge has its axis tilted at the same angle from north. The inner star-arms of the seven-sided heptagram star drawn from the Aubrey hole centres meet up almost exactly in the middle of the sarsen lintels.

Meanwhile, the inner face of the sarsen lintels, which enclose an Egyptian 'year-circle', have a circumference which is within a third of one percent of the days in one solar year, times ten, whilst the outer circumference, or rather its radius, provides the *silver fraction* ratio with respect to the Aubrey radius, being in feet what the Aubrey circle is in Megalithic yards. Added together, all of this looks nothing short of being a minor miracle, Hawkins' "eighth wonder of the world" in fact.

However, the two circles are *not* concentric, which initially prevented the writer from discovering the relationships above. In 1993, I obtained the Thoms' original tracing of Stonehenge and, using the revised data, can now suggest that the displacement of the sarsen circle may have been an integral part of the design process.

I suggest that the original surveying for the sarsen circle used the heptagram star geometry. The radius was established from this construction, from whence the centre was moved 1.73 feet northwards along the axis. The mean circumference of the sarsen circle was then marked out, divided into thirty and the sarsen uprights placed in position. The lintels were then cradled up to their lofty position more or less as described by Atkinson, using pallets and rollers, levers and muscle-power. By so doing, the location for the ritual of marking the *silver fraction* along the axis-avenue would take place *directly underneath the axis lintel (101)*, rather than on the outer circumference of the sarsen circle.

1.73 feet, the displacement figure taken from the Thom map and quoted in several monograms and books on Stonehenge, *is one half of the sacred rod*, which then places the *silver fraction* location plumb under the mean sarsen lintel circumference, because the lintels are just one rod in width. I can think of no better place in the world to mark off the silver fraction than along the axis and directly underneath the main and widest portal of the one surviving monument which proves that the cultural aspirations of a bygone age were astonishing *and* implemented; realised, along with their calendar, in a breath-taking display of design expertise combining geodetics, geometry, astronomy and extremely accurate measurement. The result is Stonehenge, a signed statement from a civilisation beyond our present history books.

The Eightfold Connection

The sarsen lintels alone have provided this most interesting picture concerning what can happen when information from various sources are allowed to mingle and connections made. The Station Stone rectangle is another major feature of the earlier stages of Stonehenge, reflecting the octagonal motif of the Earth's geometry in space, and it can be given the same treatment.

From the Thom survey plan (*facing page 1*), its dimensions can be accurately measured as 40 MY and 96 MY, whence the diagonals - the Aubrey circle diameter - follow, *à la Pythagoras' theorem*, at 104 MY.[17] The measured readings from the Thom plan are:

> *Aubrey circle diameter (hole centre to hole centre) 104.04 MY (13 x 8 MY)*
> *Long side of rectangle (nearest Heelstone) 95.88 MY*
> *Long side of rectangle (farthest Heelstone) 96 MY*
> *Short side of rectangle (left of axis) 39.79 MY*
> *Short side of rectangle(right of axis) 40.26 MY*

172

Just as seven-fold geometry locates the sarsen circle, the *silver fraction* point and the 'year-circle', the octagonal geometry built into the Station Stone rectangle offers fertile insights into the design and implementation of Stonehenge.

The Station Stone Geometry

The internal angles of the corners of the station stone rectangle are all within 0.3° of a right-angle, the indicated centres marking the best estimates of where the original stones were placed. It must be clear that in the absence of a stone (in two cases), the best estimate can only ever be the centre of the hole once occupied. We might also assume that the stones were laid out adjacent to an original Aubrey hole and on the same circumference - all but stone 92 appear to fit this assumption closely with placements on the southern side of existing holes.

It has been assumed for a long time that the station stone rectangle lay perpendicular to the 'midsummer sunrise' axis of the monument. The Thom plan clearly shows this not to be the case, the Stations are aligned to the extreme right-hand 'A' posthole, which lies three degrees off axis to the left.[18] As a lunar sightline this has little relevance, but if the 'A' postholes could ever be shown to represent an attempt to observe a different or unstable axial tilt of the planet we live on, then their significance, and that of the station stones would be historically enormous, for the date of this shift could then be estimated.

Working on the Thom plan, I was reminded of another very important site in Britain, the Merrivale complex on Dartmoor, which contains two almost identical stone rows, whose orientation differs by just 2°. They form part of a solstitial observatory (*figure 2.3(c), page 25*). Whether this was a necessary although unknown design feature of Neolithic astronomy or a common theme based on a change in the Earth's axis, here is a further piece of evidence ripe for a "rigorous search for alternatives".

The station stone rectangle is based on an octagonal geometry; as such it divides the circumference of the Aubrey circle into eight. The resulting arcs are 40.84 MY or 111 feet each in length, making the whole circumference an interesting 888 feet. If we assume that the shorter sides of the station stone rectangle are 40 MY in length, and that the sarsen circle outer diameter is 30 sacred rods, it is inset just 26.74 inches (2.22 feet) top and bottom from the longer sides. This may be cross-checked - the 'inner' heptagram star arms suggest a circle with diameter 0.356896 of the outer circle dimensions. Assuming 104 MY as the Aubrey diameter, this produces an inner circle radius of 100.89 feet - almost at the mean measured radius of the centres of the sarsen lintels. The station stone rectangle, produced as above as a completed octagonal construction, frames a inner circle whose diameter is 0.382683 that of the Aubrey circle (*figure 9.6*). This frames the sarsen circle with a minimum gap of 23 inches on all four sides.[19] This agrees with Michell's suggested geometry for the sarsen circle.

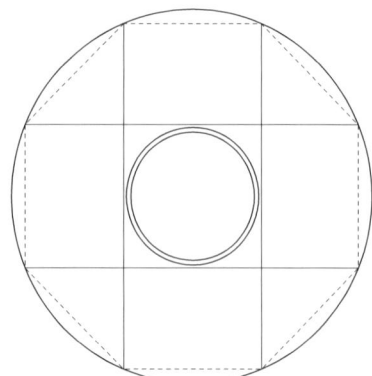

Figure 9.7 The geometry of the Aubrey and Sarsen circles. Seven and eightfold division of the Aubrey circle together generate the essential design of Stonehenge.

Seven and Eight-fold Interactions

The two constructions - seven-fold and eight-fold - may now be superimposed on the plan. Seven multiplied by eight produces the 56 marker holes of the Aubrey circle, also the minimal solution to a Sun-Moon calendar and eclipse predictor. These two numbers generate the essential design of Stonehenge.

Two 'Year-Circles' Compared

Stonehenge may be understood as based on a seven-fold design which began with the Aubrey circle. This circle, through its use as a soli-lunar calendar, is also a representation of the zodiac band through which the Sun and Moon pass in their eternal rounds of the sky. Thus the Aubrey circle is a 'year-circle' - its circumference representing the 365..242 days of the year. But, because of the lunar emphasis we find in the earlier phases of Stonehenge, it is also the 'month-circle' of the Moon. We know the dimensions of this circle to a high degree of accuracy - it has a diameter very close to 104 MY.

The Aubrey circle mean circumference (hole centres) is 104 x π, which is 326.72 MY or 888 feet. The holes have an individual average diameter of 1.06 metres[20], which enables the calculation of inner and outer circumferential figures.

The Aubrey outer diameter is then 105.25 MY, whilst the inner diameter becomes 102.7 MY. The corresponding circumferences are

> *Aubrey outer circumference, 898.81 feet (10785.67 inches)*
> *Aubrey mean circumference 888.13 feet (10657 inches)*
> *Aubrey inner circumference 877.41 feet (10528.92 inches)*

These relationships are illustrated below in figure 9.8. The outer circumference is exactly 365.242 x 29.53059. Whatever structure was originally built into the Aubrey holes[21] contained the possibility for a circumference 'year-circle' which was *exactly* the product of the solar year and the lunar month in days. If intentional, a rather good example of soli-lunar integration!

The inner year circle of the sarsen ring, connected to the Aubrey circle through the geometry of the seven-sided star, has a circumference of 3652.4 P", ten times the length of the solar year, in days. [22]

Whilst this may seem like a mish-mash of different unit systems from disparate cultures, a most interesting and original statement emerges:

> *The Aubrey 'year-circle' is 2.95053 times the diameter of the Sarsen 'year-circle',*
> *one tenth of the lunation period. This links solar and lunar numerology.*

By reference to *A Book of Coincidence*, page 114, we discover that the seven-sided star holds an inner to outer star arm ratio of 0.356896. This must be reciprocated to obtain the outer to inner ratio 2.8019. From the outer Aubrey year-circle derived above, this places the inner star arms around a circle of 100.99 feet diameter, which is 29.38 sacred rods - *within half a percent of the lunation period.* The outer diameter, 30 rods, becomes the silver fraction ratio with the Aubrey diameter; the inner diameter, 28 rods, provides a circumferential 'year-circle' where 10P" represent each day of a solar year of 365.242 days.

Geometers are used to conceiving of lines and curves having no thickness, an abstracted notion if ever there was one. To builders of real objects, curves and lines possess width and depth. Here, the indications are that the builders used the widths

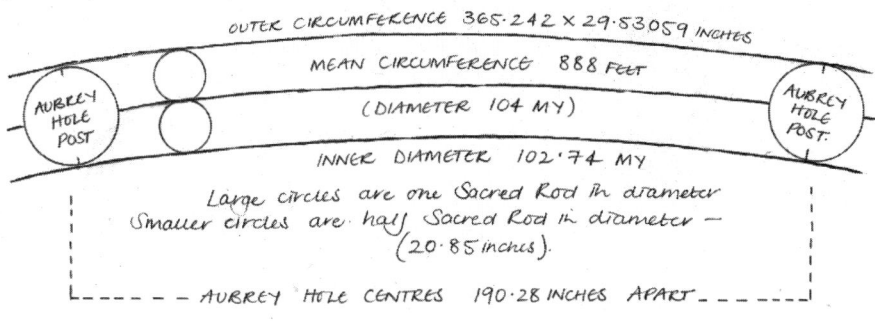

Figure 9.8 The geometry and metrology of the Aubrey circle.

of their structures in order to reconcile various measurement systems, geometrical and astronomical relationships. In Islamic doctrine the width of the 'path' of many geometrical designs is an essential part of the design process and here we find the widths of stones taking the same role.

We have not needed to dig out obscure measurements from Stonehenge to find these things, to arrive at the conclusions here the only measurements have been those of the Aubrey circle and its holes and the sarsen circle and its lintels. These are unarguably the two main features of the Stonehenge design and they are connected through the seven-sided star. The Thom plan agrees very closely with these figures in comparison with measurements taken by Atkinson and they are the same figures as quoted by Michell, North, Wood and other writers on the subject of Stonehenge.

Two other 'Year-Circles' Compared

Stonehenge, we have seen, appears based on a seven-fold design which began with the Aubrey 'year' circle. Because the design of the Great Pyramid is also based on a 'year-circle' we might now profitably compare the two.

The Pyramid of Cheops is the largest pyramid in the Giza complex. There are many books which instruct and often bamboozle their readers with astonishing information about the nature and purposes of this construction.[23] Here, I shall take

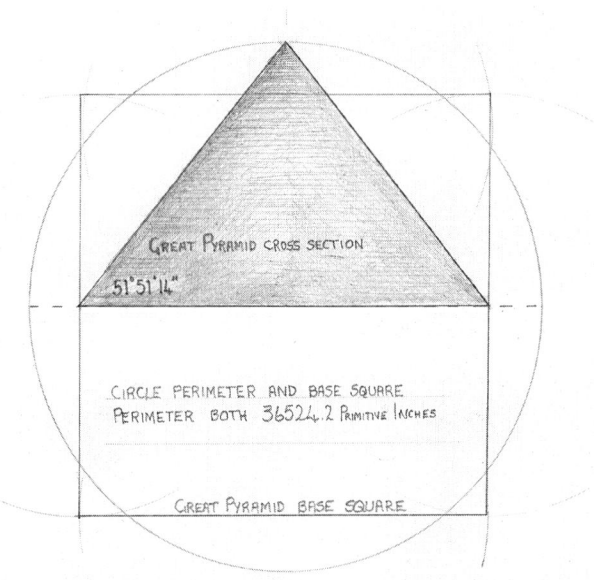

Figure 9.9 The Design of the Great Pyramid. The forming 'year-circle' is 'squared', and the resulting square defines the base of the Pyramid, whose height is then made the radius of the original circle, also setting the base angle at just under fifty two degrees.

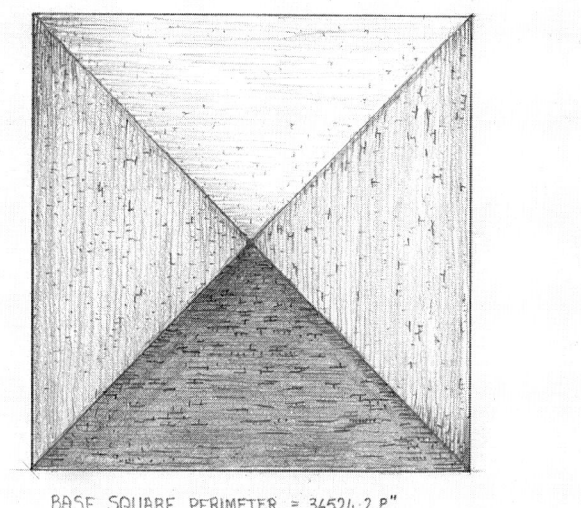

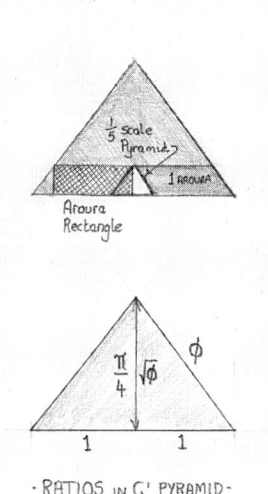

BASE SQUARE PERIMETER = 36524.2 P"
SIDE LENGTH = 365.242 SACRED CUBITS

· RATIOS IN G' PYRAMID ·

Figure 9.10 left: The elevation of the Great Pyramid design.
Figure 9.11 The external measurements of the Pyramid, with *phi* and *pi* relationship.

the exoteric and publicly available information on the design and measurements of the construction, in order to then compare it with Stonehenge. So far, the only link between these two more or less contemporaneous structures has been the interesting Great Circle described and illustrated on page 87 (*figure 5.7*).

The design of the Pyramid is quite straightforward. The four sides of its base have the same perimeter as a circle of circumference 36524 P". This is exactly the same kind of astronomical/numerical message we have found emanating from the Aubrey and sarsen year-circle material discussed. The only difference is that here one day represents 100 'primitive' inches instead of 10 for the sarsen 'year-circle'; or instead of 29.53059 British inches for the 'lunar' Aubrey 'year- circle'.

The Great Pyramid Design

The design of the Great Pyramid begins with a year-circle of circumference 36524 P". Using the same center, the ground plan of the Pyramid is obtained by constructing a square whose perimeter is identical to that of the year-circle. This is shown opposite in figure 9.9.[24]

The elevation of the Pyramid can be obtained by imagining the year-circle to be a sphere, whence the sides of the Pyramid are formed by connecting its square base to the zenith of the sphere (*also shown opposite*). Thus all the principle dimensions of the Pyramid are defined from simple geometry and the familiar year-circle constant of

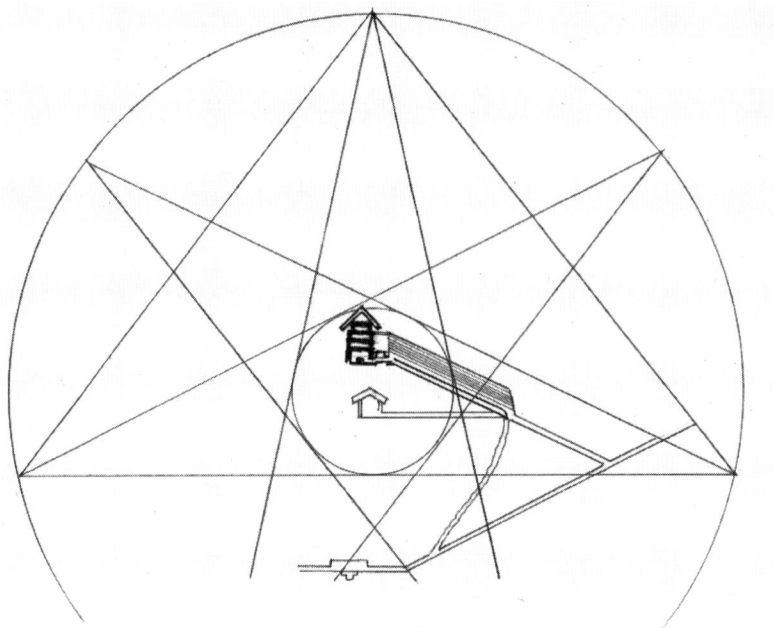

Figure 9.12 The Pyramid's key features superimposed on the heptagram star. The angle of the Grand Galler, its entrance shaft and that of the descending path to the 'well' run parallel to the geometry of the heptagram. The angle of the Pyramid being 51.85 degrees; the link between the building and seven-fold geometry is clear.

365.242, again multiplied by a power of ten, this time ten squared.

Because of the nature of the definition of the Sacred Cubit, the ground perimeter of each of the Pyramid's four sides becomes the year length, 365.242 expressed in this unit, diagram 9.9 showing the correlation. The perimeter thus becomes 1461 Sacred Cubits, the number of days in the first synchronization (four-year) cycle of the Sun. The height of the Pyramid, as designed, becomes 5813 P", although the apex capstone, of height 364 P" may never have been completed.

By now superimposing the plan of the internal passageways within the Great Pyramid we discover a connection between the Pyramid's design and the geometry of the seven-sided star. Figure 9.12 demonstrates that many of the key internal features of the building are 'framed' within the heptagram geometry, just as they were seen to be at Stonehenge.

The dimensions of the Pyramid's profile enables an important feature of its design to be appreciated, for it embodies the two constants *phi* and *pi* in its design, a novel and convincing demonstration that the ancient world understood only too well, and could manipulate, the irrational number set. In addition, figure 9.11 shows the incorporation of the *aroura* rectangle within the design.

The Stonehenge and Pyramid year-circles compared

The two year circles are shown below with their relative sizes. The linear scaling between the two is found to be 1696.2 : 5813 (radius of each year-circle in inches). This gives a scale of 1 : 3.427. It was not immediately apparent whether this figure was other than random, until the relative *areas* of the circles were considered, whence the landscape suddenly changed into a much more familiar territory to this writer:

> *The area of the Pyramid's forming circle : 106157460 sq.ins*
> *The area of the Aubrey circle : 9038730.37 sq. ins.*
> *Scaling factor 11.74 : 1, which is also 19:phi*

There are 11.74 lunations in one eclipse year. The relationship between these two sites is illustrated below in figure 9.13, first numerically and then astronomically. This is a strong pattern of the past, linking Stonehenge to the Pyramid through lunations and eclipse patterns, a connection about which we currently know nothing.

The diagram suggests that the two sites, Stonehenge and the Pyramid are connected, in time, for although the building of Stonehenge apparently began before the Pyramid, both structures were built within a few hundred years of each other; not just in space, for the Great Circle connects the two sites and many other sacred sites, and now also through their geometry and astronomical function to each other.

If the Aubrey year-circle is taken to represent one lunation (29.531 days), then the Pyramid year circle represents the eclipse year (346.6 days). 11.74 is also related to *phi* because when multiplied by *phi* it gives exactly 19, which is also a number redolent with astronomical meaning. There are 19 eclipse years in the Saros cycle, the best known eclipse cycle, which takes 223 lunations to complete (18.03 years), and 19 solar years complete the most accurate synchronization between solar and lunar rhythms (235 lunations) - the Metonic cycle.

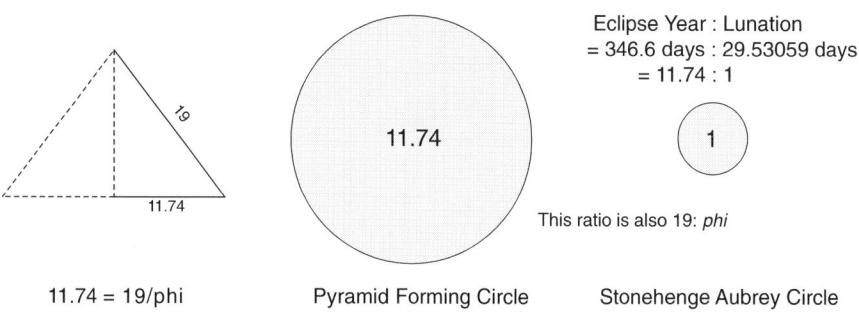

Figure 9.13 The relative areas of the Pyramid and Stonehenge year-circles. These suggest a cosmological relationship between the two sites, also involving *phi*.

Although this is not a text about astronomy *per se*, these numbers invite us to look at the Saros in a new way for,

$$11.74 \text{ lunations} = \text{eclipse year} = \frac{19}{phi},$$

$$\text{Therefore the Saros (19 eclipse years)} = \frac{19^2}{phi} = 223 \text{ lunations}$$

$$\text{And the Metonic cycle (19 solar years)} = \frac{19.50^2}{phi} = 235 \text{ lunations}$$

These are all fine coincidences, and carry much meaning. The number 19 infuses through many astronomical cycles and 19 is the number of stones in many stone circles, particularly in Cornwall and Brittany.

The Geometry of the later Bluestone Circle and Horseshoe

Our next task is to study the geometry of the other features at Stonehenge. From the Thom survey plan, the diameter of the bluestone circle was measured at 76.15 feet (14.08 MY).[25] This is 0.270769 of the Aubrey diameter. It is interesting to note that the bluestone circle has a integral radius in Megalithic yards and that it may be placed on the plan of Stonehenge by simple pentagonal or hexagonal geometry shown below (*figure 9.14*). Here, the pentagonal geometry connects Sarsen to bluestone circle within a quarter of a percent of the measured positions.

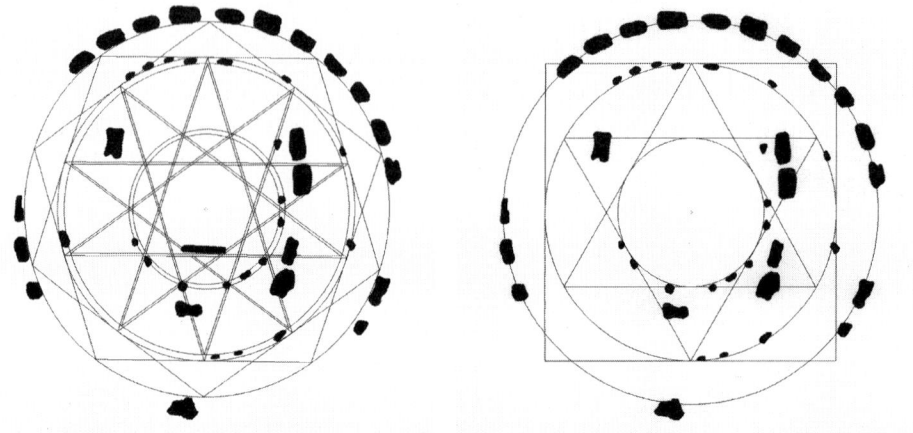

Figure 9.14 Geometrical techniques which position *both* the bluestone circle and 'horseshoe' ellipse. *Left*: a pentagonal solution from John Martineau which accounts for the stones' thickness. *Right*: a simple hexagonal technique, originally from John Michell's *Dimensions of Paradise*. (*Both pictures courtesy J. Martineau*).

The inner bluestone 'horseshoe' is also positioned to similar accuracy using the same geometric technique. That five-fold geometry was being used by megalithic architects is demonstrated by the double ring at Miltown of Clava (*figure 6.16*) whilst the trilithons at Stonehenge make a grandiose statement about five-ness. To achieve the required spacing and also account for the stones' thickness suggests that both the bluestone constructions were linked to the sarsen ring via pentagonal geoemtry.

The bluestone horseshoe is another example of recycled bluestone - with rather grander stones than those found in the bluestone circle. Its measured radius fits the geometry to better than 98%. The horseshoe originally contained 19 pillars, set at intervals of 2 MY, centre to centre, laid out as a semicircle with extended linear arms providing an enclave or focus for the Altar Stone. Because these stones are all elegant in shape and skillfully dressed to a square section, they clearly held importance, and linked with the number nineteen one might predict that they once monitored the 19 year Metonic cycle, when the phase of the Moon repeats *exactly* on the same day of the year after nineteen years - a super-annual cosmic cycle described by Diodorus in his 40 BC description,

> "Hecataeus and some others tell us that opposite the land of the Celts there exists in the ocean an island not smaller than Sicily, and which, situated under the constellation of the Bear, is inhabited by the Hyperboreans...(who)..honour Apollo more than any other deity. A sacred enclosure is dedicated to him in the island, as well as a magnificent circular temple adorned with many rich offerings. Diodorus also tells his readers that "Apollo visited the island every 19 years."[26]

The shape of the horseshoe is that of a semi-circle with linear extensions parallel to the axis and which provide an enclave in the central area of Stonehenge - the Altar stone. Atkinson gives the diameter of the inner face of the semicircle as 39½ feet, this writer measuring 39.12 feet. Because it is built from square section stones of side length two feet, we must add a further foot in order to obtain the mean diameter, which becomes 41.12 feet [15.12 MY].[27] This is 0.145384 of the diameter of the Aubrey circle centres or 0.394351 of the sarsen mean diameter, and there are two accurate ways by which this geometrical construction may be laid out, using either pentagonal or hexagonal geometry (*opposite*). The former technique accounts for the thickness of the stones for both the circle and the horseshoe.

The Trilithon Horseshoe

Although visually a most impressive feature of Stonehenge, the five trilithons have remained rather a geometric *Cinderella* until quite recently and no one thought to ask if the trilithons had been set up in any precise geometrical or astronomical pattern. In 1973, the Thom family suggested that the inner faces of four of the five trilithons were located on an ellipse of eccentricity 0.78, expressed as major and minor axes of 27 and 17 MY. The ellipse is symmetrically placed on the axis of Stonehenge but its centre is 4 feet from the sarsen centre. The Pythagorean triangle which produces such a shape has integral side lengths 17, 21 and 27 and the perimeter is very near to an integral 28 Megalithic rods.

The five trilithons, despite this clarity on their geometry, remain an enigma. Off centre in every sense, the great central trilithon is not even set on the same curve and the remaining massive upright, stone 56, is dished on its inner face. It was re-erected in 1901, and the primitive state of restoration acceptable at that time probably condemned it to a non-original position - it is not even perpendicular to the axis. But sixty ton stones are not carried 23 miles, accurately dressed and erected with lintels without very good reason. The question which needs asking is obvious whilst the answer remains, as yet, unclear.

The middle two trilithons relate to the sarsen portals such that a gap appears right through the monument when standing by Aubrey holes 15 or 42. This gap forms a corridor right through the inner parts of Stonehenge, passing just to the south of the Altar stone (*opposite, figure 9.15*). In *Stonehenge*, John North attempts the courageous task of relating this and other such sighting gaps to astronomical events (his figure 189) and makes the point that where the extremes of lunar setting were to be seen, there were also high concentrations of cremated burials (page 489). North asks if the trilithons were an independent monument (page 486) and then uses the commonality of the units of measurement - in this case the Megalithic yard - as vindication that the trilithons did, in fact, form part of an integrated design. This is exactly the same analytic technique I have applied here, amplified through a wider range of units, astronomic constants, geodetic measurements and simple geometry.

Summary

The geometry presented here allows the original positions of all the major features of Stonehenge to be accurately located using known megalithic techniques. In the absence of any firm evidence beyond the stones' placings, we may never know the finer details concerning this site. Even then, some of the stones have been moved, displaced, removed, eroded or damaged and it remains hard to know for sure what once may have been a precise geometry or an accurate astronomical sightline.

The design of Stonehenge is seen to be integrated with geometry, geodetics and astronomy. When we find repeated occurrences of logically derived lengths related to the Earth's shape, lengths still in widespread use today and which then relate to these same geometric and astronomical contexts, then we also find an opening into the mind of the architect(s) of Stonehenge. The metrology of Stonehenge has been shown to use units of length derived from the dimensions of the Earth, this strongly suggesting a knowledge of the true shape and size of the Earth. Stonehenge is thus seen to radiate a higher cultural presence than that presently accepted by mainstream archaeology.

If the geometry is taken to be merely fortunate or contrived coincidence, then we ask at what point coincidences begin to collate into something else. We ask why

Figure 9.15 The 'trilithon-sarsen circle alignment' through Stonehenge. (The author's model of Stonehenge confirms the alignment with a complete sarsen ring, relevant parts of the original are missing at Stonehenge.)

logical decimal and duodecimal divisions of the Earth's radius and circumference provide exact units of length with which we remain familiar. We further ask why these same units of length may repeatedly be found throughout the geometry of Stonehenge and we ask why numerically self-similar values of different units relate to produce astronomically meaningful relationships. Finally, we ask if repeatedly denying the cultural achievements which produced Stonehenge may suggest that our present culture cannot face something about its past. The patterns of the past presented here tell of ancient high culture from which we might today learn a great deal about living on the Earth.

The voices of our ancestors need not be audible in order for them to still speak with us.

183

Footnotes to Chapter Nine

[1] A Newnham scholar; one-time archaeological correspondent of the *Observer* and *SundayTimes.*

[2] Correspondence with the author, March 1998. Dr. Burl's *A Guide to the Stone Circles of Britain, Ireland and Brittany* is published by Yale University Press and is essential to any student of megalithic culture.

[3] In a letter concerning his father's survey in 1973.

[4] The MOW plan is an incredible 4% in error on some key linear measures. These errors are so marked that they can be seen with the eye alone when the plan is placed side by side with the Thom Plan

[5] See the reproduction postcard in the appendices. *Phi* is 0.618 to three places of decimals.

Kepler's three planetary laws are: 1. Planets move in elliptical orbits with the Sun at one focus. 2. Planets sweep out equal areas in equal lengths of time. 3. The squares of their orbital periods are proportional to the cubes of their distances from the Sun. Such succinct laws, combining geometry with astronomy, and upon which the Space Age depends!

[6] 51° 51' 14"

[7] To improve on this accuracy requires a knowledge of trigonometry (right-angled triangles) and accurate measurement of rise and set azimuths of stars - both techniques were familiar to megalithic observers.

[8] The best basic description of ancient navigation practice, including the determination of longitude using the Moon, may be read from Hogben's classic and best selling, *Mathematics for the Million.* (George Allen and Unwin Ltd, 1936.)

[9] This is 100,000,000 divided by 12, linking duodecimal to decimal number systems. It is two and a half feet.

[10] John Michell, in conversation with the author. John Ivimy writes "At no time of which records exist did either the Greeks or Egyptians use a sexagesimal (60-based) number system." [*Personal communication concerning his new work on measurements.*]

[11] J.E.Wood, *Sun, Moon and Standing Stones*, page 172.

[12] This is found to be very close to the actual plan, and where spacings were altered, for example, to make an extra foot space at the axis 'entrance' to the sarsen circle, the adjacent gaps were narrowed accordingly. Similarly, the southernmost sarsen, stone 11, is half the width of the rest and has a correspondingly wider gap on its westerly side. Therefore, the sarsen circle was originally marked out by division of its perimeter into thirty equal lengths.

[13] This is very nearly twice 56 MY.

[14] Professor John North quotes Alex Thom's measurement of the Aubrey diameter as 104.26 MY, op.cit., p494.

[15] *Sun, Moon and Standing Stones*, page 165.

[16] Within 0.06%.

[17] the measured readings are 103.8 MY (/) and 104.1 MY (\)

[18] The distance from the first posthole A from the axis is 12.75 feet, placed 242.83 feet from the Aubrey centre.

[19] The differential between 0.356896 and 0.382683 is 0.025787 - producing a 43.740 inch length between sarsen lintel centres and the 'frame' provided by the octagonal extension of the Station Stone rectangle. Almost exactly half a sacred rod, 20.85 inches, is taken up in the width of the sarsen lintels to their outer faces, leaving 22.89 inches.

[20] *Sun Moon and Standing Stones*, p 5.

[21] It is thought that a wooden henge structure may have been built around the 56 Aubrey holes, an artist's impression may be found on page 4 (*figure 1.4*).

[22] The longer 'primitive' inch being defined as one twenty-fifth of the Egyptian sacred cubit of 25 P".

[23] *The Great Pyramid Decoded*, by Peter Lemesurier (Element) is probably the best single starting text on the subject.

[24] The circumscribing sphere has a radius of 5813 P" or 178.396 MY.

[25] Atkinson, in *Stonehenge*, gives 75 feet, commenting on the fact that this circle appears not to have been as precisely laid out at the Aubrey and sarsen circles (page 37). The sarsen trilithons, erected earlier, would prevent simple radius determination for the later recycled bluestone circle - perhaps the less accurate 'chords meeting at a common centre' technique was used to lay out this later circle.

[26] Although this is 40 BC and not 2000 BC, we may note that this historical account describes Britain, Stonehenge and Avebury quite well. The nineteen year fine detail is an astronomically accurate one and tends to lend credence to the rest of Diodorus' account. Either Stonehenge was still in use in 40 BC or there were accounts of its use before that date.

[27] This is within 0.2% to 40 royal cubits [20.60 inches].

[28] Perhaps the trilithons represented the five visible planets, as the fingers of the hand still do in the ancient and largely forgotten art of palmistry, another remnant of a cultural past we have chosen to marginalise. The trilithons are placed like the fingers pushing up from the earth.

Above: The Bossinney Labyrinth, Rocky Valley, near Tintagel. The seven circuit labyrinth may be found throughout the world and is a shared cultural artefact. This example is dated to the Bronze Age, and a plaque nearby gives 1600 to 1400 BC. A second labyrinth is carved adjacent to the example above, but this is not as well executed and is thought to be much more recent. Tintagel's name connects it to the ancient tin trading route down through Cornwall to Fowey or Tywardreath. (*courtesy Paul Broadhurst*)

Chapter Ten

- THE VIEW OVER ALBION -

The cultural legacy of Stonehenge

The rich cultural heritage and history of the British Isles presently fails to include the contribution of an unique culture, one which inhabited these 'green and pleasant lands' more than five millenia ago. Yet, throughout the land, this culture's mighty achievements survive in their hundreds on moorland and mountainside, a curiosity for walkers and often merely a nuisance for farmers. Whilst Stonehenge and Avebury remain massive showpieces of the abilities of our ancestors to move huge volumes of earth and erect huge stones, a visit to either site will convince the visitor in minutes that the cultural legacy of these sites, particularly relating to their geometry and astronomy, has no public profile whatsoever and is hardly mentioned. It is therefore not surprising that for many people it is deemed either not to exist at all, or to be the product of an overactive imagination.

This is surprising, for the British race, a melting pot of many cultural inputs over thousands of years, contains and expresses many other aspects of its suppressed 'pagan' past through one of the richest folklore traditions to be found anywhere in the world. Despite the ravages of the industrial revolution, folk culture in Britain remains robust. The modern alternative movement in Britain reflects this, although it now wears the current fashion of ecological concerns as its outergarments. Underneath, pagan petticoats keep the body of our folklore warm and surprisingly well.

Many authors have explored the richness of this other world. Prudence Jones and Nigel Pennick, in *A History of Pagan Europe*, provide an accessible yet substantive overview of Britain's pagan past within European history.[1] Janet and Colin Bord have provided a popular treatment of the folklore of pre-industrial Britain in *Earth Rites*, and the work of Peter Berresford Ellis is to be recommended unreservedly for students of Celtic history, traditions and social patterns.[2]

Whilst this material does not deal directly with the time period of the megalithic culture, the folklore it contains has already been shown to contain remnants of material that are based on the practices of neolithic Sun and Moon watchers. These oral and pre-Celtic remnants are important in order to complete the historical landscape of this book, but where is the folklore of the megalithic culture to be found? The answer to this question, as provided by this final chapter, will be found astonishing.

In their book, *Ancient Celtic America*, W.R.McGlone and P.M.Leonard write,

> *"However difficult it is to discover, recover, and analyse the material culture and the biological remains of past humans, it is yet more difficult to discover and formally state the mental culture of these people. Yet it is this mental culture that archaeologists wish to know."*

We are no more than 200 generations away from the megalithic builders. At most, 70 human life-spans separate us culturally from the people who erected Stonehenge. Anthropologists attempt to connect with the human behavioural patterns woven through these generations. Dr Chris Knight, in his book *Blood Relations*, presents a theory of the origins of culture based on the menstrual cycle and hence on the rhythms of the lunation cycle.[3] The fortnightly cycle between fertility and menstruation is well known and has been known about for a very long time indeed - the *Venus of Laussal* rock carving contains this same message and the connection between marital sex and the Moon is still culturally and linguistically alive as our ritual 'honeymoon'.

That the reflected light from the central period of the lunation cycle around full Moon aided the hunting parties of our tribal ancestors is linked by Dr Knight to a model of an original lunar based social structure. However, this lunar synchronicity is not shared by other primates - chimpanzees ovulate with a thirty-six day rhythm and humans appear unique in aligning their social patterns to the lunation cycle. From such information, it is unwise to assume that our link with the Moon is purely instinctual, at least on evolutionary timescales, and we must assume that behavioural factors and "mental culture" repeatedly reinforced this cultural pattern over hundreds of generations.

Parents teach their offspring this "mental culture", and children receive it with their mother's milk. As the child grows it becomes more and more imbued with the folk-culture of the tribe; their beliefs determining what games the child plays, which toys are favourites and which superstitions and legends are valid ways of interpreting the environment. T he tribe overlays gender expectations on the child and, at puberty, the child is initiated into the tribe and learns its secrets. None of these things have fundamentally changed between Stone Age times and now, so we must ask why the importance of Sun and Moon cycles has become so diminished in our lives?

One might answer this question by suggesting that only a very few members of the tribe would have understood the inner workings of this Sun and Moon material. Dr Colin Renfrew's *astronomer-priests* were apparently an elite *corps*, yet our children today play at Kings and Queens, astronauts, secret agents and other elite members of our present culture, mimicking their behaviour to a remarkable degree. The whole tribe would have been aware of 'goings on' at Stonehenge, Avebury and other sites at propitious times of the calendar, and this must, one feels, have permeated their folk-culture in some way.

One might also argue that the human race has moved onwards in its evolutionary progress - and that the Sun and Moon are no longer very important to our cultural landscape. This suggestion disregards the evidence pouring out from from every ancient civilisation. It also disregards the esoteric writings in all the world's ancient religious texts. Finally, it disregards logic, for the Sun and the Moon are ultimately the drivers of the vast evolutionary engine of the Sun, Moon, Earth system. Evolution *is caused by* the cycles of the luminaries and Man cannot detach from their importance, if only because he is wholly formed (materially at least) by the effects of these two bodies and their ceaseless gyrations - their Sacred Marriage. In this marriage the Earth is the *Mabon*, the holy child, teeming with life, and completing a holy trinity.

These are therefore not satisfactory arguments. The reason why the mental culture associated with megalithic monuments has diminished almost to the point of extinction must be that it was forcibly replaced by a different mental landscape. There can be no other logical explanation. We therefore look through an enormous cultural barrier when we peer at those fifty ton stones at Stonehenge, a barrier far more effective than anything the MOD police ever erected. The mental blocks to our perception of this monument are far more of an obstacle than any road-block placed on the A303 at the summer solstice. Our conscious mind is steeped in that same 'new' culture which ousted the megalithic era.

This suggests that the first step in reconnecting to the megalithic culture is to actually believe the fact that prehistoric men had brains as good as ours. We can then begin to place ourselves in *their* cultural landscape and discover ways to solve the same problems that their "mental culture" asked of them. In learning to think and observe like neolithic folk, we will then understand their monuments, for these people were just ourselves minus 200 generations.

Because this old culture has gone 'underground', it resides partly as a subliminal recognition of the truths of its folklore and partly as unconscious material which, as our Jungian psychologists have shown, will periodically surface and demand expression in our conscious lives. In many of the passages which follow one can see both of these aspects at work. Folklore and religious texts provide us with an *Aladdin's Cave* of material from both categories and if megalithic culture we seek, then British people may find it within the material which bubbles up from the cracks in the cultural pavement we currently tread. That material is ancient folk-culture and it has always been brought to our attention by musicians, artists, poets, writers, clowns, fools and storytellers.

In this final chapter, we take a look at some of the main superstitions, legends, traditions and fables of Old Britain and elsewhere, and show that they too are derivatives of the cultural mind-set of the builders of Stonehenge.[4] True folklore could be defined as *a ritual practice which aligns folk to evolutionary forces*, whereby the megalithic culture ought to show more than just mere traces within our present folklore. In addition, I will show how cultural components which presently are thought disconnected in time and place share a common origin. In revealing this mystery, ancient Britain will be found intimately connected with another famous ancient civilisation thought to originate from a far distant land, yet one with a huge claim on Stonehenge.

The Song of Amergin

The Song of Amergin is in two sections, and its origins are proto-Celtic. The first comprises thirteen statements. From this, Robert Graves reconstructed what he thought was ancient calendar-lore: a thirteen month calendar, connected with the letters of the alphabet and the trees of the proto-Celtic year. The 'Tree Calendar', as it has become known, has now been consigned to the fire by many forward thinking scholars, but this does not prove that a thirteen month calendar was never used. The Aubrey calendar - the oldest in the land - invokes the structure of the 364 day, 13 month calendar and the earlier part of this book extols its virtues.

The second part of *The Song of Amergin* takes the form of six questions in the archetypal Bardic style of heralding the omnipotency of the god-head.

> *"Who but myself knows the assemblies of the dolmen-houses upon Slieve Mis?*
> (a mountain top in County Kerry, Ireland.)

> *Who but I knows truly when/where the Sun shall set?*
> *and what is the length of the Sun's month?*

> *Who is it foretells the ages of the Moon?*

> *Who brings forth the cattle from the house of Tethra and places them on due order?*
> (the stars in their courses.)

This is very interesting material. In *The White Goddess*, Graves suggests that this song is 'said to have been chanted by the chief bard of the Milesian invaders, as he set foot on the soil of Ireland, in 1268 BC.' Whilst such a story is apocryphal, dating the text to the Trojan Wars, it is undoubtedly very old indeed and we can still find echoes of it two thousand years later. The sole surviving copy of this original Old Goedelic text is written in colloquial Irish.

Saltair Na Rann

This tenth-century song contains material which also suggests the aspirations of the megalithic culture. It is thought by some to be a Christianized version of a pagan epigram,

> *"For each day five items of knowledge*
> *Are required for every understanding person -*
> *From everyone, without appearance of boasting,*
> *who is in holy orders.*

> *The day of the solar month; the age of the Moon;*
> *The state of the sea-tide, without error;*
> *The day of the week; the calendar of the feasts of the perfect saints*
> *In just clarity with their variations."*

These "five items of knowledge" are, in fact, just about as concise a curriculum of the objectives of megalithic astronomy as one could ever hope to find, and are clearly from the same cauldron that Amergin took his inspiration from. However, the text informs us of something else. It informs us that, even in the tenth century, these abilities were *still considered the prime requisites for an educated or initiated person*. By the tenth century the old Celtic world had all but coalesced with the Anglo-Saxons in Britain, yet this original quest of the megalithic astronomer was still there, floating around in the monastries, colleges, folklore and libraries, even then, and this particular piece of "mental culture" had survived down through the generations. Do we then really believe that the practical methods to obtain this knowledge would not also have been available?

Perhaps we might briefly look at how these five items of knowledge can be most easily acquired. The reader will see how the Aubrey calendar can easily provide four out of five of these, and, with a small additional refinement, it can also accurately forecast the state of the tide, "without error".[5] However, there is another little device which provides a ready-reckoner for our "understanding person" and which is also the quintessential expression of fiveness.

The Lunation Pentagram

The pentagram star or pentangle is wheeled out with tedious repetition in almost every 'B-Grade' horror movie. Like many superstitions, this one keeps on rolling through the generations like a Catherine wheel, warning ordinary folk that it contains an 'evil secret'. This is quite strange, for it may be found as part of the ornamentation in several Christian churches, most notably on the granite font at Lewannick church, in Cornwall, a church built *Augustine-fashion* on a Celtic mound and within which may also be found Ogham, labyrinth, spiral and Goddess-related carvings.

The pentagram, orientated with one of its star-points vertical, represents Man,

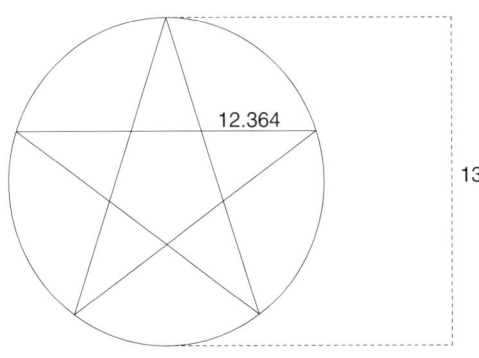

Figure 10.1 The Lunation Pentagram. If the diameter of the circle surrounding a pentagram is made 13 units, then the star arms are each 12.364 units in length. The number of lunations in one year is 12.368. The complete circuit of star arms is 61.82, which is almost 100 times *phi*, the golden section. Thus five solar years contain 100 *phi* lunations.

and as such has been immortalised within the art of Leonardo da Vinci, Robert Fludd and others. Inverted, it depicts Pan, who, in our culture, represents the forces of evil, Satan and the Devil. As the horned goat, Pan is the Earth-God, the symbol of the Devil incarnate. This too is strange, for the pentagram, either way up, contains more *phi* ratios - the *Divine Proportion* - than any other known shape. It also contains a valuable cargo when inscribed within a circle.

In figure 10.1 the length of one of the 'star' arms becomes 12.364, a length within 0.04% of the annual lunation rate (12.368). A pentagram star inscribed within a circle offers directly the length needed to perform all the lunation measurements needed for the calendar, but if *and only if* the enclosing circle diameter is taken to be 13 units. Familiar? It should be, for the Aubrey circle takes this very diameter throughout our analysis of Stonehenge. The 'star arm' lengths total five times 12.364, a figure which is 61.82 - or 100 times *phi'*, and we cannot now fail but to see that the number of lunations in five solar years is *directly* related to *phi*, the *Divine Proportion*.

This information now allows us to explore some new soli-lunar relationships:

There are 61.84 lunations (100 x phi') in five years.

or

20 x phi' = Annual lunation rate, 12.364

and

Star-arm length to circumscribing circle diameter = 12.364 : 13

Might this explain something of the enduring nature of the pentagram star and pentacle throughout history, as a carrier of sacred esoteric information about the realities of life on Earth? 12.364 is a very close approximation to the solar year length expressed as lunations, whilst 13, the diameter of the Aubrey circle, represents 13 lunar months. The ratio they form is that of the solar year to 13 lunar months (383.9 days).

$$\frac{12.364}{13.000} = \frac{365.242}{383.898} = \frac{solar\ year}{13\ lunar\ months}$$

This same ratio may be reciprocated, whence we get within a day of the eclipse year of 346.6 days.

$$\frac{13.000}{12.364} = \frac{365.242}{347.352} = \frac{solar\ year}{eclipse\ year}$$

This geometric 'coincidence' enables a calendar maker to work with very accurate values for the key calendraic constants of the Sun and Moon - and therefore eclipses - *by simply remembering how to construct a pentagram star within a circle of diameter 13 units.* The constants are delivered directly as lengths of rope or rods.

These are very interesting relationships, for the pentagon and its associated pentagram are very ancient magical symbols indeed. Even if we will never know for sure why, we have at least found a practical and calendrical application for this beautiful geometric shape - it provides data relating to the Sun, Moon, Earth system.[6]

If the reader feels that this is a fanciful contrivance, then ponder on how, in a pre-literate culture, the necessary instructions for construction of an accurate calendar could be more easily memorised. Whenever and wherever the dates of lunations or eclipses were required, this simple and beautiful geometric shape provided an answer, the double rings at Miltown of Clava and Loanhead of Daviot (*figure 6.12*); and the inner circles of Stonehenge (*figure 9.14*) demonstrating that this kind of geometric construction was certainly being explored in the Neolithic and Bronze Age period.

The Coligny Calendar

There is evidence that the Celtic world was aware of this kind of calendrical system. A Celtic calendar dating from the first century BC uses the same timeframe, described here by Peter Berresford Ellis,

> *"The earliest known surviving Celtic calendar, dated from the first century BC, is the Coligny Calendar, now in the Palais des Arts, Lyon, France. It is far more elaborate than the rudimentary Julian calendar and has a highly sophisticated five-year synchronization of lunation with solar year."*[7]

Like Stonehenge, here we find an artefact which connects Sun and Moon cycles via the calendar to an ancient icon of Sacred Geometry - the pentagram. We might suggest that the five-year synchronization between solar and lunar cycles is actually rather a poor one - there are much better ones; eight years and nineteen years are much closer to forming integral numerical ratios.

> *In 3 years there are 37.10 lunations, a three day 'miss' from exactitude.*
> *In 5 years there are 61.84 lunations, a five day 'miss'.*
> *In 8 years there are 98.94 lunations, a 1.6 day 'miss'.*
> *In 19 years (the Metonic cycle) there are 235 lunations, a two hour 'miss'.*

Unless the five year cycle was important because of the sacredness of the golden section number *phi*, then a calendar would be much better designed around an eight or nineteen year cycle. The reader may note that *phi* also crops up throughout these near-synchronous connections between lunations and solar years, for 3, 5 and 8 are consecutive numbers of the Fibonacci series, whose adjacent members approximate closer and closer to the *phi* ratio as the series is expanded.[8] The Fibonacci series is 0, 1, 1, 2, 3, 5, 8, 13, 21, 34 ...&c, where each term is the sum of the previous two. The calendar, thence the Sun and Moon, and *phi* are thus seen to be closely linked, the Coligny calendar offering us solid evidence that this was known about in the ancient world, which evidently found *phi in the sky*. And there is solid evidence of at least one calendar of gigantic proportions which appears to have been designed around the eight year synchronicity of solar and lunar cycles - *Avebury*.

The Avebury Calendar

The design of Avebury appears to draw upon the eight year cycle of soli-lunar synchronicity. Around the outer ring, a colossal two-thirds of a mile in circumference, were once placed 99 stones.[9] From the two huge flanking stones which lead to the West Kennett Avenue may be found the remains of a further eight stones, four pairs on either side of the approach to the Avenue. Added to the outer ring, the total becomes 107 stones.

To operate Avebury as an eight-year soli-lunar calendar is therefore not at all difficult - *in eight years there are 99 lunations and 107 sidereal lunar months.* The inner two rings at Avebury, once comprising 27 and 29 stones each, enable 'clocking' of both lunar cycles, sidereal and lunation. A marker is made up for both inner rings and then the count begins, at a suitably auspicious time in the calendar, by moving each of them *one stone around the inner rings per day.* When each returns to the start position, a marker can be moved one stone around the outer ring. Thus two markers move at slightly different rates around the outer ring at Avebury, one indicating elapsed lunations and the other sidereal lunar months. After three years they are three stones apart, after five years they are five stones apart, and so on. After eight

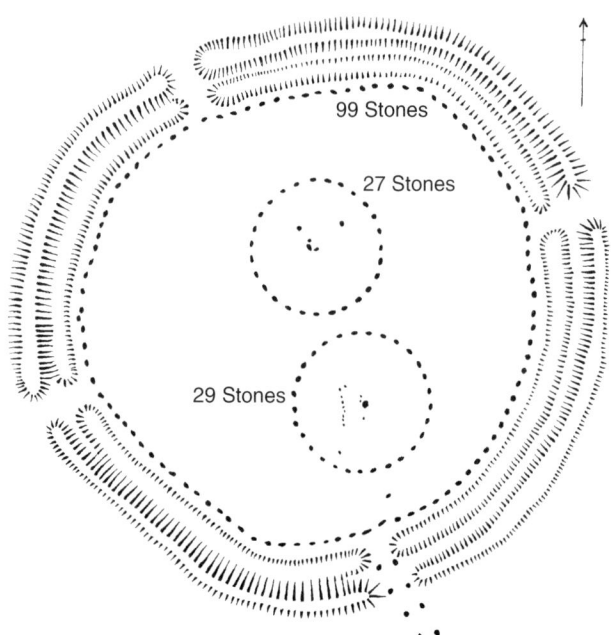

Figure 10.2 The layout of the Avebury circles. [see text for calendrical instructions]

years, if the sidereal lunar marker has been made to travel around the eight entrance stones rather than commencing a second revolution of the main circuit, it would be adjacent to the lunation marker and *one marker would lie on each side of the flanking stones*, after just eight years [99 lunations and 107 sidereal months]. The lunar markers would indicate the entrance to the processional avenue at precisely the correct time - after eight years.

Avebury readily provides the necessary hardware for meeting the requirements of the *"five items of knowledge, ...required by every understanding person."* Such a calendar offers us a reason for the design of Avebury, a reason sadly lacking in current books about the site. The astronomy gives us plenty of cause to believe that Avebury was a lunar site, and the times for festivals, celebrations and other rituals would be admirably served by the 'lunar observance' calendar scheme I have outlined above. The number patterns of known stones or stone holes suggest so perfectly the function I have described, although other aspects of the site, such as its latitude being one-seventh of the polar circumference of the Earth, the sheer scale of the ditch and bank, the proximity of Silbury Hill, and the scale and geometry of the outer ring, inform us that Avebury was once the centre for a huge cultural development, with astronomy and geometry centrally placed on the agenda.

Egyptian Phi in the Sky

An Egyptian calendrical practice provides further evidence of *phi* being used within calendrical practices. 25 years of the civil 365 day calendar were synchronized to 309 lunations (or 50 years to 618 lunations).[10]

$$25 \text{ calendar years of } 365 \text{ days } = 9125 \text{ days}$$
$$309 \text{ lunations } \left(\frac{1000 \times phi'}{2}\right) = 9124.9523 \text{ days}$$

Therefore,

$$618.00 \text{ lunations take } 50.00 \text{ calendar years of } 365 \text{ days to complete,}$$
$$\text{or } 618.4 \text{ lunations take } 50.00 \text{ solar years of } 365.242 \text{ days to complete}$$

To discover that these soli-lunar cycles, which *were* understood in ancient times, are shot through with occurrences of *phi* now connects Sacred Geometry with astronomy, and therefore to Stonehenge, Avebury and the megalithic culture - taking in ancient occult or esoteric symbols *en route*. 'Modern' sacred geometers, at least from Greek times, seem to have disassociated themselves from the link connecting geometry and its roots within the cosmos, this too easily making the subject a purely cerebral abstraction. This trend has been recently counteracted by the work of John Michell, Keith Critchlow, John Martineau, Chris Day and other architects, designers and innovators following in the wake of Rudolph Steiner and Buckmeister Fuller, who both strove to restore our links to the cosmos within a geometric context.

Finally, and to link this *phi*-theme directly with the megalithic culture, Stonehenge is sited at a latitude where, viewed from space, high above and on the Earth's axis, all the various concentric circles which form Atkinson's phases I through to III(c) take on the shape of a 'Golden Ellipse', i.e. an ellipse whose major to minor axis ratio is in the ratio *phi*:1. The pioneering psychologist Fëchner discovered in the last century that this was the ellipse shape most favoured by his volunteers - and Stonehenge is uniquely sited at the only latitude where this *phi* relationship can occur.

These few examples demonstrate that the ancient world had evidently discovered the importance of *phi* within solar and lunar cycles, and was applying it within calendraic activities.

More Phi in the Sky

The shape of the pentagram arises naturally from any study of the motion of the planet Venus in the sky. These days, one can pick up a calculator and punch in the numbers of Venus' orbital period (224.7 days) and compare this to that of the Earth (365.25 days). The ratio is within ½% of *phi*. To an observer on the Earth, this information is experienced as Venus appearing to stop every 584 days, reverse its

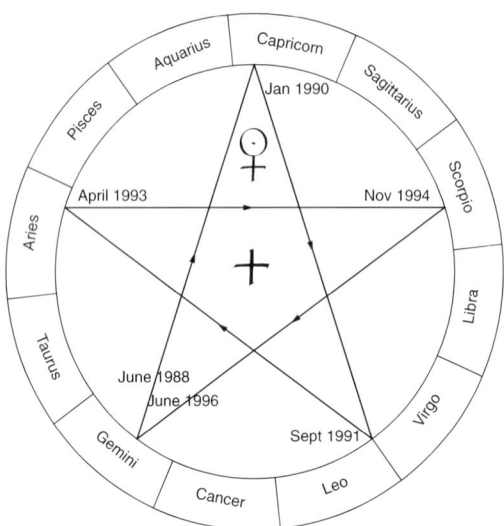

Figure 10.4 The Venus Pentagram. Every eight years, the planet Venus makes five reversals of its motion in the skies above the Earth, completing the pentagram star shown above within two days of the calendar date of the first reversal. Five and eight are both Fibonacci numbers; this confirming Venus' link with *phi*.

direction for a while, then gradually resumes normal anticlockwise motion against the fixed stars. This time period also forms a *phi* relationship to our solar year, also within $^1/_2$% accuracy. Thus our planet and Venus are locked into a little *phi*-based dance together, their relationship progressing over eight years so that Venus stops at five equally spaced places in the zodiac and thus traces out a pentagram star. In *eight* years, Venus, the Goddess of Love, stops *five* times, and again we find a *phi*-based Fibonacci numerical sequence.[13]

This phenomenon of the regular retrograde motion of Venus, every 584 days, provides a beautiful display by the planet to whom astrologers have always attributed the qualities of harmony and relationship - perhaps we have just found out why. The Mayans certainly knew of this relationship, for the number 584 is incorporated within their calendar and sacred buildings. The fact that Venus sensibly represents the fifth day of our week only strengthens the conclusion that our present culture is a relatively new sapling growing from a vast cultural tap root or tuber rooted much deeper into the past than we can presently imagine.[14]

Venus sidereal : Earth Orbit : Venus synodic
= 225 days : 365 days : 584 days
= phi' : 1 : phi

Stonehenge, Sacred Geometry and the number Seven

The rhythms and cycles of the Sun and Moon produce an exquisite geometry to those initiated into comprehending it. Evolution depends on these cycles and has developed life adapted to them. Every cell in every living object has circadian rhythms built into an evolutionary programme which dates back at least 500 million years to the time when single cells were being swilled up and down in a primordial soup by twice daily tides on the shorelines of a birthing planet.

In the last chapter we undertook to reproduce the design plan of Stonehenge by using one of the main techniques of Sacred Geometry - the division of a circle by whole numbers. Here we discovered that the heptagram star placed the position of the sarsen circle very accurately; in fact, it located the central circumference to within a few inches. Pentagonal geometry then provided accurate placements of other major features at Stonehenge, just as five-ness enabled the resolution of the twelve / thirteen month dilemma via the lunation triangle in order to 'marry' the Sun and Moon together. We have also seen, via the lunation pentagram and the Coligny Calendar, how five-ness is built into the *phi*-relationship between solar and lunar cycles.

The repeated seven-ness built into Stonehenge is reinforced so often that anyone, even a sceptic, can see that an angle of one-seventh of a circle plays a key role in the siting and design of Stonehenge. The importance of the number seven is not limited to Stonehenge however, and ancient folklore from around the world contains thousands of references to the specialness and spiritual qualities of the number seven.[11]

In *Cruden's Complete Concordance to the Old and New Testaments*, seven takes more entries than any other number, so many that, as a preface to the section, one may read,

> *'A sacred number among the Jews, also indicating perfection or completion. It was used very often in a symbolic manner for the whole of a thing. The number seven entered very largely into the religious life and observances of the Jews.'*

The Seven-fold Creation Story

One of the oldest creation stories in the world, the *Enuma Elish*, came from the Sumerian civilisation which ultimately gave way to the present Patriarchal world order. The story, perhaps originating from the third millenium BC, was adapted by the Patriarchs and may be found, almost intact and with the predictable exclusion clauses for the Moon, in the very first chapter of the best selling book in the world - the Bible. Here, in Genesis, chapter one, the seven days of creation follow a specific order where each day is represented by one of the seven visible planets [*Table 10.1*]. Mythologically, each planet related to a process within the creative cycle. Although many of us have forgotten these processes, each of the days of the week remain named after these same planets, or their mythological equivalents, in all European languages.

An observant soul may well ask why this order of the days of the week makes no astronomical sense. In answering this question we gain access into some ancient cosmology, hidden from the exoteric mind and yet delightfully explicit.

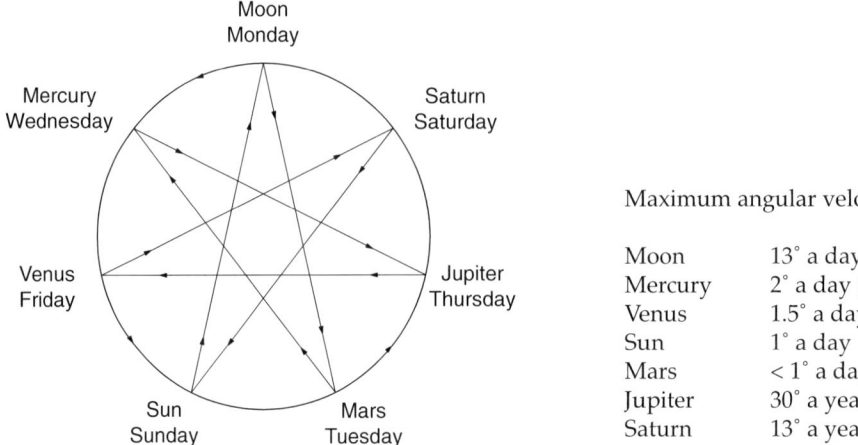

Maximum angular velocity.

Moon	13° a day (av.)
Mercury	2° a day (max)
Venus	1.5° a day
Sun	1° a day
Mars	< 1° a day
Jupiter	30° a year
Saturn	13° a year

Figure 10.3 The seven-fold days of creation and the *Chaldean Order* (by orbital velocity) of the planetary bodies as encoded wisdom.[12] Here the heptagon converts the relative speeds of the planets into the weekday order, via the heptagram star. The creation story in Genesis preserves this order.

Excluding the two luminaries and taking the five visible planets first of all, we can place these around the circumference of a pentagram in their relative orbital distance order from the Sun - Mercury, Venus, Mars, Jupiter and Saturn. Then, with five clockwise strokes of the pen one can obtain the weekday order by drawing a pentagram star beginning from Mars. The pentagon/pentagram acts as a decoding device between weekday order and the orbital velocities of the planets, and the pen doesn't even need to leave the paper!

If we now wish to include the Sun and Moon, a heptagram must now be drawn, and the relative orbital velocities of all seven bodies circumscribed around the seven points. This order is given in Table 10.2, together with the maximum angular velocities

DAY	PLANET	METAL	CREATION STORY
Sunday	Sun	Gold	Light
Monday	Moon	Silver	Division of Waters (tides)
Tuesday	Mars	Iron	Dry Land/Trees
Wednesday	Mercury	Mercury	Seasons/Astronomy
Thursday	Jupiter	Tin	Sea Beasts/Birds
Friday	Venus	Copper	Evolution/Reproduction
Saturday	Saturn	Lead	Repose

Table 10.1 The Genesis creation story and its planetary allegory.

of each body. Once more, to convert angular velocities to the weekday order, all one needs to do is to trace out the heptagram star, discovering that the *Chaldean Order*, as it is known, frames another decoding device within a geometrical icon. It preserves a great deal of astronomy and reinforces the importance of seven-ness in geometry.

To deduce the *Chaldean Order* would take a naked eye astronomer only a matter of months. Someone in antiquity decided to encode this astronomic observation into our present creation story and days of the week order via the heptagram star, just as someone once decided that the same geometric function would link the two main features of Stonehenge. The 56 Aubrey holes enable this same construction to take place with ease, every eighth Aubrey hole marking a star point.

Stonehenge, Lunations and the Musical Scale

Another fascinating insight into how cosmic cycles appear to drive the evolutionary process along may be provided by a study of the modern western musical scale. The principles of harmony and music are anchored very firmly within cosmology, and one only has to read the *Rig Veda* to recognise that *The Music of the Spheres* was alive and well thousands of year before the Christian era.

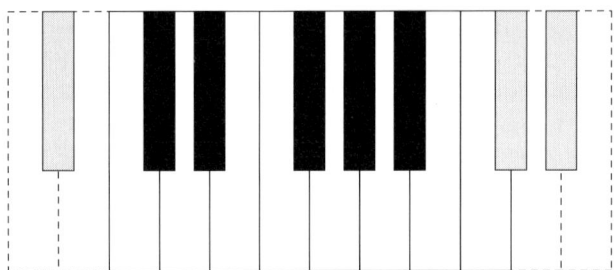

Figure 10.5 The Piano Keyboard. A musical scale consists of seven notes, yet needs the eighth, or octave, to complete musically. The chromatic musical scale comprises twelve separate notes, although it sounds distressingly incomplete without the completing octave, which makes thirteen notes. Five black keys, arranged in a 3:2 ratio complete the similarity with the numbers of the lunation triangle. Five, eight and thirteen link the keyboard structure to the Fibonacci numbers and thence to *phi*.

Today, we think, in total error, that modern musical science has replaced the curious ideas of the Hindus and those quaint Pythagoreans, and we think that we *never* think of music in terms of cosmic principles nor even relate the two.[15] But a brief look at the modern piano keyboard shows how wrong we can be. The modern chromatic scale comprises twelve notes, *plus a thirteenth* to complete the musical sense of the scale. The name given to the 12th note, which precedes the octave, is the *leading* note - indicating the sense of incompleteness *if the thirteenth note* (the octave) *remains unplayed*. You can easily demonstrate this truth for yourself on even the most rudimentary keyboard.

The structure of the equal-tempered scale enables a musician to modulate (change key) into any other key with relative ease, avoiding the howling discords formed by earlier non equal-tempered scales. Musical scales contain seven notes, with a completing eighth. In *solfa* format, we know these as *doh-re-me-fah-so-la-ti* and the completing octave *doh*. Here, although we can make connections between the seven-ness and eight-ness of the Aubrey circle, there is a much bigger cosmological connection between the structural form of the keyboard and that of the lunation triangle.

The modern keyboard shows the by now familiar connection between 12 and 13. In addition, we also discover the required five black notes arranged in a 3:2 ratio. The keyboard appears as a derivative of the lunation triangle and has the same underpinning numerology. This numerology now enables *musical* harmony to be realised; whilst to the latter it enabled *calendraic* harmony to be achieved.

Was the design of the keyboard conceived of consciously from soli-lunar rhythms? Musicologists would probably answer with a resounding "No!" However, if we were to agree with them, then concluding that the keyboard was *unconsciously* conceived begs us to enquire how many other products of human imagination are actually subsumed responses to the fundamental rhythms of the Sun and Moon. This also suggests that the luminaries may have much wider effects on human behaviour than we presently understand.

The similarity between the lunation triangle and the keyboard is perfectly obvious and suggests that the design took the only form it could take in order to optimise the creation of harmonious sound. Musical technicians, consciously or not, aligned themselves to the underpinning laws. How well they, and composers, responded to the cosmos may perhaps best be experienced by listening to the ineffable quality of the first of Bach's *Forty-eight Preludes for the well-tempered Klavier*.

Seven in Geometry and Folklore

What, if any, is the link between *phi* and seven? We have seen that Stonehenge is linked to both of these numbers, yet so far have not made the connecting link between seven-ness and *phi*.

The packing of equal sized circles around a central circle suggests a fundamental importance to six plus one as a way of filling space. The seventh circle or coin is surrounded by six identical shapes. The central circle touches six other circumferences around a hexagon. The seventh circle resembles a bee larva within its honeycomb, and such imagery assists us in understanding the evolutionary importance of the number seven.

The Egyptians named the goddess *Seshat*, also called *Sefhet*, after the number seven. She always attended the foundation ceremonies of temples and was the female counterpart of Thoth, the mistress of measure. Her emblem is a seven-petalled flower, found inscribed on temple walls from the earliest dynasties; the Egyptians had made a connection between the number seven and measure before 3000 BC. So, evidently, had the architects who sited Stonehenge at latitude 51° 10' north, also with its axis at an azimuth of one seventh of a circle.

Folklore has a lot to say about seven and much Celtic literature is well nigh obsessed with the number. The dialogues between Merlin (*Myrddin*) and *Taliesin* in *The Black Book of Carmarthen*[16] use seven as the commonest adjective throughout, and in *The*

Figure 10.6 The geometry of seven circles. Six coins arraged hexagonally around a circle, enclose a central space which perfectly fits a seventh.

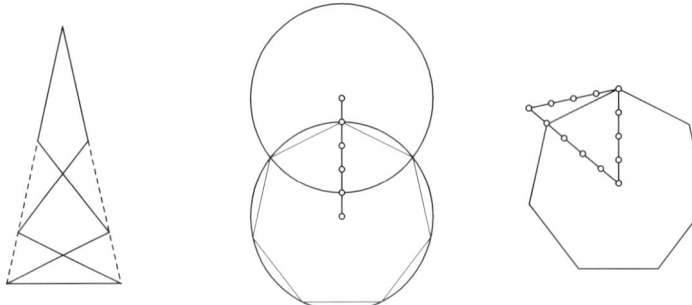

Figure 10.7 Methods of dividing a circle into seven. *Left*: the 'seven-matchstick' method, which produces an angle of one-seventh of a circle. *Above and right*: using a Druid's Cord (thirteen knots and twelve spaces) to produce a heptagon.

Tales of Taliesin one finds the same stylistic pattern. *The Birds of Rhiannon* sing men to sleep for seven years, whilst there were seven items in *Fionn's* crane-bag and the seven circles of the underworld kingdom, *Annwn*, offer us a geometrical link between circles and seven.

Similarly, *The Book of Enoch* is filled with adjectival uses of the number seven, taking its reader, through the whole 364 day calendar structure and the seven metals associated with the seven planets - here also represented as seven mountains. Genesis hammers out the *Chaldean order* of the planets as a geometric encryption base on seven-ness in the creation story, itself poached from much earlier roots. Clearly this number held an enormous importance to the ancient world as a symbol of creation or evolution. The link with *phi* shown earlier is therefore not at all surprising. But what might it all mean?

Figure 10.8 A Classical Seven Circuit Labyrinth.

Mathematically we may note that $\sqrt{2} + \sqrt{3} + \sqrt{5} + phi = 7$, why this should be the case remains a mystery, although it clearly connects *phi* with the number seven.

Labyrinths, Mazes and Seven

The history of mazes and labyrinths is as long and winding as their apparently complex form. This symbol and its family of derivatives may be traced back over 3500 years and its origins remain obscure. For a precise and intricate symbol to have travelled unaltered across so many cultural boundaries and for so long is probably due to the simplicity of its construction, a process which, once learned, is never forgotten, allowing its reproduction anywhere. In this regard, the labyrinth, like the lunation triangle and pentagram, is a geometric tool to facilitate a process. In our present culture, the attraction with the labyrinth and with mazes remains *in situ* and the shape was amongst the first to be incorporated within computer games.

The same labyrinth shape may be found in Peru, Arizona, Iceland, Crete, Egypt, India, Sumatra, Ireland and Great Britain. In its commonest form it contains seven circuits and eight paths, Sig Lonegren terming it the *Classical Seven Circuit Labyrinth*.[17] A link with the musical scale may thus be immediately appreciated.

Phi and the Goddess

Phi, through its derivative number series, the Fibonacci numbers, is found wherever *form* is being built up. It appears that this number, along with the irrational constant *e*, governs processes of growth and decay in the material world. We have met *e* directly as the value of the Megalithic yard with a form-related unit of length, the foot. We have also met *phi* incorporated into Stonehenge and the Pyramid. *Phi* and *e* may be symbolically taken to represent the 'female' side of the creative process. Whilst 'the idea precedes the form', the form is what you see, touch, smell, hear, and taste. It is matter, *mater*, and therefore it should now come as no surprise to anyone that the study of megalithic culture remains repressed within our patriarchal and dissociated society - where the functions of mind (male) and body (female) have been split by two millenia of faulty religious *thinking*.

The invading Church of Rome warred against the Celtic Church, which took a much more relaxed and holistic view on religious life, and it stamped on superstition and folklore; it burned witches, indulged itself in self-mortification and, in its attempts to eradicate the feminine side of life, created a wholly unnatural all-male Trinity. It is here where our "mental culture" was most altered, to produce the seeds of our present western society. We are still reaping the harvest of this cultural change as simultaneously the nascent New Age struggles to be born, like Yeats' 'rough beast'.

If there is one common cultural legend which is claimed uniquely by the northwest of Europe (i.e. the regions that spawned the megalithic architecture which led to Stonehenge), it is the legend of King Arthur. It is a remarkably persistent legend which is irrevocably connected with Stonehenge, and its folk-culture is indelibly written in our minds, buildings and landscapes. For the non-mathematical reader who has wrestled with my treatment of Stonehenge, and for those who have ever wondered about the roots of Britain's folk culture, there now follows a mysterious account of how the two main 'solar-heroes' of British folklore, *Jesus* and *Arthur,* became inextricably connected via the ancient megalith builders.

Stonehenge and the Arthurian Legend

The exploits of Arthur, Merlin and the Knights of the Round Table may be found throughout the folklore of England, Wales, Ireland, Scotland and France. The legend may also be found in parts of Germany, and Wagner composing the operas *Parsifal* (Perceval) and *Tristan and Isolde (*Tristram and Iseulte*)* little more than a century ago. Today, in England, the Arthurian legend centres around Glastonbury, although Tintagel is still a major Arthurian pilgrimage point for tens of thousands of visitors each year. The sole trade of this Cornish village is gleaned in servicing the requirements of tourists visiting the legendary conception and subsequent birthplace of Arthur.

Throughout the megalithic region one can find, on any map, references to Arthur's stone, Arthur's Grave, Arthur's Quoit, Arthur's Stone, Carn Arthur[18] and so on and so forth. This particular legend is alive and well, preserved through place names or local heroes-by-association who knew Arthur or Merlin.

However, it is at Glastonbury where the epicentre of the Arthurian legend resides, and whose older name of *Avalon* - the enchanted *Island of Apples* - still captures our imagination today. Here, the pilgrims flock in even larger numbers and up to 600,000 souls attend the summer festival there. Glastonbury has also become the focal point for the entire alternative movement in Britain, and the Arthurian legends evidently fulfil emotional and spiritual needs for men who want to be heroes, like Arthur and his knights; and women who want to be beautiful and fay, like Guinevere and Vivienne. Glastonbury is the New Age's spiritual home.

However, at Glastonbury, the Arthurian legend is quite inextricably entwined with a much older story - the Christian legend. Here, at one small town in Somerset, these two legends have collided. For Merlin, we find Joseph of Arimathea, for the twelve knights we find twelve disciples, for Judas we get Sir Lancelot, for the crucifixion and the resurrection we are treated instead with the *Avalon* story and for the Round Table we get...what? The last supper?

Christianity arrived in Britain very soon after the crucifiction. St Joseph of Arimathea, Jesus' uncle and a tin merchant, allegedly alighted on Wearyall Hill at Glastonbury, with eleven followers, and planted his staff there, which became the famed Holy Thorn. He brought the Chalice with him. Fuelled by the folk legends, town names and old miner's traditions in Cornwall and at Priddy on the nearby

Mendip Hills, a persistent tradition that Jesus spent time in Glastonbury and environs has endured. It has been suggested that Jesus attended a Druid college at Glastonbury, thus making sense of the otherwise inexplicable connections between early Christianity and Druidic lore.[19] Treharn's concise commentary in *The Glastonbury Legends* confirms the spiritual importance of Glastonbury when he writes,

> *"When the English arrived at Glastonbury soon after 658 they found a great and famous Celtic monastry already established and flourishing there, a monastry already venerated as the holiest place in Britain, with a primacy in time springing from great antiquity stretching back to a lost origin before firm history begins in this part of the land."*

Twelve holy anchorites also founded the first Christian church in Wales, according to legend, in 56 AD, at or near Llantwit Major. The leader, St Ilid, was a Jew from Rome. In the sixth century, this original foundation was totally regenerated by St Illtud, whose name is remarkably similar in pronunciation. We shall show that the ancient monastry / college, founded by Illtud at Llantwit Major around 480 AD, is also heavily connected with the Arthurian story.[20] This remarkable man was instrumental in the promotion of Christianity and learning in Celtic Britain during that critical time, between 450 and 550 AD, when the invading Anglo-Saxon barbarians threatened the annihilation of the Celtic cultural tradition. This links Llantwit Major and Glastonbury with the very beginnings of Christianity in Britain, and Treharn's quote does not rule out the possibility that Glastonbury may have already been a holy centre before St Joseph arrived.

St. Illtud's disciples included Gildas, St Sampson, Paul Aurelian and Prince Maelgwyn of Gwynedd. St Sampson was very travelled in Cornwall and eventually became Archbishop of Dol, in Brittany. Near to Llanilltud Fawr - the Welsh for Llantwit Major - may be found Llancarfan, another town written into the Arthurian legend; founded by St. Cadoc, who was also active in Cornwall. In France, Arthur and his exploits may be discovered throughout the northern regions and particularly in Celtic Brittany.[21] The main regions which include the Arthurian story within their folk-lore are therefore seen to be indistinguishable from the stamping grounds of these few Celtic monks. These people, the keepers of the vast repository of Celtic and pre-Celtic wisdom, all operated between 450 and 600 AD, within which period lies the identified period for the life of Arthur. After his death, was the Christian story tagged onto a hero and a legend more suited to Britain?

A motive for so doing can be easily suggested:- Celtic Britain was being invaded by foreigners - the Anglo-Saxons. Simultaneously, with the final collapse of the Roman administrative system around 450 AD, the nation was sliding into anarchy and the constant threat of civil war. The Celtic world was attempting with all its might to resist the English invasion and was succeeding with this venture in the west of the country, Wales and Cornwall. The original message of Christianity had already been incorporated into the earlier wisdom of the Celtic Church and this was recognised as a foreign import. The Celts were understandably becoming very unimpressed with foreign imports during this period, making it imperative for these Celtic priests to reset the Christian jewels within a new crown - it became a politico-religious necessity. Having once battled with invading Romans, and lost most of their territory, the new mission statement was to adapt the favoured Christian message and promote it as a force *against* the invaders and their barbarian culture, to recreate the Nazarene 'solar hero' as a Celtic warrior who, through his sacrifice, saves and redeems the Celtic world.

The end of Roman Britain coincided with the age of Arthur, which is also the beginning of modern British history. The style of the middle ages can be said to have been born with Arthur's death around 515 AD. In *The Age of Arthur*, Dr John Morris concludes,

> *"Therein lies the importance of the little short-lived realm that Arthus salvaged from the ruin of Rome. The tales that immortalised his name are more than a curiosity of Celtic legend. Their imagery illuminates an essential truth. In his own day, Arthur failed, and left behind him hope unfulfilled. But the measure of any man lies not in his own lifetime, but in what he enables his successors to achieve. The history of the British Isles is funnelled through the critical years of Arthur's power and of its destruction, for thence came the modern nations. The age of Arthur is the foundation of British history; and it lies in the mainstream of European experience."[22]*

Earlier in the same text, Morris informs us that, "The initial vigour of the British monks was confined to the decades about 550, and its strength lay in South Wales, Dumnonia (Cornwall) and Brittany." The legend could only have been fabricated after the real Arthur's demise, and the above date is therefore perfectly placed.

Exoterically, the Arthurian legends are about the original Britons and their struggle against the invading and barbaric Teutonic tribes - the Anglo-Saxons. As such, the legends are truly Celtic and predominate in those parts of western Europe which are considered 'Celtic', a label which, although vague, includes the Welsh, Cornish, Bretons, Irish, Manx, northwestern English and some Scots. These are the nations where our folklore is richest, and from where the epic tales of Arthur, Taliesin, the Fionne, the Tutha de Danaan, Culchulain and Manannan originated. Esoterically, the Arthurian material is the same human struggle to obtain spiritual truths and redemption, just as are the inner meanings of the Christian story. Because, in earlier chapters, we found important astronomical truths buried within the Christian texts, we must now look for similar material lodged within Arthurian folk-lore.

In *The Black Book of Carmarthen* may be found an epic poem which appears to connect Stonehenge, and the bluestones' epic voyage from the Preselis, with the Arthurian legend. It is supposedly written by none other than Merlin himself, and is basically a whinge about the state of the Celtic world since the collapse of Roman rule and the constant threat of English invasion, and is entitled *The Ohs of Merlin*. I quote the relevant section:

> *'Oh little piglet, don't doze off. A tragic tale will reach our ears, of paltry chiefs who do not keep their words. Stingy little stewards poring over a penny, when speedy men will come from over the sea, two-faced with war-horses under them, two heads to their inexorable spears. Of plots with no harvesting in an unquiet world, better to be dead*

than to be poor and needy; women with peaks on their four cornered hats and when men
full of lust will be on the job, a morning of reckoning it will be on Salisbury Plain.'
'Oh little piglet, oh restless grunter, Chwyfleian tells me a wondrous tale: and I prophesy
a summer of discontent: from Gwynedd, treachery between brothers when peace will
long be banished from the land of Gwynedd. And seven hundred ships will wend their
way with the Northern wind and their meet will be Milford Haven.'

I include this charming text, not because it derives from the Stonehenge period nor its builders, but because it is a mythic tale which names precisely the same non-mythical places involved in the Stonehenge story. It contains something embedded within our folk-culture, just as does the persistent legend of Merlin having originally brought the bluestones from Ireland to Stonehenge.

Merlin is apparently still busy weaving his spells today. The mythic tales of T.H.White's *The Once and Future King*, is described by Geoffrey Ashe as 'an exuberant best-seller', upon which the famous musical *Camelot* and subsequent film were based. The author then raises something which deals with an issue of importance to this text. I quote Ashe:

> *".. and the bit of dialogue where we confront an issue evaded ever since Wace[23]: 'You*
> *could never sit a hundred and fifty knights at a round table. Let me see...'*
> *Merlyn, who hardly ever intervened in the arguments now, but sat with his hands folded*
> *on his stomach and beamed, helped Kay out of the difficulty.*
> *'It would need to be about fifty yards across,' he said. 'You do it by $2\pi r$.' "*

Here we find the number 150, not very far from 153, connected with a magician and a geometrical problem and, again, none of it very far different in concept from St John's Gospel, last chapter, a story encoded with the design plans and meaning of the lunation triangle. A subliminal theme is being repeated and we must now look much further into the astronomy and geometry of the Arthurian legend.

The Map of Arthurian Britain

In *The Quest for Arthur's Britain*, Geoffrey Ashe gives a map showing all the sites mentioned in the book which have been identified with the Arthurian legend. It is reproduced overleaf and the sites for the southern and western parts of Britain listed. The map clusters sites connected with the legends in certain places. A band from Tintagel down to Fowey, in Cornwall contains no less than thirteen sites, whilst around Glastonbury (Avalon) we find seven sites. Stonehenge is given (Amesbury) as are the important sites, including Windmill Hill, near Avebury, and the epic battle-site of Mount Badon. There are twelve sites up and down the Bristol Channel plus St David's.

Strangely, Lundy is not listed and neither is Caldey Island although both of these islands feature prominently throughout Celtic literature.

"In mythology, islands feature as sacred places, or as entrances to the 'otherworld'. Lundy, in particular, holds an importance to the Welsh as Annwn, the realm of Gwyn Ap Nudd and the place to which departed souls go. The most popular holder of the title 'Annwn' is of course Glastonbury Tor. There may, however, be a good case for Lundy as Annwn, and the island is mentioned in The Mabinogion."[24]

Arthur and his knights are depicted in a cryptic Welsh poem going over water in quest of a magic cauldron, which is held in *Annwn*, a Celtic Otherworld similar to *Avalon*, where Arthur and other departed heroes lie sleeping, according to the legend. Interestingly, the tenor bell at St Helena's church on Lundy bears the inscription, in Latin, "Farewell to the departing souls."

With the mention of a magic cauldron we find similarities to the myth of the Holy Grail, which also features in pagan Celtic myth as a fertility symbol and source of inspiration and creativity, whence it is now part of the blended Arthur/Christian legend of Glastonbury. The Quest for the Grail has become a symbol for this unified myth, which despite its essentially romantic gloss still casts a spell today. In *The*

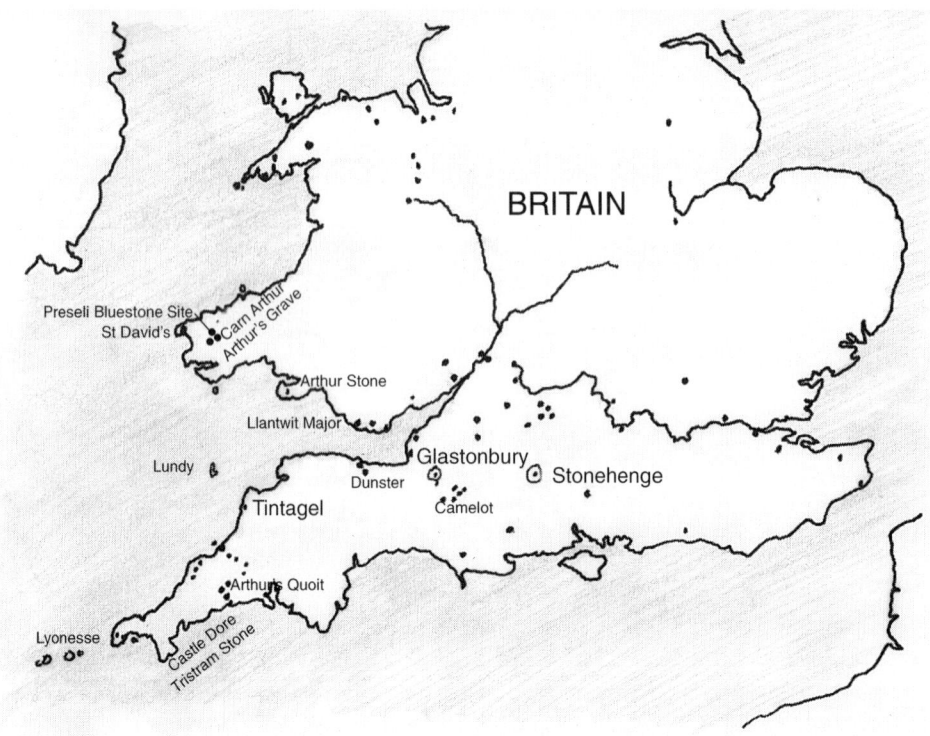

Figure 10.9 Arthurian Britain with key sites marked (*after Ashe*).

208

Triads of Britain, we find St Illtud and St Cadoc defined as Knights of St Arthur and Guardians of the Grail (Triad 121), but what really underpins this blended story?

A clue may be found in the story of Joseph of Arimathea's landing on Wearyall Hill, then an island in the Somerset wetlands. He is said to have arrived with eleven followers carrying the Chalice of the Last Supper, plus two cruets, one containing the blood of Jesus, the other the sweat from the crucifixion. Heraldic shields associated with Glastonbury still exist depicting these relics. But there is no obvious enigmatic thirteenth saviour figure within this story in the traditional solar-hero style. However, persistent folklore weaves a mystery concerning Joseph having brought "Mary" with him, whilst Templar traditions regard Mary Magdalene as a saint, the guardian of the Holy Grail and therefore the keeper of the sacred bloodline.

Although there is a long running controversy as to whether Mary of Bethany and Mary Magdalene were the same person, the Gnostic gospels and folklore both inform us that Jesus and "Mary" were lovers, in which case might not the thirteenth 'saviour' figure have been carried in the "Chalice" or "Grail" of Mary's womb, thus perfectly aligning the story with the earlier Pagan traditions. Is this not the folklore of the "Old King - New King" now presented with a Christian gloss? Can a pregnant Mary have represented the Chalice, in this story, where the cruets now contain the traditional contents of the Chalice, sweat and blood, leaving it available to contain a *living* saviour and thereby preserving the Royal lineage?

The Recurrent Myth of Twelve and Thirteen -

Both Arthur and Jesus were 'solar heroes'. This concept has, in recent times, been taken up widely by the Jungians. Carl Jung wrote that,

> *"It is not enough for the primitive to see the Sun rise and set; this external observation must at the same time be a psychic happening: the Sun in its course must represent the fate of a god or hero who, in the final analysis, dwells nowhere except in the soul of man"*[25]

Arthur and Jesus were both part of a group containing twelve lesser mortals, the twelve knights or disciples. As such, the familiar calendrical and therefore numerical and social choices we faced in the first half of this text are directly highlighted by *both* the Arthurian legends and the Christian story. But both versions of this story contain a third component - *Stonehenge*. The monument is the vital and sole man-made component in the giant lunation triangle connecting Lundy, Caldey, the Preseli bluestone site and Stonehenge. It is Stonehenge which ultimately defines this triangle and Stonehenge and Lundy are seen to be common components within the myths and exploits of the Arthurian legends and also within the Christian story, via the lunation triangle described by St John.[26] These two myths are almost mirror images of the same story, centred on the same east-west line which connects Stonehenge and Lundy, and it is from there we will find our best view over Albion.

Tintagel

Arthur's birth-place is associated with Tintagel. Uther Pendragon, Arthur's father, once held a great court and summoned all his barons. The King of Tintagel at the time, King Gorlois, went to this court and took his wife Ygerne, and "she was the fairest dame in any kingdom". To cut a long story short, in a spectacle of shape-shifting, deception and sexual mistaken identity, predictably aided and abetted by Merlin's magic, Uther Pendragon eventually has his way with Ygerne, and Arthur, a predictable time later, is the result of this union whilst poor old King Gorlois, in line with all other Old King myths, is speedily dispatched to the Otherworld. A sexual union, albeit contrived, thus brings our hero into the world, a far cry from the Virgin Birth but nevertheless identifying an unusual conception which produces a Saviour King. Tintagel is uniquely stamped as the place where this union of male power and female pulchritude took place.

According to C.A.Ralegh Radford's conclusions following the excavations undertaken at Tintagel in the mid 1930's, the Tintagel headland had previously been the site of an extensive Celtic monastry. However, very significant finds of pottery from the eastern Mediterranean were excavated there and dated to the fifth or early sixth century.[27] A Roman settlement at nearby Bossinney, the older Cornish name for Tintagel takes the importance of this site even further back, whilst Ashe informs us "The point is not without importance. A Celtic monastry implies a certain concentration of population within a reasonable distance."

However, as Paul Broadhurst informs us in his *Tintagel and the Arthurian Mythos*, Tintagel Island appears in several ways less and less as an insular monastic shelter for hermit-like monks, and more and more like an important festival or celebration place.[28] Historian and archaelogist Professor Charles Thomas, upon reopening the eight large boxes of pottery from the Ralegh Radford excavations, in 1980, discovered the pottery shards to show considerable craftsmanship and to have been tall pottery jars (amphoras) used to store the finest wine, oil and comestibles - to be consumed on the Island. The shards are dated directly to the Arthurian period and are not those of medieval domestic ware.

> 'They had been imported from the Mediterranean in post-Roman times, and were unique in British archaeology, no other examples of this type having been reported. Such a considerable amount, about three hundredweight, suddenly increased Tintagel's early significance, and linked it directly with the Arthurian Age of orthodox history'. (quoted from *Tintagel and the Arthurian Mythos*, page 139.)

The archaeological evidence from Tintagel supports the image of a powerful centre, with ancient and strong cultural and trading ties to Mediterranean centres of power. Its importance would therefore have been expected to have entered the folk memory of Britain. Paul Broadhurst goes on to ask if Tintagel Island was a citadel, and makes the valuable point that the Island is practically uninhabitable in the winter. He also points out that the Island forms part of an alignment to the summer solstice sunset and winter solstice sunrise, through a 'Round Table' of Cornish sites of importance centred on *The Cheesewring*, on Stowes Hill. This is familiar material for this text and no further commentary is needed.

The chapel on Tintagel Island, described by John Leland as *'a pretty chapel with a tumbe on the left side, dedicated to Uletta alias Uliane'*, takes us into other familiar waters. More recently, this dedication has become St Juliot, or St Julitta, a shadowy figure whose arrival on Tintagel Island was dated to 500 AD, again contemporaneous with the Arthurian and Illtud period and whose name appears etymologically connected to the *Uil-* or *Ill-* root seen earlier in the original name for Lundy Island and the dedication of its original church (*page 77-79*). This same root may also be found at Caldey, where St Illtud built the original church on the island.

Modern Poets and Visionaries

If the archaeological, astronomical and etymological evidence confirms an historical importance for Tintagel, then so too does the impressive catalogue of eminent poets, religious sages and occultists who have been drawn to the island. Amongst these was Lord Alfred Tennyson, whose *Mort d'Arthur* echoed the same title which had earlier flowed from the pen of Thomas Malory. Tennyson's work inspired many of the Pre-Raphaelites, who produced the scores of romantic Arthurian pictures now to be seen popularised in every New Age shop throughout the land.

In August 1924, the occult philosopher Rudolf Steiner visited the Island of Tintagel and later that same week spoke of the forces there,

> *"Into the twelve Knights of the Round Table flowed the inspiration from the zodiac;..*
> *..the inspirations from the spiritual forces of the Sun and Moon were represented by*
> *Arthur and Gwenhwyvar (Guinevere). Thus we find the cosmos humanized..."*[29]

Steiner's work continues to influence aspects of our modern world. A pioneer in methods of holistic education and agriculture, Steiner schools and his methods of education are promoted world-wide and anthroposophy formed an important root source for the nascent alternative movement in the sixties. Steiner's "spiritual forces of the Sun and Moon", mirrored in Arthurian folk-lore, remain to be quantified.

Castle Dore and the Tristram Stone

The fine pottery which was being used at Tintagel was also to be found at another Cornish site some twenty miles to the south. Deeper still into Cornwall, just north and west of Fowey and the southern edge of Bodmin Moor, one can find a cluster of place names on Ashe's map. The area is steeped in megalithic monuments, such as Arthur's Quoit, the bizarre pent roofed burial chamber at Trevethey. The Fowey

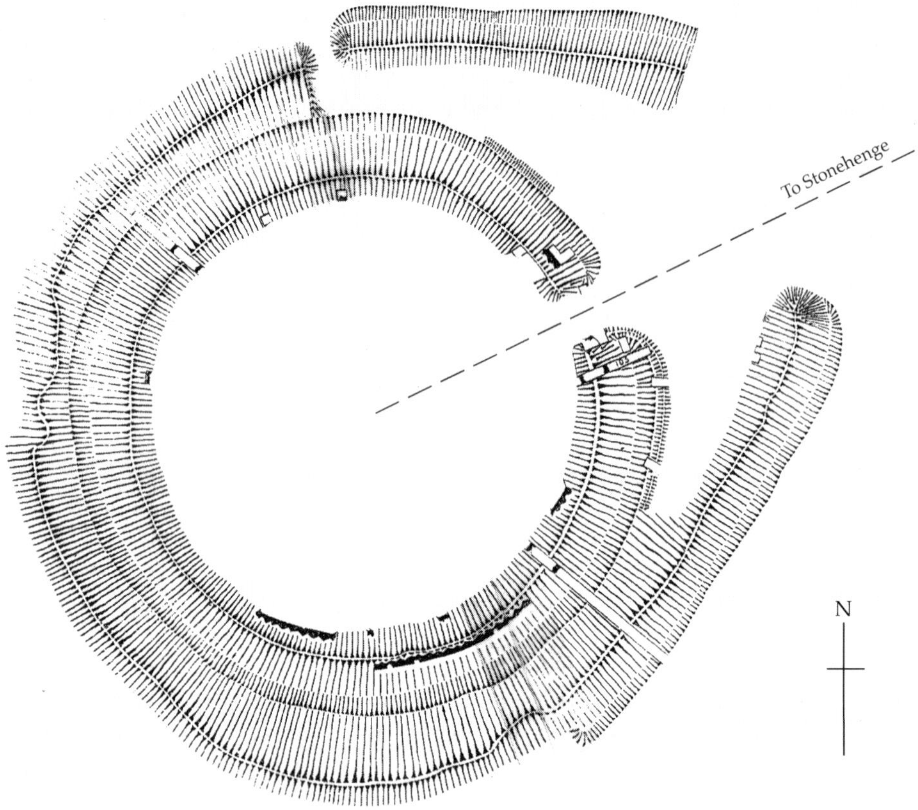

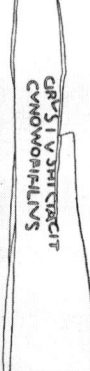

Figure 10.10 Castle Dore, Cornwall. This huge henge-like structure is over 370 feet across. It resembles a Sun and Moon motif or a giant eye looking towards Stonehenge.

peninsula contains a Bronze Age trackway which runs alongside Castle Dore, a huge henge-like structure some 370 feet in diameter, and which was variously occupied throughout history by Romans and then by Celtic chieftains, probably including King Mark, one of the last of the Cornish Kings and the uncle of Tristram. It appears to have been the court of Cynvawr, Tristram's father, a sixth century Breton.

Many names linked to the Arthurian legends may be found within a few miles of Castle Dore, most notably the reset standing stone (*left*) dedicated to Tristram, son of Cynvawr. It reads, in Latin, "DRUSTANUS HIC IACIT CUNOMORI FILIUS" (here lies Tristram, son of Cynvawr). Castle Dore lies on the Parish boundary of St Sampson in Golant and this augments the importance of this region within our tale, for Sampson was educated by Illtud, like Gildas, in the monastic school at Llanilltud Fawr in Wales. He finally travelled to Brittany, becoming Archbishop of Dol. The church of St Sampson is linked with the secular story of *Tristram and Iseulte*, which, although traceable back only to the 12th century, dates from much earlier, Sampson having been a sixth century saint. The standing stone also eloquently confirms the time of Tristram's life and his lineage.

Castle Dore is a most impressive site. In his book, *Prehistoric Henges*, Aubrey Burl first defines his territory by quoting the definition of a henge taken straight from *A Dictionary of Archaeology*,

> 'Henge. A type of ritual monument found only in the British Isles and consisting of a circular area, anything from 150 to 1700 feet [46 to 518 metres] across, delimited by a ditch with a bank normally outside it.'[30]

Burl then begins his book with, 'Henges are strange places. To the casual eye they seem dull, no more than a circular bank of earth and rubble surrounding a turf-covered interior. There is nothing else to see. Yet henges were places vitally needed by their builders, places for gatherings at the great times of the year, places where sacred objects were ritually buried, *places of the sun and moon* [italics mine], of the axe, perhaps even of sacrifice.'

There are nearly one hundred henges to be found in Britain and Ireland, and Castle Dore fits the above definition perfectly. It is built on a high ridge running north-south and adjacent to an ancient trackway and trading route dating back to the Bronze Age. However, it is not presently considered to be earlier than the fourth century BC, described vaguely as 'pre-Roman or Iron-Age', and remains excluded from the list of British henges. In Arthurian times, the inner circle contained a wooden building, some 90 feet by 40 feet, built along the lines of the famous Great Hall at Tara, Court of the Irish chieftains. Castle Dore was undoubtedly a most auspicious place in the earlier centuries AD.[31]

The plan of the site, shown below, shows the circular flat inner plateau, 228 feet in diameter, surrounded by a high bank some four or five feet high. It commands a superb view of the nearby Tywardreath beach and, from the centre, looking northwards, one can see the Cornish sacred high ground sites of *Brown Willy* and *Roughtor*, whilst directly north one can see the high plateau near Tintagel and Boscastle, some twenty miles distant. The entrance of this henge-like structure is placed to face northeast, - a central azimuth of 68° - *and is aligned to Stonehenge.*

The construction is more complex than just a circular henge. Symmetrical to the henge entrance, a crescent shaped addition may be found outside of the bank, this feature also being defined by its own bank and ditch. The effect, from the air, is to make Castle Dore resemble a combined Sun and Moon symbol, the central circle eclipsing a 'lunar' crescent. It also resembles a giant eye looking in the direction of Stonehenge.

Just as for Tintagel, this site also generates sufficient mystique to attract modern romantics who draw from its ancient folk-lore, most notably its connection with the tragic love story of Tristram and Iseulte. *Castle Dor* is the title of a novel adapted by no less an author than Daphne du Maurier. The story has recently been adapted for the stage.

We now have sufficient information to confirm my earlier suggestion that the Arthurian legends, whatever they came to represent in the Dark Ages and medieval Britain, are subsumed within a much older story, the Christian story, which we have shown to have tagged itself onto a still older story dating back to Stonehenge. The druids, monks and priests, holding the keys to the ancient wisdom and wishing to promote the Christian message, melded our present version of the Arthurian story into the mythic landscape of Britain, a landscape already waiting with sites that fulfilled perfectly the legend we read today. The Celtic warrior-hero, King Arthur, was born.

Tintagel Island and Castle Dore clearly form the central Cornish locations for the Arthurian legends. They share the same north-south line of longitude, and are separated by 21 miles. Meanwhile Lundy Island, on the same longitude line, is some 35 miles from Tintagel. These three sites therefore form *a second lunation triangle* - almost a mirror image of the Stonehenge-Preseli triangle and one which shares the same 'solar 12' side between Lundy and Stonehenge (*figure 10.11*). The axis entrance of Castle Dore aligns directly to Stonehenge, some 135 miles distant, as confirmation.

The complex of 'islands' rising from the Somerset marshes at Glastonbury, which John Michell relates to the circumpolar constellation of *Arth Fawr* - the Great Bear[32], straddle the 'solar 12' side from Stonehenge to Lundy at just three tenths of its length, with Glastonbury Tor located at latitude 51° 9' to Stonehenge's 51° 10'. Another huge natural high spot, Ben Knowle hill, at Wookey, lies at 51° 12'.

The Arthurian Triangle

The Arthurian legend takes on a whole new context once this triangle is added to the original lunation triangle, as does its connection with Christianity. Lundy and Stonehenge become the foundations upon which these two geometric constructions are built into a cohesive pattern of mythology themes, folk-lore and their astronomical truth. The original lunation triangle provided an essentially spiritual meaning to its astronomical basis, whilst the latter 'Arthurian' triangle is essentially secular. It is an earthly reflection of the cosmic truths incorporated into the Stonehenge-Preseli triangle, this fitting the ancient adage, 'as above, so below'.

This remarkable construct is another example of the connections which can be made once conventional subject boundaries are dissolved and allowed to cross-pollinate each other. I suspect that many people will reject what I have uncovered here simply because it will not fit any version of reality that makes sense to them. The apparently 'eternal recurrence' of the same mythic theme, preserved across the British landscape for five thousand years, is not the version of heritage many people were brought up to appreciate, nor what they want to hear, yet it is the root of true

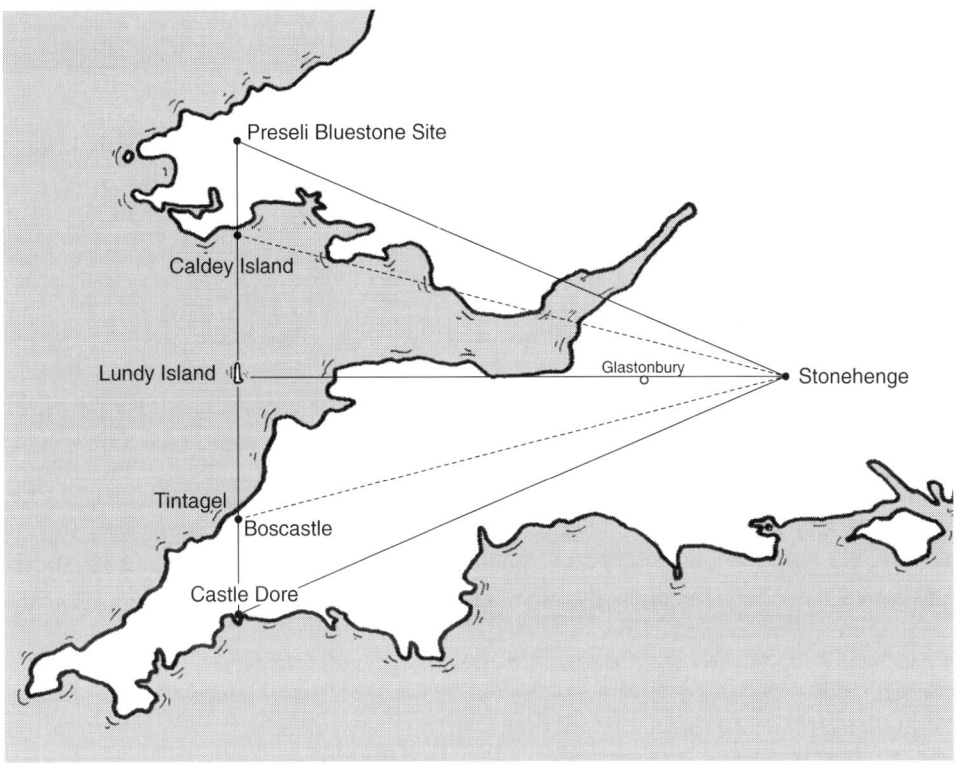

Figure 10.11 Myths, Maths and Megaliths - The 'Arthurian' lunation triangle, with the Preseli triangle it reflects. It is not quite as accurate as the Preseli triangle, although the longitude of the north-south line is shared. If made exact, the 'Tintagel' 3:2 point would lie in the sea north of Boscastle (*see appendix five, page 234*).

folklore, with mythic roots burrowing deep into British soil and the British soul. The original 'hardware' of this folklore - the geometry and siting of these lunation triangles - is directly traceable to the work of the megalithic builders, preserved in an aspic of myth and legend - the 'software' - which has refused to disappear, perhaps because it speaks of fundamental truths about being human. The program runs in all of our heads whether we like it or not - it is the stuff of the banished glee-men of old, the minstrels, the clowns, poets and storytellers - the Bards that were once the repository for the Ancient Wisdom. This underpinning wisdom was shared by the very Celtic saints after whom the key sites are named or to whom their churches are dedicated.

Like Parsifal, all one has to do to rediscover that wisdom is to begin asking the right questions.

A Glimpse of Troy

At Bossinney, adjacent to Tintagel, may be found a maze carved upon a rock. It is identical in shape to the maze at Knossos, Crete, where Theseus slew the Minotaur and is dated to the same period - 1800 - 1400 BC. The illustration below shows its design stamped on a coin minted in Knossos, Crete (*figure 10.12*). We should perhaps ask why the same cultural artefact occurs in Britain and in Crete, and then go on to ask why the same designs were formally known as "troys".

Could it be that the same design evolved spontaneously throughout the world, through an unconscious process about which we presently know nothing or is it more likely that people travelled much more in prehistory than we believe, carrying with them the simple secret of the maze?

In the standard design, one makes seven turns to reach the centre of the labyrinth. Why is this shape carved on a rock immediately adjacent to Tintagel, near the 3:2 point of the second lunation triangle? By now, the reader will understand, I hope, that the folklore of Tintagel and Castle Dore is that same one of male and female union, which, whilst very earthy in comparison to the spiritual symbolism of the lunation triangle, is symbolically the same material. The story of Helen of Troy and Paris is also thematically the same - the Troy myths being epochal tales about human cultural development, set in a period of rising Patriarchal and declining Matriarchal society when the Greeks and Trojans held centre stage for this drama of cultural change.

King Minos of Crete offended Poseidon because he did not carry out his promised sacrifice of the white bull. In retribution, Poseidon set the stage for the energies of the gods to be united with those of humans. He made the bull irresistible to Queen Pasiphäe, and their union produced a monster with a human body and a bull's head

Figure 10.12 A close up of classical seven-coil labyrinth in Rocky Valley at Bossiney, between Tintagel and Boscastle. *Right*: A Minoan coin from Knossos dated 1200 BC.

- the Minotaur. The Goddess oriented Minoans held feminine energy in high esteem but their civilisation was in decline. They sent King Minos' son, Androgeus, an androgynous symbol of the ambivalence of Troy at that time, to face the bull, but he was killed. King Minos, who ruled the seas, had won a campaign against the Greeks and had demanded seven boys and seven girls as an octennial tribute, to be given in sacrifice to the Minotaur in the labyrinth. One of these boys, Theseus, the hero of the story, a Greek and one of the Patriarchs, went into the Cretan labyrinth and killed the Minotaur, with Ariadne's help.

The numerology of this tale connects both to the labyrinth itself, which has the number seven written through its form like lettering through sea-side rock, and the eight year cycle of the Sun and Moon, which we have seen to be enshrined in stone at Avebury. This cycle is given by Frazer in *The Golden Bough* as the astronomical reason for the sacrifices made to the bull every eight years, which eventually, in more modern times, became the sacrifice of the bull itself as a substitute. The renewal of the powers of the Minoan king every eight years by intercourse with the god-head is described by Frazer and demonstrates the similarity between the annual pagan sacrifice of the Old King and the birth of the New King, and this eight-year cycle of Sun and Moon.

We still commemorate the annual cycle through the birth of Jesus at the winter solstice, but our culture has apparently forgotten the eight-year cycle and, as a consequence, cannot make sense of Avebury. In *The Myth of the Goddess*, we read that, "This marriage of the priest-king and the priestess-queen was also an imitation on Earth of the marriage in heaven, when the Sun and the Moon returned after eight revolving years to 'the same heavenly bridal chamber where first they met'."[33] All over the Near East this sacrifice was enacted as the ritual slaying of the bull - the Minotaur legend is a cycle of sacred marriages between the Sun, as bull, and Moon, as priestesses or princesses. In Minoan ritual, these sacred marriage rituals at Knossos were celebrated by the priestess-queen and priest-king wearing the horned masks of cow and bull. That a Minoan labyrinth may be seen on a rock at Tintagel, adjacent to where the union between the godlike (and disguised) Uther Pendragon and Queen Ygerbe produced Arthur, confirms the importance of this location.

We may now suggest that Avebury was indeed set up specifically to observe this same eight-year cycle and further suggest that the incorporation of the planet Venus into this ritual *could not possibly have been avoided*, for after eight solar years have elapsed, Venus is placed precisely in the same angular relationship to the Sun that the planet enjoyed at the start of the process. Never far from the Sun, as a morning or evening 'star', Venus would be a permanent and loyal consort to the Sun in this octennial ritual, the Moon slipping backwards around the zodiac by seventeen degrees after each elapsed eight year period. Venus rules the sign Taurus, the bull, the sign where the Moon is exalted, this connecting the eight year cycle and the Minoan rituals with ancient astrological lore.

The *geometrical* story of the marriage of the Sun and Moon is overlain on Tintagel - where there is a labyrinth. The Arthurian story began here, at the 3:2 point on a lunation triangle - as *defined by Stonehenge*, but is now centred on Glastonbury, where there is also a labyrinth - on the Tor itself.

The Geomantic Habits of the Celtic Monks

The early Celtic Church in Wales left several important sites which survive as buildings today. The best known, in Wales, is the town of St David's, now with its magnificent Cathedral visited by tens of thousands of people every year. St Illtud's church at Llanilltud Fawr (Llantwit Major), the site of the monastry and college is less well known. This latter site has the almost the same latitude as Avebury and both sites are placed precisely on the circumference of a circle, centred on Lundy Island, whose radius is the same as the '5-side' of the lunation triangle. Llantwit Major is thus equidistant from Lundy and Caldey Islands.[34]

Can all these things be a pure coincidence? The circumference also takes in the Preseli bluestone site and passes by Merlin's Hill, near Carmarthen. This geomantic display places a new dimension onto the activities of the early Celtic Church and may be measured off a map by anyone (*figure 10.13*).

The *Welsh Triads* are verses of great antiquity that incorporate the wisdom and the traditions of the indigenous people of Britain back into prehistory. In one of these *Triads*, Llanilltud Fawr, Glastonbury and Stonehenge are described as the being the "three perpetual choirs" of Britain. That they are equidistant from each other and located as points on a decagon on the perimeter of a circle 63 miles in radius, which is itself a sixty-third of the Earth's polar radius might also raise an eyebrow. The centre of this circle lies in the Malvern Hills, at a place called Whiteleafed Oak, where the three counties of Hereford, Worcester and Gloucester all meet. Clearly, there is a geomantic undertow to these locations, these three "perpetual choirs" being linked in historical context, (time) and also in space.

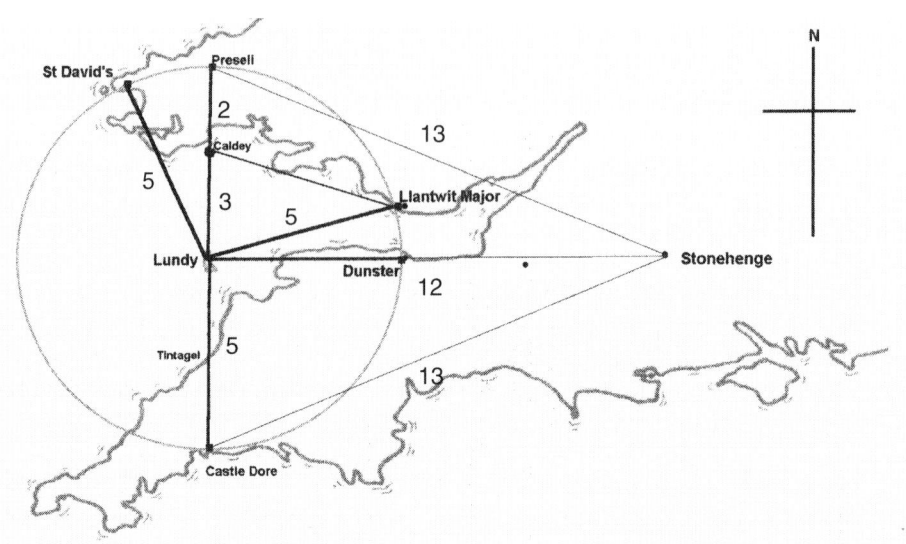

Figure 10.13 The Geomantic habits of the early Celtic monks.

Figure 10.14. Inside St Illtud's Church, Llantwit Major. Amongst the inscribed gravestones for early Celtic kings (*above right*), may be found an oddity - the 'lingam' stone shown above (*left*). Circular in cross section, it more resembles Indian and Middle Eastern ceremonial stones than Celtic, although the knotwork is typical.

Across the Bristol Channel, this same circle also encompasses the Somerset town of Dunster, whose latitude is identical to that of Stonehenge and Lundy. Dunster thus lies on the '12' side of both lunation triangles, dividing it into the ratio 7:5. In *The Life of St. Carannog*, Dunster is named as the centre of Arthur's activities, for when the saint arrived in the West Country from Wales, searching for his lost altar stone, he found Prince Arthur intending to use the altar stone as a table, only nothing could be made to remain on the table. The altar stone was duly returned to Carantoc (St.Carannog) in return for help in capturing and taming a serpent, which had been ravaging the nearby region of Carrum. Whilst Dunster may not be the central site in the Arthurian legend, the town with its castle and huge mound overlooking the coast does lie directly across the Bristol Channel from Llantwit Major and is certainly geometrically connected with the lunation triangle geometry. That so many other Celtic sites are also connected must be seen as proof of an intent about which we currently know very little.

Figure 10.15 The Coat of Arms (*left*) and the Holy Thorn at St Illtud's Church, Llantwit Major (*right*). The link with geometry and Glastonbury could not be clearer.

The Celtic saints, Illtud, Sampson, Gildas, David, Patrick, Juliot and Carantoc, must have understood the original secret of the lunation triangle for so many of the monastries and churches named after them to have been sited according to its geometry. The Arthurian legends are centred on the key sites of Glastonbury, Tintagel and Castle Dore.[35] The central figure in all of this appears to have been St Illtud, a man who single-handedly spearheaded the religious renewal of Britain, more particularly in Celtic Britain and Wales, although churches dedicated to Illtud are also to be found in Brittany, from where he is thought to have originated in the late fifth century. St.Illtud established what is reputed to be the oldest centre of learning in Britain at Llanilltud Fawr monastry and he died around 510 AD, St. Sampson succeeding him as abbot.

Tud, translated from Old Welsh means 'measuring', (in the sense of a measuring stick. *Tud fach* is a stilt and *tudlath* is a measuring rule). The root *Ill*, literally means *they*, but linguist and historian David Elkington, in a conversation with the author, quite independently gave the linguistic roots of *Illium*, the old name for Troy, as relating *"to both triangle and circle"*. The *Illiad* stems from the same root.

At the modern church of St Illtud, built on the site of the original monastry, may be found several ancient Celtic artefacts, including a decorated lingam stone and the decorated gravestones of several important Welsh kings from the Dark Ages. A thorn tree, a scion from the original Holy Thorn from Wearyall Hill, Glastonbury, flourishes against the church wall. The heraldic crest paved into the floor of the church doorway is of interest in that it shows *three* bishop's mitres and *two* bishop's crooks. That the latter resemble the measuring sticks of Egyptian pharoahs, and the former express the *vesica piscis* - and carry the same name as a right-angled joint - gives further food for thought.

Ashe says of St Illtud,

> *"Illtud became, in the words of St Gildas (who, however, does not name him, any more than he names Arthur), 'the polished teacher of almost the whole of Britain.'*
> *'Illtud may have attended one of the schools set up by Germanus, and it is said, though on no very safe authority, that he served as a soldier under Arthur. After some years as a hermit, he founded the monastry of Llantwit Major in Glamorgan. His monks reclaimed land and pioneered an improved method of ploughing."*

The Old Welsh word for ploughing is *troi*. The farming fable above therefore connects us to an inner message, for a Welsh dictionary also informs us that,

> **troi**, *v, to turn, to revolve; to turn over, to overturn, to upset; to wind, to twist; to stir; to convert; to become; to plough.*

Apart from informing us why the labyrinth was formerly called a 'troy', I also sense that the ploughing story, which is hardly a spiritually enlightening anecdote, is designed to connect St Illtud with a culture much older than 4th century Britain.

The Troy Symbol

One of the most ancient symbols known is the 'troy-symbol' of three radiating lines. It may be traced back to 8000 or 9000 BC, according to David Elkington, and thence to Old Kingdom Egypt. Linguistically it is conected with the unspoken name of God, which in more recent times has become Jehovah or Jahweh, although the

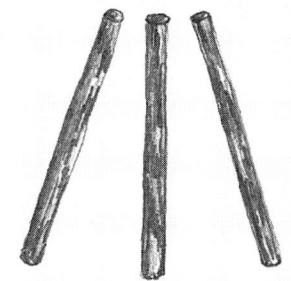

Figure 10.16 Above: The 'Troy' symbol of three rods remains the symbol of modern Druidry. *Left*: This 19th century engraving of an Arch-Druid may be fanciful, but it shows a cultural reverence for the elders - wise men of the past. St Illtud was certainly amongst these, and made a profound influence on British history.

letters AWE were how it was originally linked to the troy-symbol.[36] This is so geometrically and symbolically similar to the form of the two triangles radiating out westwards across the Bristol Channel that a connection between the 'Troy-symbol' and Britain may now reasonably be assumed.[37] The symbol remains the sign of the modern Druidic movement and has also been adapted by the British Astrological Association as its *logo*.

Summary

Although folklore cannot be treated in quite the same objective and practical manner as the geometry of huge stones arranged in circles, it is nonetheless as real because it usually carries a deep meaning. In the last few pages we have seen how folklore, coupled with other historical information relating to ancient sites, has enabled us to link large sections of the historical landscape together to reveal a wholly new perspective. Once again, it is the lunation triangle which has allowed access to these interesting connections. An important secret, held silently by Stonehenge for thousands of years, is now revealed.

In this revised history there are as yet no experts, only explorers. British history becomes the cycles of the Sun and Moon translated into stone temples, cathedrals, castles, mythology and an incredibly rich folk heritage. These cycles have been shown throughout this text to permeate much deeper into our social fabric than anyone had previously thought, and our story dates back at least 5000 years.

The early Celtic saints are seen to have overlaid the Arthurian legends onto the earlier Christian story, and are thereby seen to have had access or spiritual insight into the legacy left by the megalith builders and geometers of an even earlier epoch. Perhaps the Celts themselves fabricated the second 'Arthurian' triangle, yet the antiquity of the Bossinney labyrinth and the dating, style and orientation of the henge at Castle Dore suggest otherwise.

Two lunation triangles, each the reflection of the other, are written into the geographical landscape with indelible features. Together they indicate the entrance into Troy itself, and certainly to our national temple, Stonehenge, where the heavenly measures were enshrined in stone. These triangles are the true *Triads of the Island of Britain*, once the sign for Troy, and they remain the sign for the modern Druidic movement.

At the apex of this sign and these triangles, to the East, can be found Stonehenge. Despite all those passing years, the pattern of the past has remained resolutely in place, both in hard stone and in folklore, patiently waiting for its message to be revealed. In due course, the high culture of the past may once again take its rightful place and our story completed.

Footnotes to Chapter Ten

[1] *A History of Pagan Europe* by Prudence Jones and Nigel Pennick. Routledge (1995).

[2] *Earth Rites*, published by Paladin (1982). Peter Berresford Ellis has published over thirty titles. *The Celtic Empire - The First Millenium of Celtic History 1000 BC - 51 AD* (Constable) is recommended as a starting point.

[3] *Blood Relations - Menstruation and the Origins of Culture*. by Dr Chris Knight, published by Yale University Press (1991).

[4] This is not a new concept. Professor Stuart Piggott expressed the view that the legend of Merlin having "thrown the bluestones' from Ireland to Stonehenge was a remnant of a truth preserved within the oral traditions.

[5] See *A Key to Stonehenge*, page 59-60. The Aubrey calendar can predict the tides as accurately as modern tide tables.

[6] To 0.06% accuracy.

[7] *The Celtic Empire*, p 17.

[8] The Metonic cycle of 19 years comprises two 8 year cycles plus a 3 year cycle and the errors in each fortuitously cancel each other, resulting in a two hour error between solar and lunar cycles after 19 solar years [235 lunations].

[9] Figures quoted here taken from various books on Avebury, most notably *Avebury* by Dr. Caroline Malone (English Heritage)

[10] *Serpent in the Sky*, by John Anthony West. Julian Press, NY (1987), p 106. This calendar, discovered by Schwaller de Lubicz, synchronizes to within 1.14 hours, *better than the Metonic cycle*, although based on a calendar year rather than the 365.242 day solar year. (The true value of *phi* to four decimal places is is 0.6180).

[11] See *The Modern Numerology* by John King. Blandford Press (1996). Also *Seven, the Number of Creation* by Desmond Varley. G.Bell(1976)

[12] The word *planet* comes from the Greek word for *wanderer*, something both the Sun and Moon do quite a lot of when viewed from the Earth; i.e. geocentrically observed. This is why astrologers call the two lights *planets*.

[13] After eight years, Venus has moved just two degrees along the zodiac - the pentagram is almost a perfect regular shape.

[14] This places the Moon as the first day of the week and the Sun as the seventh. See *Sun, Moon, Man, Woman* by the author for a full exposition on the relationship between the planets, their attributed qualities and the naming of the days.

[15] See *The Myth of Invariance* by Ernest G. McClain (Shambala 1978). Not an easy read but a seminal text on the relationship between the musical scale, mythology, cosmology and geometry.

[16] *The Black Book of Carmarthen*. Published by Llanerch Enterprises(1989). A Translation by Meirion Pennar, with a letter-for letter Welsh text, of a 1250 AD text which originates from a much earlier date. Carmarthen is *Caer Myrddin* - Merlin's city -in Welsh. *Caer* can also mean castle or fortress and *Caer Gwydion* means *Milky Way*.

[17] *Labyrinths, Ancient Myths and Modern Uses*, by Sig Lonegren. Gothic Image Publications, Glastonbury.

[18] In Wales, the town of Carmarthen ('Caer Myrddin' but linguistically mutated to *Caerfyrddin*) is named after the magician alleged to have guided Arthur's destiny. Merlin's Hill and Merlin's Bridge are to be found locally.

[19] *New Light on the Ancient Mystery of Glastonbury*, John Michell. Gothic Image (1997 edition). Page 79.

223

[20] *Illtud* is pronounced, approximately, as *Ich-tid*.

[21] See *The Quest for Arthur's Britain*, edited by Geoffrey Ashe. (Paladin, 1968)

[22] *The Age of Arthur - A History of the British Isles from 350 to 650*. Dr John Morris. (1993). Dr Morris was senior lecturer in history at London University.

[23] Wace was a chronicler, born in Jersey, who in 1155 AD produced an important account of the Arthurian material. The Round Table was a paramount feature, alongside the problems of 150 knights becoming seated there.

[24] From *Archaeology of Lundy - Sacred Island of Annwn?* Sharon Higgins. A summary of recent fieldwork undertaken by the National Trust Archaeological Survey. *The LeyHunter Journal*, no.130.

[25] *Archetypes of the Collective Unconscious*, from *Collected Works*, vol 9, part 1, (trans. Hull) RKP, 1959.

[26] Other stories in the Bible confirm Jesus as a solar hero. See *Culture and Cosmos*, 'An Astronomical Basis for the Myth of the Solar Hero' by the writer. Vol 1, No 1, Spring/Summer 1997. Reproduced in Appendix 1.

[27] From *The Quest for Arthur's Britain*.

[28] *Tintagel and the Arthurian Mythos*, by Paul Broadhurst, Pendragon Press, PO Box 888, Launceston, Cornwall.

[29] Public lecture given on the 22th August 1924, in the Town Hall, Torquay.

[30] *Prehistoric Henges*, Aubrey Burl, published by Shire Archaeology (1977). *A Dictionary of Archaeology*, W.Bray and D.Trump. (1970).

[31] The excavation of Castle Dore is described in *The Journal of the Royal Institution of Cornwall*, New Series, Volume 1, appendix 5, 1951.

[32] *New Light on the Ancient Mystery of Glastonbury*, John Michell. Gothic Image Publications (1997 edition).

[33] *The Myth of the Goddess*, Anne Baring and Jules Cashford. Penguin Arkana (1991), page 140. Quote from *The Golden Bough*, by Sir James G. Frazer, Vol 4, *The Dying God*, p 76.

[34] I am grateful to a well known clown, Goffi, for discovering the geomantic link between Caldey, Lundy and Llantwit Major. The original church on Caldey is dedicated to St Illtud; the later church is dedicated to St David.

[35] In addition, within half a mile of the Preseli bluestone site may be found *Carn Arthur* and *Bedd Arthur* - Arthur's Grave - an important megalithic site. Thus, four of the four sites defining the western ends of the two geodetic lunation triangles are identified with King Arthur, only Caldey Island is not.

[36] In modern Welsh, *Awel* means *Breath* or *breeze* and biblical literature connects *breath* with *Spirit* and *God*.

[37] The 'W' consonent, phonetically 'OE', suggests the western direction of the middle leg of the troy-symbol. The middle leg of the double lunation triangle points west.

Epilogue

The contribution from the indigenous people of Britain will one day have to be incorporated within our concept of heritage. Despite the research of many people indicating that the megalith builders were practising high astronomy and geometry before 3000 BC, it still remains true that this culture is wholly undervalued as a vital component of our history. My aim in writing this text was to lay out an easily accessible, readable and coherent study of the whole megalithic context, one which will then hopefully act as a springboard for other people to take the various areas further on along the road that leads to better understanding.

When exploring new territory, there are no experts and, mercifully, there is no dogma. Whilst there are some truths emerging from this exploration, another central purpose of this text was to make available material which, for various reasons, is scattered throughout many rather rare and often inaccessible textbooks. The personal explorations I have made convince me that a proper and realistic history of this culture is now becoming a possibility.

Stonehenge and Avebury remain the two most potent symbols of the megalithic culture in Britain. The manner by which these sites are connected, astronomically, geomantically and culturally has been demonstrated in this text, and the coherent cultural linkages connecting their hundreds of sisters and cousins has also been shown.

If it is argued that the Preseli triangle and its reflection, the 'Arthur triangle' are not precise constructions, then a visit to any of the sites which define this extraordinary construction would show in a few moments both the suitability and the necessary compromises made to exactness at these locations. If the true purpose of these constructions was to perpetuate a cosmic truth, then they have succeeded brilliantly in that task - the message has been received. Mathematical exactness is just one component in the cultural equation whereby the correct sites are found to align soli-lunar truths with earthly location. With real designs, exactness is often subsumed by other considerations, such as beauty.

We must allow our overheated left-brains to take some repose as other factors in the geometry and siting of this geomantic expression take their due importance. Apollo's temple must, in the final analysis, bow to Sophia, and her handmaidens in these islands, Brigit, Ceres and Diana. Ultimately, they are the traditional rulers of our sacred spaces.

Appendix One

An Astronomical Basis for the Myth of the Solar Hero

Extracted from an article in *Culture & Cosmos,*
Spring 1997, by Robin Heath.

Introduction

Our increasing knowledge of the megalithic culture of the British Isles in the 2nd and 3rd millenia BCE tends to confirm the proposition that megalithic astronomers measured celestial positions with considerable accuracy. The evidence indicates that they understood the 18.61 year nodal period and the moon's nine minute declination wobble.[1] They also had sufficient geometrical ability to reproportion spacings between lines, divide circles into whole number polygons and divide lines into equal integere spacings.[2] We should therefore ask whether there is evidence of such early astronomy in the numbers which recur in certain myths. The following should be viewed as preliminary arguments.

The Thirty-Three Year Cycle

If our interest is megalithic astronomy then we could search for relevant evidence in the myths of the British Isles. One of the most recurrent numbers in the stories of the Tuatha de danaan who, according to tradition, inhabited Ireland before 1500 BCE, is thirty-three.[3] We are told, for example, that the first battle of Mag Tuired was fought by the saviour hero Lug and thirty-two other leaders. In the same vein, Nemed, another hero, reached Ireland with only one ship, while tirty-three were lost on the way; Culchulainn slays thirty-three of the Labraids in the Bru battle whilst a late account of the second battle of Mag Tuired names thirty-three leaders of the Fomorii, thirty-two plus their highest king.[4]

This material contains one clear and obvious theme. Repeatedly, it reinforces an originally oral message which told the knowing listener to look to the number thirty-three as something relevant to a hero, a saviour. In his analysis of the Welsh White Book of Rhydderch, Dr N.L.Thomas writes that 'Both three and eleven were equally symbolic, the multiplicand thrity-three particularly so. It has frequently been used to imply supra-human attributes, regal authority and deification.'[5]

We find evidence of an astronomical and mythical significance of a thirty-three year cycle in other cultures. Perhaps the best known example is found in the tradition that Christ began his ministry at age thirty and was crucified at age thirty-three.[6] The solar tradition in early Christianity is well recorded, with the wirdespread identification of Christ with Helios and the fixing of Christmas to coincide witht the older festival of Sol Invictus, a few days after the winter solstice, and Easter close to the spring equinox.[7] It is partly on ther basis of such evidence, together with the argument that epic myths such as those of Gilgamesh and hercules represent solar cycles, that modern comparative mythology has produced the notion of the solar hero.[8] I am arguing that the numerical evidence in the Celtic tales provides astronomical evidence that they too could be considered solar heroes.

Megalithic Astronomy and the Solar Cycle

Many megalithic standing stones have been shown to relate to extreme Sun and Moon rising and setting azimuths against the local horizon. While the link at some sites is tenuous it is beyone doubt in others, as for example at Stonehenge.[9] The practical solar year is 365 days long. I say *practical* because most reference books claim that there are 365 and a quarter days in the year, a confusion between the Earth's orbital period around the Sun. Every fourth year an extra day slips in to make it 366 days. Thus, in four years there are 1461days. It is fairly easy to observe the Sun's behaviour and thereby measure this number.

An equinoctial sunrise marker, of which many still exist around the British Isles will, each year, deliver the vernal equinox from a slightly different position on the horizon. The 'quarter day effect' means that the Sun, each year, is displaced about a quarter of one degree from the marker stone. During three years of observation, the Sun appears to be slipping ever more away from the alignment until, at the fourth year, two remarkable and very observable things happen simultaneously: the Sun rises once more very close to the marker stone, and the day count is found to be 366 and not the more familiar 365. Observation does not stop there, a good human eye can detect much more miniscule angular changes than a quarter of a degree from watching sunrises.[10]

The truth about solar year measurements carried out at the equinox is that the result is always 365 days unless sustained observations are conducted over many years. In this case the result is 365.25 days, a figure which, under optimum conditions, could be realised after four years (see figure 1).[11] This figure is within eleven minutes of the period of the tropical year (365.24219 mean solar days).

For longer periods of time something else happens. Every once in a whole number of years the chance arises to measure the year with even greater precision. This can be achieved by observing certain key years when, once again, the Sun rises precisely behind the foresight - be this a stone marker or a distant mountain peak - in other words, *a perfect repeat solar cycle*.

1 year	365.242199 days (error from integer, +5.812776 hours)
4 years	1460.968796 days (error from integer, - 44 minutes)
21 years	7670,086179 days (error from integer, - 124 minutes)
29 years	10592.02377 days (error from integer, - 34 minutes)
33 years	12052.99257 days (error from integer, - 11 minutes)

Table One. Solar Repeat years. Integer day count with errors.

After thirty-three years one can observe an exact repeat of an original equinoctial sunrise behind a marker stone (see Table 1 and figure 2). To a megalithic astronomer this same phenomenon would have bee seen as an exact repeat rising (or setting) , whilst a modern astronomer would note that the Sun's declination will be identical on the same calendar date thirty-three years after the value read from a book of tables today; thirty-three years is a true solar cycle. If we can assume that the megalithic astronomers made exact angular observations over many years, as the current evidence suggests[12], then this phenomenon would have been a familiar one to them.

However one interprets the dats, this presents a possible astronomical source to the use of the number thirty-three in heroic myths. Thus when Christ's resurrection occurs at age thirty-

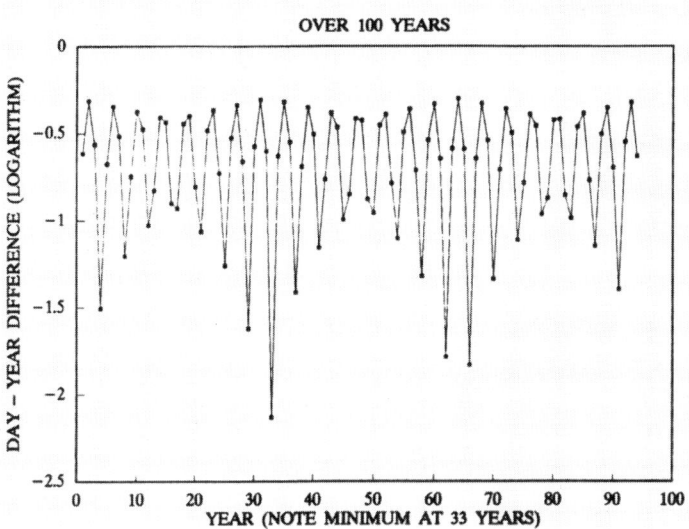

Figure Two: Graphical representation of Table One.

three, witnessed as it was at sunrise at Eastertime, we may be faced with a sophisticated astronomical/calendar metaphor. Even the rolling away of the stone to reveal the resurrected saviour may plausibly be argued to represent the emergence of the Sun from behind the marker stone, inaugurating another thrity-three year cycle.

Conclusion

Contemporary archaeology has established the astronomical sophistication of the megalith builders to a previously unsuspected level. So far the arguments, naturally enough, have rested primarily on the the archaeological record. However, a second line of argument may be derived from the mythical record, even though we have to account for the problem that the written sources are necessarily of a much later date than the stone remains. It is clear that myth may provide evidence of ancient astronomical knowledge, while astronomy may also provide an additional perspective on ancient myths.

Footnotes to Appendix One

[1] Alexander Thom, *Megalithic Sites in Britain*, (Oxford University press, 1967, pp 59, 165). Thom reckoned that good observation can detect angular changes as small as 2.5 minutes of arc (correspondence from Archiue Thom to the author, 1994). John E Wood, *Sun, Moon and Standing Stones* (Oxford University Press 1980), wrote ' the Temple Wood observatory shows inherent accuracies of declination measurement to around one hundredth of a degree.'
[2] Wood, *Sun, Moon and Standing Stones*, pp 36-56.
[3] The best source for the early myths is the Royal Irish Academy's edition of *The Book of Leinster*, 1880, a facsimile of the Leabar na Nuachonghbhala (also sometimes known as the Book of

Glendalogh). This contains the earliest known version of the Leabhar Gabhala, the 'book of invasions', the primary source for the stories of the Tuatha de Danaan. The most reliable version of this work is lebor Gabala Erenn: *The Book of the Taking of Ireland*, ed. R.A.S.MacAlister, Irish Text Society, 5 vols, 1938, 1939, 1940, 1941 and 1954.

[4] Dr N.L.Thomas, *Irish Symbols of 3500 BC*, (Mercia Press, Corl, 1988), page 83.

[5] Thomas, Op cit, page 76. For the *White Book of Rhydderch* see Llyfr Gwyn Rhydderch, with an introduction by T.M. Jones, (University of Wales Press, Cardiff, 1973, reprint of the 1907 edition edited by J. Gwenogvrryn Evans). The original manuscript is National Library of wales MSS Peniarth 4. Also see Rees, Alwyn and Brinley, *Celtic Heritage* (Thames and Hudson, London 1961), pp200 f., 318 ff., 338. Although *The White Book of Rhydderch* is dated to 1300 -1325, like other similar texts, it is widely believed to represent the written account of a much earlier oral tradition.

[6] St Luke 3.23, Acts 2, record that Christ's ministry began at age thirty.

[7] The earliest reference to the celebration of Christmas on Sol Invictus, Dec 25th, is the Philocalian Calendar of 336. There are different formulae eastablishing the celebration of easter. The standard is the Roam version: Easter Sunday falls on the first Sunday after the full moon following the spring equinox. See also Henry Chadwick, *The Early Church*, Harmondsworth, Middlesex, for discussion of Christian reverence for the sun in the 1st - 3rd centuries.

[8] The concept of the solar hero has been particularly popularized by the Jungians. Jung wrote that, 'it is not enough for the primitive to see the sun rise and set; this external observation must at the same time be a psychic happening: the sun in its course must represent the fate of a god or hero who, in the last analysis, dwells nowhere except in the soul of man'; C.G.Jung, '*Archetypes of the Collective Unconscious*', Collected Works, Vol. 9, part 1, page 6, translated by F.R.C.Hull (RKP, London, 1959).

[9] For Stonehenge see Hugh Thurston, *Early Astronomy* (New York 1994), pp 45 - 55.

[10] Thom, *Megalithic Sites in Britain*, page 108.

[11] Lockyer argued that simple observation was sufficient to establish these figures: 'Had ignorance led to the establishment of a year of 360 days, yet experience would have led to its rejection in a few years... If observations of the Sun at solstice or equinox had been alone made use of, the true length of the solar year would have been determined in a few years." Norman Lockyer, *The Dawn of Astronomy*, (Cambridge, 1894), pp245-6, reprint MSI, 1964.

[12] At Loghcrew, In Ireland, Cairn F, stone C1, there are a set of 62 inscribed markers, whilst nearby, at Fourknocks Passage, one may count three columns of eleven chevrons, totalling 33, picked onto a stone. See Dr N.L.Thomas, *Irish Symbols*, page 73. Sixty-two years is another solar repeat, less than 24 minutes from integer, at 22645.01634 days.

Appendix Two

- Units of Length and Area -

(see also figure 9.4 on page 167)

Fundamental Measurements (in order of length).

The Inch - Primitive. One twenty-fifth of the Sacred Cubit. *See page 82-84*

The Inch - Imperial 'British'. One twelfth of the *Silver Fraction*, expressed in Megalithic yards. One primitive inch equals 1.001064 British inches. *See page 83.*

The Foot - 'Megalithic'. *The Silver Fraction*, expressed in Megalithic yards - 0.368266228 MY = 1.00105 'British feet' or twelve primitive inches. *See page 82.*

The Foot - Imperial 'British'. One thousandth part of a degree of arc along the Earth's equatorial circumference, divided by 365.242199 (the solar tropical year). *See page 165-167.*

or, one thousandth part of a degree of arc along the polar circumference, divided by 364. *See page 165.*

The Remen. An Egyptian unit, 14.58 inches in length discovered by John Ivimy to be related to the Royal Cubit and the Megalithic yard by the irrational factors √2 and √5 respectively. *See page 86-88.*

The Royal Cubit. The Megalithic yard minus the foot, i.e. the remainder of a MY when the lunar 'over-plus' is removed - 0.632 MY. (20.63 British inches). *See pages 84 - 86.*

The Sacred Cubit. One ten-millionth of the Earth's polar radius, divides into 25 primitive inches or 25.0265 British inches. *See page 165.*

The Imperial Yard. Three British feet or 36 British inches. *Alternatively, see page 83.*

The Sacred Rod. One six-millionth of the Earth's polar radius. (3.4757485 British feet or 41.709 British inches - note that this is very close to two Royal Cubits). *See page 165.*

* * * * * * * * * * * * *

Earth's polar radius, 3949.89 miles
Polar circumference 24,817.95 miles

Earth's equatorial radius, 3963.42 miles
Equatorial circumference, 24,902.95 miles
(see pages 165-167)

Sacred Geometers use 3960 miles as the Earth's radius, and 1080 miles for that of the Moon. Both numbers contain a most useful range of divisors. This reinforces their use within a *Canon of Measure*.

* * * * * * * * * * * * *

Units of Area.

The Aroura *(see pages 143-145, 177, 179)*. An Egyptian unit of area equal to a square of side length 100 Royal Cubits. One quarter aroura is the area of a circle of circumference 36524.2 Primitive inches in length - the Egyptian 'Year-Circle'.

Appendix Three

Another method for constructing Type A Flattened Circles.

This technique is very similar to that employed for the Type B (*see figure 6.6 on page 104*). The author terms it a Type A1: it is practically indistinguishable from the Type A, yet is much simpler to produce. There is a more obvious commonality of design with the Type B.

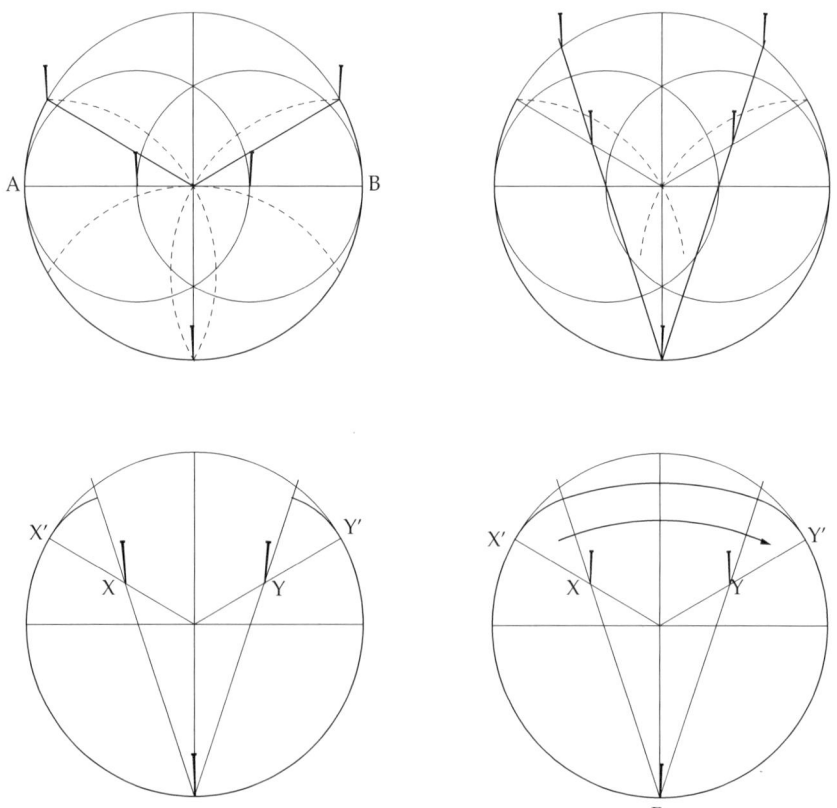

Order of Construction.

Top Left: Divide a line AB into three, using two circles arranged as a *vesica piscis*. Proceed as shown in figure 6.6 to generate the large circle. Then, using the technique shown in figure 6.7, divide the circumference into six.
Top Right: Take a rope from point P and drive pegs in at points X and Y.
Lower Left: With centres on the upper pegs, trace radius around small arcs X-X'; Y-Y'.
Lower Right: With rope pegged at 'P', walk around flattened section PXX' to PYY'.

232

Appendix Four

The Chartres Labyrinth

The Labyrinth is totally designed around the factors of the thirteen month, 364 day calendar discussed on page 30-32. It is also capable of being used as a working analogue of the motions of the Sun and Moon as seen from the Earth (*see chapter three, page 49*). There are 112 hemispheres around the circumference (twice 56) and the central 'flower' is based on the division of a circle into thirteen. There are 28 turns, the central 'flower' design is based on six circles plus a circle radius, making six and a half, which is half thirteen.

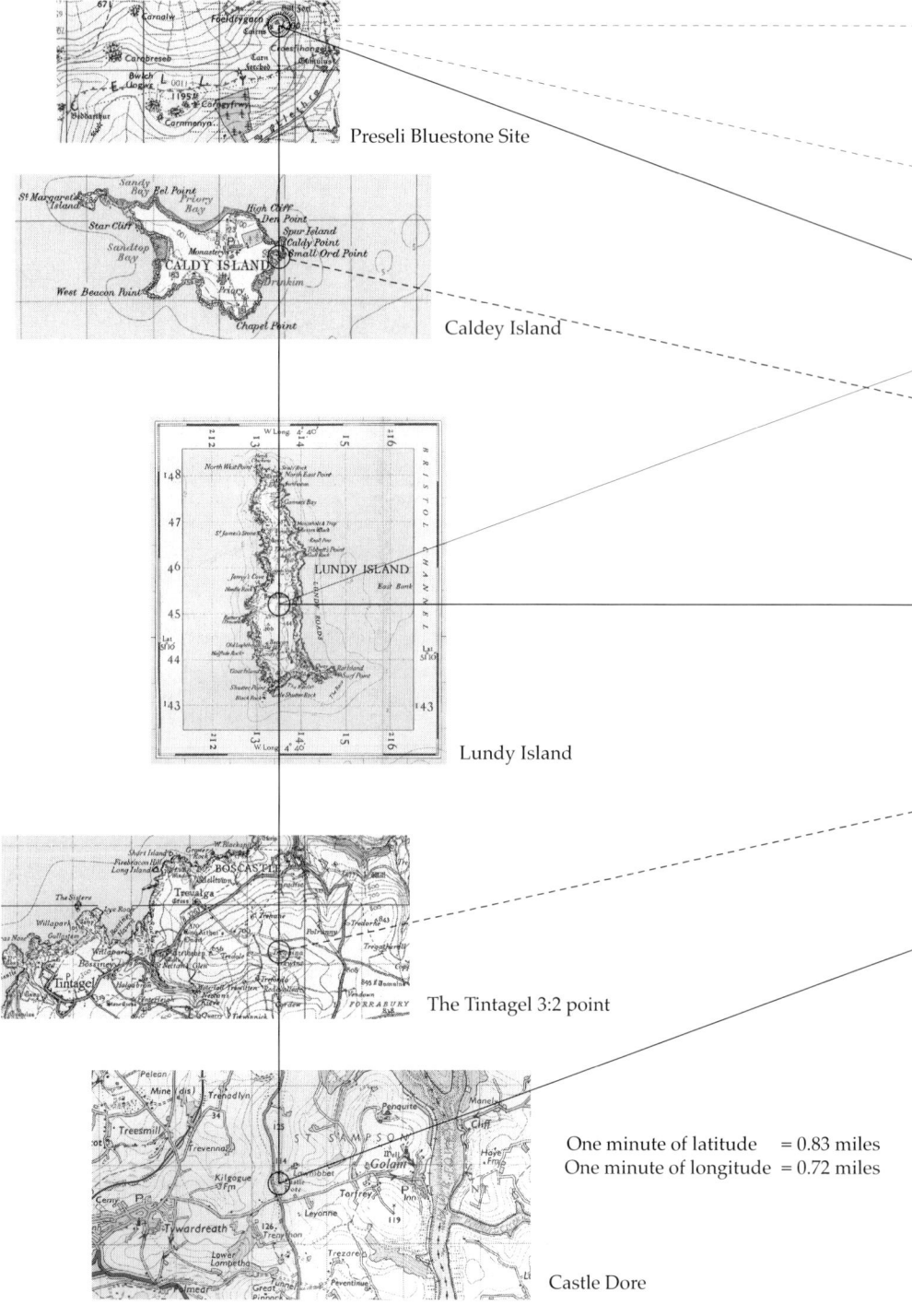

Preseli Bluestone Site

Caldey Island

Lundy Island

The Tintagel 3:2 point

One minute of latitude = 0.83 miles
One minute of longitude = 0.72 miles

Castle Dore

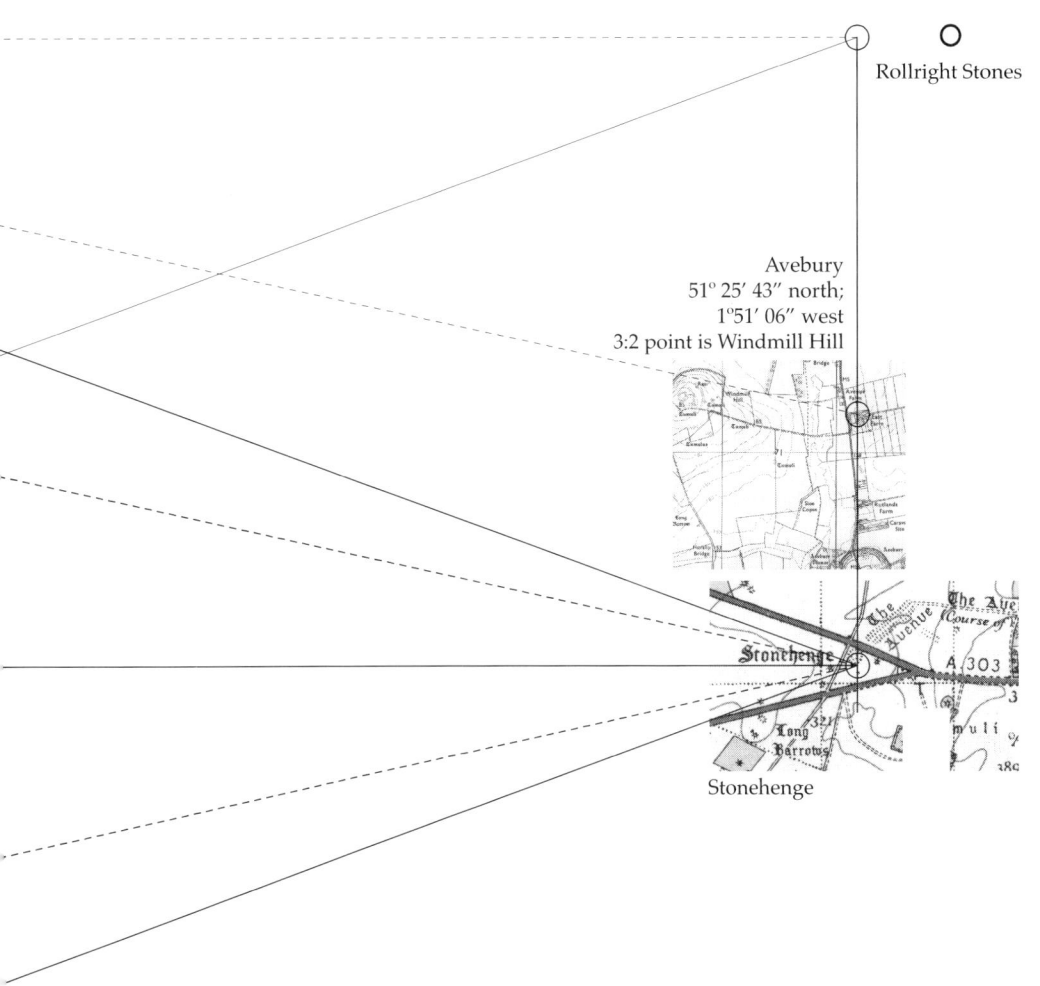

Rollright Stones

Avebury
51° 25' 43" north;
1°51' 06" west
3:2 point is Windmill Hill

Stonehenge

Appendix Five
Locations of the Lunation Triangle sites

Sources: PF = O.S. Pathfinder 1:250000,   OS = O.S. 7th Series

Preseli Site	51° 57' 44" north; 4° 42' 05" west (PF)
Caldey Island (St Helena's Church)	51° 38' 13" north; 4° 41' 01" west (OS)
Lundy Island (Tibbett's Hill)	51° 10' 33" north; 4° 39' 52" west (PF)
Stonehenge (Centre)	51° 10' 42" north; 1° 49' 30" west (PF)
Tintagel Island	51° 40' 42" north; 4° 45' 30" west (OS)

(The actual 3:2 point lies between Boscastle and St Genny)

Castle Dore	50° 21' 42" north; 4° 40' 01" west (PF)

Appendix Six

Astronomical Constants

All the calculations in this text have been derived from the following astronomical constants. It is uncertain by what tiny percentage these figures might have changed since the megalithic era. [Sources : *Astrophysical Constants*, by C.W. Allen(1973) and/or *General Astronomy*, by the Astronomer Royal, Sit Harold Spencer Jones (1951)].

Solar Cycles:

Solar Tropical Year ... (SY) ... **365.242199 days**.   Sidereal Year ... 365.256360 days
Precessional Year ... (assuming a 50.2" precessional rate per year) ... **25,800 years**.

Lunar Cycles:

Synodic Lunar Month ... (from new Moon to new Moon) ... **29.53059 days**.
(The Lunation Cycle)
Sidereal Lunar Month ... (successive passages past a given fixed star) ... **27.32166 days**.
(Lunar Orbital Period)
Lunation Rate per year ... **12.36826623 lunations**.
Sidereal Lunar Rate per year ... **13.36822869 orbits**.

The Lunar Year ... (12 Synodic Lunar Months) ... **354.36708 days** (0.970224911 SY)
The Sid. Lunar Year ... (12 Lunar Orbits) ... **355.18158 days** (0.972454938 SY)

Differential between Lunar and Solar Year ... **10.875119 days** (Enoch's 'Over-plus')
Period of Moon's nodes ... **18.618 years** (6793.6 days)
The Eclipse Year ... (conjunction of Sun to one of the nodes) ... **364.62 days** (0.949014108 SY)

Superannual Soli-lunar Cycles:

The Saros Cycle ... **223 lunations** ... or **18.03001293 years** ... **6585.32157 days**
The Metonic Cycle ... **235 lunations** ... **19.00023784 years** ... **6939.68865 days**.
(The difference between 235 lunations and 19.00 years is 2.084856 hours)

236

Publisher's Note.

Sun, Moon & Stonehenge is published by one of the growing number of small publishers. If you wish to order another copy of this book and cannot find a bookshop which stocks it, please write to the address below, enclosing a stamped, addressed envelope. We will send you a list of stockists and details of how to order.

Bluestone Press, (Sales), Maes yr Awel, Cwm, St Dogmaels, Cardigan, Pembs, Wales. SA43 3JF
Telephone : 01239 613224